BIOLOGY
Exploring Life

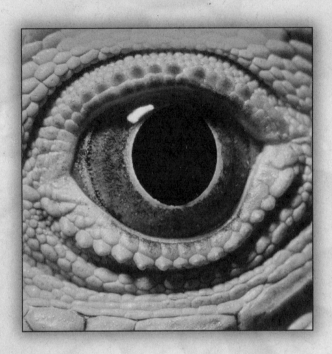

Laboratory Manual
Teacher's Edition

Diane Sweeney
Biology Instructor
Prince of Peace Lutheran School
Fremont, California

Brad Williamson
Biology Instructor
Olathe School District
Olathe, Kansas

PEARSON
Prentice
Hall

D1361256

Boston, Massachusetts
Upper Saddle River, New Jersey

ISBN 0-13-064267-3

9 10   12 11 10 09 08

TEACHER'S EDITION CONTENTS

Dear Colleagues,

Imagine you had time . . . nearly three years' time to search out and find exciting, innovative, and workable laboratory activities. Imagine you could spend time with incredibly creative biology educators from all over the country and they were willing to share their brilliant ideas with you. Imagine you had time to make meaningful improvements to the labs you have been doing for years. Imagine the lab program that could come from that kind of time and focus.

I was given that opportunity and I am so excited to share the result with you! The *Biology: Exploring Life Laboratory Manual* is an expression of my passion for teaching biology, the joy that comes from teaching high school students, and my deep respect for teachers.

These labs had their beginnings in my classroom, on my kitchen table, or in my garage. Insect pupae, various enzymes, agar, and plasmid DNA have all taken up residence in my refrigerator during the past few years. I chuckle to think what people passing by my open garage door must think when they see me peering intently through a microscope or removing an aortic valve from a pig heart. Of course, the most critical part of my testing came from putting the labs into the hands of high school students. As you know, no lab idea is useful unless it is understandable and repeatable by real kids in real classrooms.

I would love to be a mouse in the corner of each of your classrooms as your students get their hands on (and into) these activities. I hope that they are amazed and awed by the precision of enzymes, the intricacy of DNA, and the sounds of their own heart valves. Capture those moments and share them with me by e-mail (posted in the **UsingExploringLife.com** teacher community Web site) or at the next NABT or NSTA meeting!

Diane Sweeney
Biology Instructor
Prince of Peace Lutheran School
Fremont, California

Dear Colleagues,

It's my opinion as a teacher that successful biology classes are built around great laboratory experiences for students. Nothing quite sparks a student's interest like a good laboratory investigation, and nothing else works quite so well at breaking down the "I'm too cool" barrier that some high school students build around themselves. Labs are an essential component to experiencing and learning biology—and good labs provide a leaning environment that is also fun and motivating for students.

While many programs claim new and innovative laboratory programs, I'm sure you'll quickly notice that the laboratory program in *Biology: Exploring Life* delivers on that claim. Teacher and biologist Diane Sweeney spent more than two years designing and testing new laboratory investigations as well as adapting new approaches to more familiar labs. She met with innovators such as Paul Williams from the Wisconsin Fast Plant program and Charles Drewes of "California blackworm" fame to glean their ideas and methods in order to introduce new model organisms to the high school biology laboratory. As you'll see in this manual, Diane has a unique approach to making labs interesting to students while keeping the learning of biology as a central goal. Additionally, the first laboratory investigation for each chapter features a Lab Online Companion found on the *Biology: Exploring Life* Web site. The Lab Online Companions, a unique element of the program, provide real-world contexts for labs and offer tutorials in new techniques, increasing student motivation and understanding and increasing student success in the actual hands-on lab.

The laboratory program is one of the three essential components of the *Biology: Exploring Life* program. It provides the "messy, hands-on" experience that complements the text and Web activities so that all three together ensure active and comprehensive student learning. The labs run the spectrum from open-ended inquiry labs that emphasize the process of science to labs that ask the student to role-play being a paleontologist, animal behaviorist, cytogeneticist, endocrinologist, or medical technologist. The *Biology: Exploring Life* author team is proud of this set of laboratory investigations. I have no doubt that you'll find that they add a spark of excitement to your classroom.

Brad Williamson
Biology: Exploring Life Program Author
Olathe School District
Olathe, Kansas

Structure and Design of Laboratory Investigations

The investigations and activities in the *Biology: Exploring Life Laboratory Manual* are designed to strengthen students' laboratory, inquiry, and critical thinking skills and to provide a practical application of material presented in the student textbook. The easy-to-follow format of each Investigative Lab allows students to complete the investigations on their own, perhaps after an overview and brief explanation from you. This gives you an opportunity to provide the necessary help to those individuals or groups of students who require teacher assistance.

Each Laboratory Investigation has the following format:

Title Each lab title has two parts—a short, "fun" title to catch your student's attention and invite their questions, and a formal subtitle to describe the topic of the investigation.

Question(s) Each Investigative Lab challenges the student by introducing a problem in the form of a question or series of questions. Students should be able to answer the question(s) upon successful completion of the Investigative Lab. In those labs that are designed to be open-ended opportunities for student inquiry, the question may be broadened and stated as an Inquiry Challenge.

Lab Overview This section provides a brief summary of what students should accomplish in each Investigative Lab. In the Teacher's Edition, you'll find annotations near the Question and Lab Overview describing the objective of the lab, the inquiry skills the lab will foster, and a breakdown of the time each part of the lab can be expected to take.

Introduction This section provides students with basic information to prepare them for the investigation.

Background The Background provides more detailed information that students need to complete the investigation, provides a real-world context for the lab investigation, or relates the Investigative Lab to specific concepts discussed in the student textbook. In a few cases, this section may also provide new concepts and terms specific to the investigation.

Prelab Activity and Questions Some Prelab Activities are designed to prepare students for particular steps in the Investigative Lab. Other Prelab Activities demonstrate how the lab ties into concepts they are studying in the textbook. Prelab Questions may ask students to identify the roles of certain materials or reasons for specific steps in the investigation procedure. The questions will prepare them for active understanding needed to take full advantage of the Investigative Lab.

The 36 primary chapter labs (the labs without an "A" following the chapter number) feature a corresponding online component on the *Biology: Exploring Life* Web site. The **Online Lab Companion** for each of these labs includes an interactive Prelab Activity that will prepare the students for a particular part of the investigation procedure or give them background information that will enhance their learning experience in the lab.

Materials This section lists all materials required to conduct the investigation. The quantity of material for each investigation is generally indicated for each lab group (groups of 2 to 3 students are recommended). Teacher annotations for advance preparation and for alternate materials when applicable are found near the Materials section. The necessary equipment and materials for all of the Investigative Labs are listed alphabetically and by category on pages Txi–Txxi.

Safety and Disposal You are alerted to specific safety and disposal precautions in the Safety and Disposal annotation found near the start of the Procedure. Share this information with your students to make them aware of potential hazards before the investigation begins.

Procedure This section provides a detailed step-by-step outline of the Investigative Lab procedure. Diagrams are included where necessary to further explain a technique or illustrate an experimental setup.

The Procedure contains symbols and instructions that guide students as the lab is performed. Safety symbols signal students to follow specific safety precautions for the entire lab or during parts of the procedure. **CAUTION** statements in steps of the Procedure warn students of possible hazards and indicate how accidents can be avoided. **NOTES** in the Procedure direct students' attention to special directions or techniques. At the end of some steps in the Procedure, students may be instructed to make predictions, record data, or answer questions. Observations are often recorded by filling in data tables, graphing data, labeling diagrams, and drawing observed structures, as well as by answering general questions.

Analysis and Conclusions Questions in this section are designed to assist students in answering the investigation's Question(s), relating the investigation to concepts learned in the textbook, and drawing conclusions about the results of their investigation. Using data gathered during the investigation and knowledge gained from the textbook and Background, students are asked to analyze and interpret their experimental results. Many questions emphasize possible applications of the experiment and allow students to relate the investigation to real-life situations.

In the Teacher's Edition, annotations for sample data and answers to Analysis and Conclusions questions are printed in blue on the pages corresponding to the student pages. These annotations include answers to objective questions, sample graphs and diagrams, and anticipated student data when these can be predicted.

Extension Each Investigative Lab concludes with a section entitled Extension. This section suggests additional activities that may be used to enrich or supplement the investigation. Some Extension activities may also be used as alternatives to the Investigative Lab.

Inquiry Investigations Several labs throughout the Laboratory Manual ask students to develop their own experiments. Instead of beginning with a Question, these labs pose an Inquiry Challenge. The Prelab Activity helps guide students in planning their experiments. Two examples of Inquiry Investigations are Investigative Lab 3 and Investigative Lab 22.

Modifying the Investigative Labs

School schedules often do not permit long laboratory periods. The *Biology: Exploring Life Laboratory Manual* provides a number of options to help you circumvent the difficulties associated with having limited laboratory time. The investigations are often divided into two or more parts. This provides flexibility by allowing you to select the parts of the investigation that best suit your needs, objectives, and laboratory situation. In addition, you can often schedule the parts of an investigation to be performed during different class periods. A number of the investigations have annotations that suggest specific ways in which the investigation may be modified to shorten its duration.

Correlation Between Textbook Chapters and Investigative Labs

This laboratory manual is designed to accompany Prentice Hall *Biology: Exploring Life* by Neil Campbell, Brad Williamson, and Robin Heyden in the presentation of a comprehensive biology program for high school students. When used in conjunction with the textbook, the manual reinforces, expands, and enhances the student's experiences of reading the textbook and participating in classroom discussions. Although the investigations are numbered to correspond to chapters in *Biology: Exploring Life,* they can be used with any high school biology program.

Guidelines for Laboratory Safety

Safety should be an integral part of the planning, preparation, and implementation of a laboratory program. Both the biology teacher and the student are responsible for creating and maintaining an enjoyable, instructional, and safe environment in the biology laboratory.

A number of general safety concerns are discussed. You should also refer to pages x–xv in the Laboratory Manual Student Edition for a detailed discussion of safety rules and procedures. You may want to expand or modify the safety guidelines, procedures, and rules suggested here according to local and state government regulations and policies, as well as school regulations and policies. The school administration should be able to provide you with specifics on local safety requirements.

General Safety Considerations

Emphasis on proper safety precautions for each laboratory investigation is an essential part of any pre-laboratory discussion. Prior to each investigation, demonstrate the proper use of the required equipment. Demonstrate any potentially hazardous procedure used in that investigation. Always wear the required safety protective devices during the demonstrations and the investigations. If students are required to wear safety goggles, you and any visitors to the class must also wear them.

During an investigation, move about the laboratory to keep constant watch for potentially dangerous situations. Behavior that is inappropriate to a laboratory situation should be curtailed immediately. Wild play and practical jokes are forbidden in the laboratory. Once students realize that the practice of safety is a required part of the course, they will accept a serious approach to laboratory work.

Any laboratory investigation a student performs should have your prior approval. Students should never work in the laboratory without adult supervision. At the conclusion of the lab investigation, cleanup should follow authorized guidelines for waste disposal. The laboratory should be restored to a safe condition for the next class.

Classroom Organization

Furniture and equipment in the laboratory should be arranged to minimize accidents. Assign students to laboratory stations. Each station should be equipped with a flat-topped table and laboratory bench. Do not use desks with slanted tops. Provide several locations where students can obtain needed supplies. Control traffic flow in the room to prevent collisions between students who are carrying or handling equipment. Tell students to leave their personal property in a designated location, away from the laboratory stations. Do not use the floor and benches for storage area. Stress that good housekeeping is important in maintaining safe laboratory conditions. Students should keep all laboratory work areas clean. Unnecessary papers, books, and equipment should be removed from working areas.

Be sure that water faucets, hot plates, gas outlets, and alcohol or Bunsen burners are turned off when not in use.

Safety Equipment

Any classroom where laboratory investigations are done should contain at least one of each of the following pieces of safety equipment: (1) fire extinguisher, (2) fire blanket, (3) fire alarm, (4) phone or intercom to the office, (5) eyewash station, (6) safety shower, (7) safety hood, and (8) first-aid kit. If any of these basic pieces of safety equipment are not available, you may need to modify your laboratory program until the situation is remedied.

Make sure students know the location and proper use of all safety equipment. Where appropriate and practical, have students handle or operate the equipment so that they become familiar with it. Make sure all safety equipment is in good working order. All malfunctions should be promptly reported in writing to the proper school or district administrator.

Fire Equipment At the beginning of the school year, you may wish to give each student the opportunity to operate a fire extinguisher, as the sound and action of a CO_2 fire extinguisher can be quite alarming to those who never used one.

You may also want to have students practice smothering imaginary flames on one another with the fire blanket.

Eyewash Station The eyewash station should be used if chemicals are splashed onto the face or eyes. The exposed area should be left in the running water for 15 minutes.

Safety Shower The shower is used when chemicals are spilled on a student's skin or clothing. The student should remove contaminated clothing and stand under the shower until the chemical is completely diluted. Have a bathrobe or some other replacement clothing handy in case the student's clothing must be removed.

You may want to set up one or two spill kits in your laboratory. The contents of a spill kit are used to neutralize chemicals such as acids and bases so that they can be cleaned up more easily. Baking soda (sodium bicarbonate) can be used to neutralize acids. Vinegar (acetic acid) can be used to neutralize bases. Commercial spill kits for acids, bases, and a number of other chemicals are available from biological supply companies.

Safety Hood Use a safety hood whenever students are working with volatile or noxious chemicals. Make sure that the room is well-ventilated when students are using any kind of chemicals or are working with preserved specimens. Warn students of the flammability and toxicity of various chemicals.

First-Aid Kit A typical first-aid kit contains antiseptics, bandages, gauze pads, and scissors. Most also contain simple instructions for use. Be sure to read the instructions if you are not familiar with basic first-aid procedures. A first-aid kit should be taken on all field trips. For field trips, you may wish to add such items as a bee-sting kit, meat tenderizer, tweezers, and calamine lotion. Do not dispense medication (including aspirin).

Cleanup

Before beginning an investigation, instruct students in the proper cleanup procedures. Mark certain containers for the disposal of wastes and the collection of soiled glassware and equipment. Have students dispose of broken glassware in a separate trash container. Before the end of the laboratory period, have students unplug microscopes and other pieces of equipment and put them away in their proper location. Have students wash glassware, wipe up spills, and do whatever else is necessary to clean up their work area. At the conclusion of the laboratory investigation, the room should be restored to a clean and safe condition for the next class. You may wish to institute a policy of not dismissing the class until the laboratory area meets with your approval.

Preparations and the Storage Room

Reagents stored in the biology stockroom should be clearly labeled and stored safely. Take inventory of reagents frequently and keep up-to-date records of their use. Check local and state regulations for maximum permissible amounts of reagents allowed in school. In case of fire or vandalism, inform the authorities of possible hazards to the community. Keep all chemicals in a locked storage area that is accessible only to you or individuals under your direct supervision.

Some chemicals are incompatible and should be stored separately. Check local and state laws for regulations on storage of flammable liquids. The National Fire Protection Association recommends that flammable liquids be stored in vented, flame-resistant cabinets. Store large containers near floor level. Make sure that storage shelves have a raised lip at the front to prevent containers from sliding forward.

Hazardous Materials

Some reagents can be explosive and should not be on the premises. If found, they should be removed by trained fire or police bomb squads or by other qualified officials.

Known carcinogens and probable carcinogens have frequently been found in biology stockrooms and should be removed by health authorities or a licensed commercial company. If you have doubts about the hazards of any reagent in the stockroom, contact an appropriate agency, such as NIOSH or a local health agency.

Known carcinogens commonly found in school science laboratories include the following:

arsenic pentoxide	benzidine
arsenic powder	chromium powder
arsenic trichloride	formaldehyde
arsenic trioxide	lead arsenate
asbestos	sodium arsenate
benzene	

Probable carcinogens include the following:

acrylonitrile	chloroform
cadmium chloride	ethidium bromide
cadmium powder	ethylene oxide
cadmium sulfate	nickel powder
carbon tetrachloride	

Exercise great care in using refrigerators. Never store flammable liquids in a refrigerator unless it is explosion-proof. Do not store food where microbial cultures are stored. Clean refrigerators frequently and safely discard old material.

Laboratory Glassware

Probably the most common school laboratory accidents involve cuts from chipped or broken glassware and burns from hot glassware. Discard any glassware that has a crack or chip. Use only borosilicate glassware. Fire-polish the ends of glass tubing. Allow hot glassware to cool on a hot pad for several minutes before picking it up. If an accident should happen, first aid for minor cuts and burns is immersion in cool running water. For cuts that are bleeding heavily, apply pressure with folded toweling or gauze. Call a health professional immediately.

To insert glass tubing into a stopper, lubricate the stopper hole and the tubing. Wrap the tubing in several layers of toweling and gently work the tubing into the stopper, using a twisting motion and keeping the hands as close together as possible. Wear heavy gloves. Remove the tubing in the same manner as soon as possible. Tubing that is stuck is nearly impossible to remove without cutting the stopper.

To avoid unwanted cultures, clean glassware frequently by using laboratory detergent. Most deposits can be removed with dilute hydrochloric acid or sodium hydroxide solution. Do not permit students to eat or drink from laboratory glassware.

Measuring small amounts of liquids with pipettes is common in investigations. But never pipette by mouth. Use rubber suction bulbs designed for use with pipettes or pipette fillers.

Safety Procedures With Microbial Cultures

Never culture pathogenic bacteria. However, treat all bacterial cultures as if they are pathogenic. Firmly seal with clear tape any bacterial plates that are used for student inspection. For sterilization, use a high-temperature gas flame rather than an alcohol burner or candle flame.

Cultures should be killed before disposal. Autoclave all cultures and contaminated glassware at 15 pounds pressure per square inch (103.4 Pa) for 20 minutes. Disposable plates should be incinerated.

Safety Procedures With Microscopes

Never use direct sunlight as a light source for the microscope. The lenses may concentrate the light and cause permanent retinal damage. With a soft cloth dipped in isopropyl alcohol, clean the eyepiece of each microscope between viewers. Make sure any electrical cords are out of the main traffic pattern of the classroom.

Safety Procedures With Dissections

Handle sharp and pointed instruments with care. Make sure the specimen is firmly secured on a dissection tray or cutting board. Caution students never to dissect a hand-held specimen. Make sure that the scalpels and scissors are sharp and adequate for the job. If razor blades are used for cutting tissues for slide mounts, use only single-edge noninjectable blades. Dissecting tools should not be removed from the laboratory and should be stored in a locked cabinet.

Formaldehyde has been identified as a carcinogen and mutagen. Although supply companies may still initially preserve specimens in formaldehyde, they should be stored in a different preservative. Any specimens stored in formaldehyde solution in the stockroom or classroom should be removed from the school site by qualified health authorities or a licensed commercial company.

Follow the instructions on the package for preparing specimens for dissection. Most should be rinsed in running water before use. Some may need to be soaked in water overnight if the preservative is particularly strong-smelling. Specimens that have not been preserved should be used sparingly and only for a short time. Use only healthy specimens. Instruct students to wear masks and gloves to guard against infection. After dissection, specimens should be discarded in separate containers that can be transported to an incineration site.

Field Investigations

Before taking students on a field investigation, examine the area for possible safety hazards. Look for terrain or water hazards and poisonous plants and animals. Obtain the necessary written permission from parents and school authorities. Instruct students on proper dress and behavior. Make sure that students are thoroughly familiar with the investigation they are to conduct. If students are to form small groups, decide in advance when and where they will reassemble. Do not allow any student to travel alone.

Identify any students who have special health problems, especially allergies. Alert these students to potential hazards. Be sure they are adequately prepared to deal with emergencies.

Master Materials List

Item	Quantity*	Used in Investigative Lab
Aceto-orcein stain	1 dropper bottle	9
Acrylic box, small	1	24
Aerating stone	1	21A (optional)
Agar cubes, dyed blue	2	6
Agar plates	1	19
	2	16A
Agarose gel	1	13A, 14A
Alcohol, rubbing	50 mL	30
Aluminum can	1	7
Aluminum foil, heavy-duty	Several sheets	7, 10A
Antacid medications, two types	1 dose of each type	4A
Antibiotic disks	2	16A
Apple	1	19
Applesauce, unsweetened, or crushed apples	80 g	5A
Artemia cysts	50	24A
Aquarium, 5–10 gallon	1	25
Aquarium pump	1 per 5 groups	21A
Bacterial culture	2	16A
Balance	1	2A, 5A, 7, 18, 21, 26A
Beaker, 250 mL	1	8A
Beaker, 400 mL	2	5, 13
Bean plant in 4-inch plastic pot	1	22A
Benedict's solution	5 mL	32
Bile solution	5 mL	29
Binoculars	1 pair	3A (optional)
Biuret reagent	12 drops	32
Bleach solution, 10%	100 mL	13, 16A
Bone, bird (chicken)	1	26A
Bone, mammal (pig)	1	26A
Bottle, plastic, 2 L	1	13, 34A
Bowl, plastic (disposable)	1	10, 19, 26
Bread or crackers	Several small pieces	29A
Bread spreads, various, with labels showing nutrition and price information	Samples	29A
Bromothymol blue solution	1 bottle	21A
Bucket	1	2A, 5, 11A, 21A, 35
Buffer capsule, pH 5	1	5
Cardboard, white (or plastic foam block)	1 piece	9A, 28
Cards, small	50	35A
CellServ Kit 4	1	12
Cellulase, IndiAge®	2 g	5
C-Fern® spores	1 vial	19
Cheesecloth, squares, 2 layers thick	1 piece	11
	2 pieces	5A
Chicken wing, raw	1	27
Clay, modeling	1 large ball	25
Cloth, 1-cm² pieces	5	36A
Cloth, sari, or other new and old cotton cloth	2 pieces	16
Cloth strips, yarn, or stickers, colored	2	9A
Coffee stirrers	5	36
Container, graduated, 1 L	1	2A
Container, opaque with lid	1	34
Coomassie blue stain	1 bottle	14A

Item	Quantity*	Used in Investigative Lab
Copepods	Culture	16
Cork	1	7
Cotton balls	1	12
	2–4	24, 30
Cotton swabs	2–5	24
Craft sticks, wooden	10	30A
Cups, foam	1	8A, 13, 32
	3	7A
Cups, paper	1	6
	2–5	4
Cup, opaque paper, 8 oz.	1	34A
Cup, plastic (large)	1	6, 10A, 13, 16A, 21
Cups, plastic, clear	2	4A, 5A, 8A, 20A
	5	36
Cups, plastic, clear, 16 oz., with lids with straw holes	2	21A
	4	16
Cutting board, plastic	1	8A
Dawn® liquid detergent	1 bottle	36A
Demo slide culture tube	4	34
Demo slide culture tube stage	1	34
Destain solution	1 bottle	14A
Detergent, liquid	1 drop	8
Detergent solution	10 mL	11
Dissecting probe	1	25A, 30A
Dissection tray and pins	1	23, 25A, 30A, 33A
DNA fragments, PCR-generated	3 samples	13A
Dowel, wooden, 1/8-in. dia.	1	7
Dropper, plastic	1	16, 25A, 26
Dye, Congo red	Few drops	17
Egg, raw (unfertilized)	1	26
ELISA medical diagnosis lab kit	1	31
Enviro-bond™ 403	1 tbsp	36A
Ethanol, 90%	5 mL	11
Ethanol, denatured, 70%	200 mL	8A
Extraction buffer	1000 µL	14A
Fabric, dark blue denim	3 7-cm² swatches	5
Feather, flight	1	15, 26A
Feather, down	1	26A
Fern frond	1	19A
Fetal pig, preserved	1	33A
File folder	1	23A
Film canisters, black	2	22
Film canisters, white or clear	5	18
Filter paper	Few sheets	10
Fingernail polish, clear, fast-drying	1 bottle	19A, 21
Fixative acid solution	1 dropper bottle	9
Flashlight, mini	1	28
Flask, 1 L	1	13
Flatworm (planarian) or segmented worm (*Lumbriculus*)	1	23A
Flour	110 g	18
Flower, large	1	20
Flowers, varying colors, sizes, and scents	A variety	20
Food coloring, red or blue	1 dropper bottle	18, 21
Food samples, including peanuts	A variety	7
Forceps	1	8A, 9, 16A, 20, 24A, 34A
Frog, preserved	1	25A

Item	Quantity*	Used in Investigative Lab
Fruit, strawberry, fresh or frozen	1	11
Funnels	2	5A, 11
Fur	Sample	26A
Gel electrophoresis chamber	1	13A, 14A
Geranium plant, potted	1	8A
Gloves, cloth	1 pair	34A
Graduated cylinders, 50 mL	1	36A
	2	4A, 5A, 7, 26A, 36
Graduated cylinder, 100 mL	1	2A, 4A, 7, 26A, 36
Graduated cylinder, 500 mL	1	13, 16
Growing containers with soil (see instructions in lab)	1 or 2	11A, 19
Guar gum or methyl cellulose	Sample	17
Hammer	1	4A, 7
Hand lens, 10×	1	5, 23, 24, 34A
Heating pad	1	18, 34
Hole punch, single	1	8, 21A
Hot plate	1	7A
Hydroponic solution	1 quart	21A
IAA (indoleacetic acid) paste (auxin)	Spoonful	22A
Ice, crushed	1 cup	13
Ice chest, foam	1	7A
Immersion oil (for 1000× only)	1	12
Incubator	1	13
Inoculating loop, plastic	2	11, 16A
Iodine solution (IKI)	40 mL	8A
Knife, large	1	2A
Knife, plastic	1	6, 14A, 21A
Labels and markers	A variety	14A, 16A, 21A, 24
Lamp, bright	1	8, 34A
Lamp, UV (long wavelength)	1	13
Leaf, angiosperm	1 or 2	19A
Leaf, freshly collected	1	2
Leaf, gymnosperm (pine needle)	1	19A
Leaves, ivy, from same plant	1 dark green, 1 light green	8
Leaves from selected greens	A variety	15
Leaves, with long petioles or narrow stems	5	21
Lens (200 mm focal length)	1	28
Light box	1 per class	14A
Light source, fluorescent	1	8A, 10, 34
Marker, permanent	1	2, 4A, 5A, 10, 10A, 11A, 12, 13, 16A, 17A, 18, 19A, 20A, 21, 21A, 22A, 26, 30A, 31, 34A, 35
Markers, colored	A variety	4, 5, 8, 23A, 28, 36
Marvel® Mystery Oil	60 mL	36A
Matches, safety	1	7
Measuring cups	1 set	7A
Measuring spoons	1 set	36A
Measuring tape, metric	1	2A
Methylene blue stain	1 bottle	7A (optional), 13A
Mexican jumping bean	1	1A
Meter stick	1	35
Microcentrifuge tubes	1	11
	4	7A
	8	14A, 32

Item	Quantity*	Used in Investigative Lab
Micropipette and tips	1	13A, 14A
Microscope slides and cover slips	1	1, 1A, 12, 21, 23
	2	7A, 17A, 19
	3	26A
	4	9, 19A
Microscope, compound	1	1, 1A, 6A, 7A, 9, 12, 16, 17, 17A, 19, 19A, 21, 24A, 26, 26A, 27A, 33
Milk, 2%	1 pint	7A
Milk, whole	12 mL	29
Mint sprigs	2	20A
Muscle tissue samples	4	14A
Mushroom growing kit	1	18A
Nail	1	7
Oat bran or wheat bran	1 tbsp (15 mL)	36A
Onion, with actively growing root tips	1	9
Paint brush, small	1	3, 15, 24, 24A
Pancreatic juice solution	2 mL	29
Paper clip	1	2, 28A
Paper, construction, black	1 sheet	28
Paper, construction, colored	A variety	28
Paper towels	Several	2A, 5, 5A, 9, 10A, 12, 14A, 15, 19A, 22, 24A, 29A, 31, 33A
Paramecium	Culture	17
Pectinase	0.5 mL	5A
Pencils, colored	1 set	1, 2A, 6A, 17, 17A, 19, 27, 27A, 33
Pennies	About 150	2
Pens, assorted ballpoint and felt-tip	Several	3
Petri dishes	1	3, 10, 15, 23A, 24A
	2	10A
	4	36A
Petri dish, top or bottom	1	9, 12, 34A (optional)
Petroleum jelly, in tube	1	21
pGLO™ transformation kit	1	13
pH paper	Several pieces	7A
Phenol red	1 bottle	29
Pig heart, preserved	1	30A
Pin	1	7
Plants in plastic six-pack pots	3	21A
Plastic containers, with cover	1	14, 13A, 14A
	2	17A
Plastic film squares	4	29
Plastic loops	6	7A
Plastic milk container, 1 gal.	1	21A
Plastic freezer bag	1	33A
Plastic sandwich bag, self-sealing	1	4A, 14
	2	2
Plastic storage bag, self-sealing	1	11, 34A
	2–5	4, 20, 36A
Plates, paper	1	23, 25A, 27, 33A
	2	15
Plastic wrap	1 piece	8A
Pots, plastic, 10-cm dia.	1	21A
	2	19, 22
Potting soil	1 bag	11A, 21A
Power supply	1	13A, 14A
Protein solution	0.5 mL	32
Protractor	1	25
Pumpkin	1	2A

Item	Quantity*	Used in Investigative Lab
Razor blade, single-edge	1	8A, 9
Ring stand, 4-in	1	7
Rubber band	1	23A
Ruler, metric	1	1A, 2A, 4, 8, 11A, 13A, 16A, 18A, 19, 19A, 25A, 28A, 34A
Ruler, transparent, metric	1	1, 16
Running buffer (Tris-Glycine-SDS)	1 container	13A, 14A
Saucepan, large	1	7A
Scalpel	1	25A, 30A, 33A
Scissors	1	1A, 5, 10, 10A, 15, 15A, 17A, 20, 20A, 21, 21A, 22, 22A, 23, 23A, 24A, 25A, 26A, 27, 28, 33A, 34A
Screening, rain gutter (1/8 inch) or hardware cloth	1 square	34A
Sea water, artificial	30 mL	24A
Seed starting mix	1 bag	22
Seeds, albino tobacco	50	10A
Seeds, Fast Plant™	30	10
	5	19
	2	22
Seeds, radish, exposed to cobalt-60	10	36A
Shears	1 pair	34A
Shoe box	1	28
Shoe box, plastic	1	18
Simulated bird food, candies, unshelled nuts, beans, etc.	2 types	14
Skewer or dissecting probe	1	23
Slide, prepared, animal cells	2	6A
Slide, prepared, mammalian epididymis, cross section	1	33
Slide, prepared, mammalian oviduct, cross section	1	33
Slide, prepared, mammalian skin, cross section	1	27A
Slide, prepared, mammalian testis, cross section	1	33
Slide, prepared, mammalian vas deferens, cross section	1	33
Slide, prepared, plant cells	2	6A
Sodium bicarbonate, (baking soda)	1/2 cup + 1/2 tsp	8
Sodium polyacrylate	1 tsp (5 mL)	36A
Soil testing kit, rapitest® or Lamotte	1	4
Spatula	1	13A (optional), 14A
Specimens from protist, fungus, plant, and animal kingdoms	A variety	1
Sponge, small kitchen	1	17A, 36A
Spoon, large stirring	1	2A, 7A
Spoon, metal	1	26
Spoon, plastic	1	7A
	2	4A, 5A
	Several	29A
Spray bottle	1	18A
Squid	1	23
Staining tray	1	13A, 14A
Stereomicroscope	1 per class	3, 20, 23, 23A, 24, 26
Stethoscope	1	30
Sticky notes, large	1 pad	23A
Stirring rods	1	11
	5	36

Item	Quantity*	Used in Investigative Lab
Stopwatch or clock with second hand	1	3A, 5A, 6, 8, 8A, 13, 25, 29, 30, 34A
Strainer	1	2A
String	1 m	17A, 33A
Sugar	25 g	18
Sugar solution	0.5 mL	32
Syringes	2	8
Tape	1 roll	10, 15A
Tape, colored plastic	8-cm piece	8A
Tape, double-sided	1 roll	24A
Tape, duct	1 roll	34A
Tape, labeling	1 roll	11A, 29
Tape, mailing, clear	1 roll	1A, 21, 21A
Tape, masking	1 roll	2, 4, 4A, 5A, 10, 18, 20A, 21A, 22A, 36, 33A, 36A
Termite, worker	1	3
Test-tube rack	1	9, 11, 14A, 21, 29
Test tubes	1	9
	2	11
	4	29
Thermometer	1	7, 7A, 9, 13, 34A
Thread	Several pieces	7A (optional)
Tongs	1	32
Toothpicks	1	17, 22A, 23A, 24
	2	19
Transfer pipettes	1	1A, 4A, 5A, 7A, 9, 17, 19, 21A, 23A, 26A, 33A, 34
	2	17A, 29, 36
Transfer pipettes	3	12
	6	1, 31
	10	21, 32
Trowel, garden, or small shovel	1	4, 34A
Tub, plastic, small	1	19
Tubing, aquarium	3 5-cm pieces	21A, 24
Tubing, aquarium Y or T connector	1	24
Twist tie	1	22A
Universal pH indicator	1 dropper bottle	4A, 36
Urine samples, simulated	3	32
Utensil, plastic	1	14
Vermiculite	1 qt. bag	19
Vinegar solution	100 mL	4A, 21A
	500 mL	6
Washer, metal, large	1	17A
Water	Various amounts	4A, 5, 7, 8, 8A, 10, 10A, 11A, 13, 14A, 17, 18A, 20A, 21, 21A, 22, 22A, 25, 26, 26A, 29, 32, 36A
Water, simulated "acid rain"	50 mL	36
Water, simulated Blue Mountain Lake	50 mL	36
Water, simulated Brant Lake	50 mL	36
Water, distilled	50 mL	36
Water, drinking	1 cup per student	29A
Water, lake, local	50 mL	36
Water, sterile	5 mL	19
Well slides with cover slip	Several	1, 16, 17, 19
White cabbage butterfly larva	3	15
Wire, copper or brass, 28 gauge	0.5 m	25
WOWBug pupae culture	1	24

Item	Quantity*	Used in Investigative Lab
Yarn	1 15-cm piece	28
Yeast, dry active	1 pkg.	17
Yeast, quick-rising baker's	1 pkg.	18
Yeast powder, blended	1 container	24A
Yogurt, plain, or yogurt culture	Spoonful or half a packet	7A

*per group

Materials Inventory

Equipment

Item	Lab	Item	Lab
Acrylic box, small	24	Measuring tape, metric	2A
Aerating stone	21A (optional)	Meter stick	35
Aquarium, 5-10 gallon	25	Microscope, compound	1, 1A, 6A, 7A, 9, 12, 16, 17, 17A, 19, 19A, 21, 24A, 26, 26A, 27A, 33
Aquarium pump	21A		
Balance	2A, 5A, 7, 18, 21, 26A		
Binoculars	3A (optional)	Nail	7
Bucket	2A, 5, 11A, 21A, 35	Paint brush, small	3, 15, 24, 24A
		Pencils, colored	1, 2A, 6A, 17, 17A, 19, 27, 27A, 33
Container, graduated, 1 L	2A		
Container, opaque with lid	34	Pennies	2
Cutting board, plastic	8A	Pens, assorted ballpoint and felt-tip	3
Demo slide culture tube	34		
Demo slide culture tube stage	34	Plastic containers, with cover	14, 13A, 14A, 17A
Dissecting probe	25A, 30A		
Dissection tray and pins	23, 25A, 30A, 33A	Pots, plastic, 10-cm dia.	19, 21A, 22
Dowel, wooden, 1/8-in. dia.	7	Power supply	13A, 14A
Dropper, plastic	16, 25A, 26	Protractor	25
Flashlight, mini	28	Razor blade, single-edge	8A, 9
Forceps	8A, 9, 16A, 20, 24A, 34A	Ring stand, 4-in	7
		Ruler, metric	1A, 2A, 4, 8, 11A, 13A, 16A, 18A, 19, 19A, 25A, 28A, 34A
Funnels	5A, 11		
Gel electrophoresis chamber	13A, 14A		
Gloves, cloth	34A		
Growing containers with soil (see instructions in lab)	11A, 19		
		Ruler, transparent, metric	1, 16
Hammer	4A, 7	Saucepan, large	7A
Hand lens, 103	5, 23, 24, 34A	Scalpel	25A, 30A, 33A
Heating pad	18, 34	Scissors	1A, 5, 10, 10A, 15, 15A, 17A, 20, 20A, 21, 21A, 22, 22A, 23, 23A, 24A, 25A, 26A, 27, 28, 33A, 34A
Hole punch, single	8, 21A		
Hot plate	7A		
Ice chest, foam	7A		
Incubator	13		
Knife, large	2A	Shears	34A
Lamp, bright	8, 34A	Skewer or dissecting probe	23
Lamp, UV (long wavelength)	13	Spatula	13A (optional), 14A
Lens (200 mm focal length)	28		
Light box	14A	Spoon, large stirring	2A, 7A
Light source, fluorescent	8A, 10, 34	Spoon, metal	26
Marker, permanent	2, 4A, 5A, 10, 10A, 11A, 12, 13, 16A, 17A, 18, 19A, 20A, 21, 21A, 22A, 26, 30A, 31, 34A, 35	Spray bottle	18A
		Staining tray	13A, 14A
		Stereomicroscope	3, 20, 23, 23A, 24, 26
		Stethoscope	30
Markers, colored	4, 5, 8, 23A, 28, 36	Stopwatch or clock with second hand	3A, 5A, 6, 8, 8A, 13, 25, 29, 30, 34A
Measuring cups	7A	Strainer	2A
Measuring spoons	36A	Syringes	8

Item	Lab
Test-tube rack	9, 11, 14A, 21, 29
Thermometer	7, 7A, 9, 13, 34A
Tongs	32
Transfer pipettes	1, 1A, 4A, 5A, 7A, 9, 12, 17, 17A, 19, 21, 21A, 23A, 26A, 29, 31, 32, 33A, 34, 36
Trowel, garden, or small shovel	4, 34A
Tub, plastic, small	19
Tubing, aquarium	21A, 24
Tubing, aquarium Y or T connector	24
Washer, metal, large	17A
Wire, copper or brass, 28 gauge	25

Glassware

Item	Lab
Beaker, 250 mL	8A
Beaker, 400 mL	5, 13
Flask, 1 L	13
Graduated cylinders, 50 mL	4A, 5A, 7, 26A, 36, 36A
Graduated cylinder, 100 mL	2A, 4A, 7, 26A, 36
Graduated cylinder, 500 mL	13, 16
Microcentrifuge tubes	7A, 11, 14A, 32
Micropipette and 5 tips	13A, 14A
Microscope slides and cover slips	1, 1A, 7A, 9, 12, 17A, 19, 19A, 21, 23, 26A
Petri dishes	3, 10, 10A, 15, 23A, 24A, 36A
Petri dish, top or bottom (optional)	9, 12, 34A
Stirring rods	11, 36
Test tubes	9, 11, 29
Well slides with cover slip	1, 16, 17, 19

Chemical Supplies

Item	Lab
Aceto-orcein stain	9
Alcohol, rubbing	30
Benedict's solution	32
Bile solution	29
Biuret reagent	32
Bleach solution, 10%	13, 16A
Bromothymol blue solution	6, 21A
Buffer capsule, pH 5	5
Cellulase, IndiAge®	5
Coomassie blue stain	14A
Destain solution	14A
Dye, Congo red	17
Enviro-bond™ 403	36A
Ethanol, 90%	11
Ethanol, denatured, 70%	8A
Extraction buffer	14A
Fixative acid solution	9
Guar gum or methyl cellulose	17
Hydroponic solution	21A
IAA (indoleacetic acid) paste (auxin)	22A
Immersion oil (for 10003 only)	12
Iodine solution (IKI)	8A
Marvel® Mystery Oil	36A
Methylene blue stain	7A (optional), 13A
Pancreatic juice solution	29
Pectinase	5A
Phenol red	29
Protein solution	32
Running buffer (Tris-Glycine-SDS)	13A, 14A
Sodium bicarbonate, (baking soda)	8
Sodium polyacrylate	36A
Sugar solution	32
Universal pH indicator	4A, 36
Urine samples, simulated	32
Vinegar solution	4A, 6, 21A

Organisms

Item	Lab
Artemia cysts	24A
Bacterial culture	16A
Bean plant in 4-inch plastic pot	22A
C-Fern® spores	19
Copepods	16
Flatworm (planarian) or segmented worm (*Lumbriculus*)	23A
Geranium plant, potted	8A
Mexican jumping bean	1A
Paramecium	17
Plants in plastic six-pack pots	21A
Seeds, albino tobacco	10A
Seeds, Fast Plant™	10, 19, 22
Seeds, radish, exposed to cobalt-60	36A
Specimens from protist, fungus, plant, and animal kingdoms	1
Squid	23

Item	Lab
Termite, worker	3
White cabbage butterfly larva	15
WOWBug pupae culture	24

Preserved Specimens

Item	Lab
Fetal pig, preserved	33A
Frog, preserved	25A
Pig heart, preserved	30A

Prepared Microscope Slides

Slide, prepared, animal cells	6A
Slide, prepared, mammalian epididymis, cross section	33
Slide, prepared, mammalian oviduct, cross section	33
Slide, prepared, mammalian skin, cross section	27A
Slide, prepared, mammalian testis, cross section	33
Slide, prepared, mammalian vas deferens, cross section	33
Slide, prepared, plant cells	6A

Consumable Supplies

Item	Lab
Agar cubes, dyed blue	6
Agar plates	16A, 19
Agarose gel	13A, 14A
Aluminum can	7
Aluminum foil, heavy-duty	7, 10A
Antacid medications, two types	4A
Antibiotic disks	16A
Apple	19
Applesauce, unsweetened, or crushed apples	5A
Bone, bird (chicken)	26A
Bone, mammal (pig)	26A
Bottle, plastic, 2 L	13, 34A
Bowl, plastic (disposable)	10, 19, 26
Bread or crackers	29A
Bread spreads, various, with labels showing nutrition and price information	29A
Cardboard, white (or plastic foam block)	9A, 28
Cards, small	35A
CellServ Kit 4	12
Cheesecloth, squares, 2 layers thick	5A, 11
Chicken wing, raw	27

Item	Lab
Clay, modeling	25
Cloth, 1-cm^2 pieces	36A
Cloth, sari, or other new and old cotton cloth	16
Cloth strips, yarn, or stickers, colored	9A
Coffee stirrers	36
Cork	7
Cotton balls	12, 24, 30
Cotton swabs	24
Craft sticks, wooden	30A
Cups, foam	7A, 8A, 13, 32
Cups, paper	4, 6
Cup, opaque paper, 8 oz.	34A
Cup, plastic (large)	6, 10A, 13, 16A, 21
Cups, plastic, clear	4A, 5A, 8A, 20A, 36
Cups, plastic, clear, 16 oz., with lids with straw holes	16, 21A
Dawn® liquid detergent	36A
Detergent, liquid	8
Detergent solution	11
DNA fragments, PCR-generated	13A
Egg, raw (unfertilized)	26
ELISA medical diagnosis lab kit	31
Fabric, dark blue denim	5
Feather, flight	15, 26A
Feather, down	26A
Fern frond	19A
File folder	23A
Film canisters, black	22
Film canisters, white or clear	18
Filter paper	10
Fingernail polish, clear, fast-drying	19A, 21
Flour	18
Flower, large	20
Flowers, varying colors, sizes, and scents	20
Food coloring, red or blue	18, 21
Food samples, including peanuts	7
Fruit, strawberry, fresh or frozen	11
Fur	26A
Ice, crushed	13
Inoculating loop, plastic	11, 13, 16A
Knife, plastic	6, 14A, 21A
Labels and markers	14A, 16A, 21A, 24
Leaf, angiosperm	19A

Item	Lab	Item	Lab
Leaf, freshly collected	2	Shoe box, plastic	18
Leaf, gymnosperm (pine needle)	19A	Simulated bird food, candies, unshelled nuts, beans, etc.	14
Leaves, ivy, from same plant	8	Soil testing kit, rapitest® or Lamotte	4
Leaves from selected greens	15	Sponge, small kitchen	17A, 36A
Leaves, with long petioles or narrow stems	21	Spoon, plastic	4A, 5A, 7A, 29A
Matches, safety	7	Sticky notes, large	23A
Milk, 2%	7A	String	17A, 33A
Milk, whole	29	Sugar	18
Mint sprigs	20A	Tape	10, 15A
Muscle tissue samples	14A	Tape, colored plastic	8A
Mushroom growing kit	18A	Tape, double-sided	24A
Oat bran or wheat bran	36A	Tape, duct	34A
Onion, with actively growing root tips	9	Tape, labeling	11A, 29
		Tape, mailing, clear	1A, 21, 21A
Paper clip	2, 28A	Tape, masking	2, 4, 4A, 5A, 10, 18, 20A, 21A, 22A, 33A, 36, 36A
Paper, construction, black	28		
Paper, construction, colored	28		
Paper towels	2A, 5, 5A, 9, 10A, 12, 14A, 15, 19A, 22, 24A, 29A, 31, 33A	Thread	7A (optional)
		Toothpicks	17, 19, 22A, 23A, 24
Petroleum jelly, in tube	21	Twist tie	22A
pGLO™ transformation kit	13	Utensil, plastic	14
pH paper	7A	Vermiculite	19
Pin	7	Water	4A, 5, 7, 8, 8A, 10, 10A, 11A, 13, 14A, 17, 18A, 20A, 21, 21A, 22, 22A, 25, 26, 26A, 29, 32, 36A
Plastic film squares	29		
Plastic loops	7A		
Plastic milk container, 1 gal.	21A		
Plastic freezer bag	33A		
Plastic sandwich bag, self-sealing	2, 4A, 14	Water, simulated "acid rain"	36
Plastic storage bag, self-sealing	4, 11, 20, 34A, 36A	Water, simulated Blue Mountain Lake	36
Plates, paper	15, 23, 25A, 27, 33A	Water, simulated Brant Lake	36
		Water, distilled	36
Plastic wrap	8A	Water, drinking	29A
Potting soil	11A, 21A	Water, lake, local	36
Pumpkin	2A	Water, sterile	19
Rubber band	23A	Yarn	28
Screening, rain gutter (1/8 inch) or hardware cloth	34A	Yeast, dry active	17
		Yeast, quick-rising baker's	18
Sea water, artificial	24A	Yeast powder, blended	24A
Seed starting mix	22	Yogurt, plain, or yogurt culture	7A
Shoe box	28		

Additional Resources for Inquiry Investigations

Adamovic, Charles and Hedden, Carol J. 1997. Problem-solving Skills. *The Science Teacher* 64(4):20-23.

Ardizzone, Leonisa. 1997. A Course for Each Student. *The Science Teacher* 65(2):38-40.

Chiappetta, Eugene L. and Fillman, David A. 1998. Clarifying the Place of Essential Topics and Unifying Principles in High School Biology. *School Science and Mathematics* 98(1):12-18.

Colburn, Alan and Clough, Michael P. 1997. Implementing the Learning Cycle: A Gradual Shift to a New Teaching Approach. *The Science Teacher* 64(5):30-34.

Council for Environmental Education. (2000). *Project Wild: K–12 Activity Guide*. Gaithersburg, MD: The Council for Environmental Education.

Eyster, Linda S. 1997. A Comprehensive Rubric: Helping Teachers Grade Process-Oriented Tasks. *The Science Teacher* 64(9):18-21.

Francis, Joseph W. 2000. Use of Internet Resources in the Biology Lecture Classroom. *The American Biology Teacher* 62(2):90-93.

Goodman, L. and Berntson, G. 2000. The Art of Asking Questions: Using Directed Inquiry in the Classroom. *The American Biology Teacher* 62(7):473-477.

Heuschele, Ann. "It All Looks the Same to Me": An Exercise in Critical Observation. *The American Biology Teacher* 61(6):434-437.

Hinman, Richard L. 1998. Content and Science Inquiry. *The Science Teacher* 65(7):25-27.

Holyoak, Alan R. 1998. A Plan for Writing Throughout (not just across) the Biology Curriculum. *The American Biology Teacher* 60(5):186-190.

Johansen, Carol K. and Harris, David E. 2000. Teaching the Ethics of Biology. *The American Biology Teacher* 62(5):352-358.

Klapper, Michael H. 1995. Beyond the Scientific Method: Should Science Be Taught As a More Creative Process? *The Science Teacher* 62(6):36-40.

Krest, Margie and Carle, Daria O. 1999. Teaching Scientific Writing: A Model for Integrating Research, Writing, and Critical Thinking. *The American Biology Teacher* 61(3):223-227.

Lawson, Anton E. 2000. Managing the Inquiry Classroom: Problems and Solutions. *The American Biology Teacher* 62(9):641-648.

Liggitt-Fox, Dianna. 1997. Fighting Student Misconceptions: Three Effective Strategies. *Science Scope* 20(5):28-30.

Lord, Thomas. 1998. Cooperative Learning that Really Works in Biology Teaching: Using Constructivist-based Activities to Challenge Student Teams. *The American Biology Teacher* 60(8):580-588.

McCormick, Terry L. 1995. Problem-Solving Projects: Integrating Technology into the Science Classroom. *The Science Teacher* 62(3):27-29.

Melear, Claudia. 1995. Multiculturalism in Science Education. *The American Biology Teacher* 57(1):21-27.

National Research Council. (2000). *How People Learn: Brain, Mind, Experience, and School: Expanded Edition*. Washington, D.C.: National Academy Press.

National Research Council. (2000). *Inquiry and the* National Science Education Standards: *A Guide for Teaching and Learning*. Washington, D.C.: National Academy Press.

Pheeney, Pierette. 1998. A Portfolio Primer: Helping Teachers Make the Most of this Assessment Tool. *The Science Teacher* 65(7):36-39.

Pierce, Wendy. 1998. Linking Learning to Labs. *Science Scope* 21(4):17-19.

Smithhenry, Dennis. 1997. Creating a Scientific Community: Set the Tone Early for Yearlong Cooperative Learning. *The Science Teacher* 64(8):44-47.

Wright, Emmett L. and Govindarjan, Girish. 1995. Discrepant Event Demonstrations: Motivating Students to Learn Science Concepts. *The Science Teacher* 62(1):24-28.

Young, Jay A. 1997. Chemical Safety – Part I: Safety in the Handling of Hazardous Chemicals. *The Science Teacher* 64(3):43-45.

Young, Jay A. 1997. Chemical Safety – Part II: Tips for Dealing with Laboratory Hazards. *The Science Teacher* 64(4):40-43.

Lab Procedures

The purpose of this section is to provide some general information about making growing containers for plants, preparing solutions and media, making substitutions for pH indicators, and culturing live materials. For more specific information regarding the preparation and use of solutions, media, and organisms in a particular Investigative Lab, consult the on-page annotations.

Growing Containers

For the latest recommended Fast Plant growing and lighting systems, see the packaging information that arrives with your seeds or go to the Wisconsin Fast Plants program Web site at www.fastplants.org.

Solutions

General guidelines for preparing solutions and media include the following:

1. Prepare necessary solutions well in advance of the investigations in which they will be used. Each solution should be clearly labeled with its name, concentration, date of preparation, and any appropriate warnings such as toxic or flammable.

2. Always use clean glassware that has been washed with a low-sudsing laboratory soap. All glassware should be rinsed thoroughly in distilled water before use.

3. Mix each solution in a beaker or flask that holds 100 to 300 mL more than the amount of solution being prepared.

4. Use distilled water to make all preparations. Tap water may contain chemicals that alter the properties of solutions.

5. Pour concentrated acids and bases into water, stirring constantly. Never pour water into concentrated acids or bases.

6. Add solvents to solutes. Stir until solute is completely dissolved.

7. Store stains in dropper bottles.

Percentage Solutions: Volume/Volume To prepare a solution of a given percentage, dissolve the number of milliliters of solute equal to the percentage in enough solvent to make 100 mL of solution. For example, a 10% solution of hydrochloric acid (HCl) can be made by adding 10mL of concentrated HCl to enough distilled water to bring the volume to 100 mL.

Percentage Solutions: Mass/Volume To prepare a solution of a given percentage, dissolve the number of grams of solute equal to the percentage in enough solvent to make 100 mL of the solution. For example, a 3% solution of sodium chloride (NaCl) can be made by adding 3 g NaCl to a graduated cylinder and then adding enough distilled water to bring the volume to 100 mL.

Reducing the Concentration of a Solution To reduce the concentration of an existing solution, pour the number of milliliters of the existing solution that is equal to the percentage of the new concentration into a graduated cylinder. Add enough distilled water to bring the volume in milliliters to an amount equal to the percentage of the original solution. For example, to reduce an 80% glucose solution to 20%, pour 20 mL of 80% glucose solution into a graduated cylinder. Add enough distilled water to bring the volume to 80 mL of 20% glucose.

Indicator Substitutions

In the biology laboratory, the pH indicators that are suggested for use can often be replaced by others that are equally effective. The table on the next page lists some common indicators, the pH values at which they undergo a color change, and the expected color change.

Live Organisms

The live organisms used in the *Biology: Exploring Life Laboratory Manual* are readily available and can be cultured and maintained in a classroom or laboratory environment. Organisms are available from biological supply companies and often from pet stores or supermarkets. Some organisms can be collected from local ponds, streams, fields, and forests.

In many schools, circumstances require that laboratory supplies, including live organisms, be ordered a year in advance. If this situation exists at your school, you may need to maintain cultures of organisms for long periods of time. The following directions on how to care for and maintain live organisms can be easily followed by you or a student laboratory assistant.

Careful attention to directions and the use of proper equipment and materials is important in caring for live organisms. Be especially careful when using glassware. Be sure that all glassware is clean and free of any soap residue.

Ideally, glassware used to culture organisms should be new and untouched by chemicals, including soap. Laboratory glassware often retains traces of the chemicals it has contacted even after it has been cleaned—and even the faintest traces of some chemicals can have a serious impact on live organisms. Because the organisms used in the Investigative Labs usually are quite hardy, they can be cultured under less than ideal conditions. However, you may want to set aside some glassware to use exclusively for culturing organisms and preparing media. This glassware should not come in contact with chemicals harsher than laboratory soap.

Some of the following notes pertain to organisms not used in these Investigative Labs. You may wish to culture these organisms for enrichment activities, independent student projects, or teacher demonstrations.

Algae Order specific species of algae such as the brown alga *Fucus* from a biological supply company. Follow the instructions provided by the supplier to

Indicator	pH Value at Which Color Change Occurs	Color Change
thymol blue (acid)	1.5–2.5	red to yellow
bromphenol blue	3.0–4.5	yellow to blue
Congo red	3.0–5.0	blue to red
methyl orange	3.0–3.5	orange-red to yellow
litmus	4.5–8.5	red to blue
alizarin red	5.0–7.0	yellow to red
bromcresol purple	5.5–7.0	yellow to purple
bromothymol blue	6.0–7.5	yellow to blue
phenol red	6.5–8.0	yellow to red
neutral red	7.0–8.0	red to yellow
cresol red	7.0–9.0	yellow to red
thymol blue (alkaline)	8.0–10.0	yellow to blue
phenolphthalein	8.0–10.0	colorless to red
alizarin yellow	10.0–12.0	colorless to yellow

maintain the algae cultures. A salt mixture for preparing artificial seawater for *Fucus* culture can be purchased from an aquarium supply shop. Loosely place algae in jars of artificial seawater. Store the uncovered jars in a cool room beneath fluorescent lights.

Anoles Anoles and other small lizards may be raised in a terrarium constructed from a fine mesh cage or from a glass aquarium. If an aquarium is used, the top of the lizards' living quarters should be made of screen for good ventilation. The living quarters should contain some twigs on which the lizards can climb. Spray the plants in the terrarium daily to supply water for the lizards; they will lick up droplets of moisture from leaves but will seldom, if ever, drink water from a dish. The lizards subsist mainly on live insects. You may feed the lizards by offering them small crickets or occasionally mealworms held with forceps. Or, you may place live insects such as crickets and fruit flies in the terrarium. You may wish to cover the top of the terrarium with a few layers of cheesecloth.

Aquatic plants Aquatic plants are common freshwater aquarium plants and are generally available from pet stores. Aquatic plants can also be collected throughout most of the year from ponds and slow-moving streams. To maintain aquatic plants in the classroom, fill an aquarium or large (4-L) glass jar with pond or spring water. If pond or spring water is not available, fill the container with tap water and set it aside for at least 24 hours before introducing the aquatic plants. Float aquatic plants loosely on the surface of the water. Overcrowding of the aquatic plants will cause them to deteriorate. Replenish water as necessary due to water loss from evaporation. Nutrients for aquatic plants can be provided by adding six to eight guppies or mature duckweed culture to the aquarium. Do not add snails to the aquatic plants: they will quickly eat and destroy the plants. Nutrients also can be provided by adding dilute (1%)

commercial fertilizer (5–10–5) to the water. Provide a minimum of 15 hours of fluorescent light each day.

Bacteria Pure cultures of bacteria can be obtained from a biological supply company. Make sure that you are familiar with bacteriological techniques and have all necessary equipment and supplies—autoclaves, incubators, media, plates, slants, etc.—before using any bacteria in the biology laboratory. Never use pathogenic bacteria, but always treat all bacteria cultures as if they were pathogenic.

Bacteria are easily cultured in tubes of nutrient broth. To prepare the nutrient broth, bring 350 mL distilled water to a boil in a 500-mL beaker. Slowly add 3 g dehydrated nutrient broth, stirring constantly. Pour the broth into small test tubes and insert a cotton plug into each tube. Sterilize the tubes of broth for 15 minutes at 15 pounds pressure in an autoclave or pressure cooker. The sterilized tubes can be stored in a refrigerator until they are used. Transfer bacteria to the tubes of sterile nutrient broth using an inoculating loop and following sterile technique. Store inoculated tubes at room temperature for two to three days to allow the bacteria to grow. Tubes of bacteria can also be incubated at 37°C for 24 hours and used immediately. Subcultures and dilutions of the cultures can be made at two-week intervals. Cultures remain viable stored in a refrigerator for several weeks.

Bacteria may also be cultured on agar plates or slants. Biological supply companies often provide bacterial cultures on slants. Make subcultures of bacteria as soon as possible after receiving the original cultures. You can extend the life of slant cultures by covering the slants with a thin layer of sterile mineral oil and storing them in a refrigerator. These oil-covered slants will usually survive for several months.

Brine shrimp The brine shrimp *Artemia* is a good source of food for hydras, fish, and other aquatic animals. It is also rather interesting to observe in its own right, as it exhibits a strong positive response to light.

Brine shrimp eggs are available from pet stores, tropical fish stores, and biological supply companies. Hatch brine shrimp eggs in a shallow glass dish containing a dilute (4%) solution of sodium chloride. Sprinkle 0.5 mL brine shrimp eggs on the surface of the water. Larvae will hatch in 18 to 72 hours, depending on the temperature of the water. At a constant temperature of 21°C, brine shrimp eggs usually hatch within 48 hours. Aerating the water with an aerating stone increases the hatching success rate.

Brine shrimp will grow to maturity in about 20 days if they are cultured in a well-aerated aquarium at temperatures below 25°C. They can be fed a yeast suspension supplemented with scrapings of algae from the sides of aquaria.

To capture brine shrimp for observation or for feeding to other organisms, shine a light at one side of the container. Siphon off the brine shrimp with a piece of plastic tubing or a kitchen bulb baster. Before being fed to hydras or other fresh-water organisms, brine shrimp must first be washed with distilled water to remove any traces of salt. To wash the brine shrimp, pour them through a filter or fine mesh net. Rinse them thoroughly with a gentle stream of tap or distilled water. Brine shrimp can survive only a few hours in fresh water, so remove and wash only as many as are needed.

Daphnia *Daphnia* are available from a biological supply company. To culture *Daphnia,* nearly fill a 4-L jar with pasteurized spring water or tap water that has been allowed to stand at room temperature at least 24 hours. To the water add green unicellular algae or 100 mL of an established *Euglena* culture. Add several *Daphnia* to the jar and place the jar near a light source. Replenish the water and *Euglena* culture as necessary. Subculture the *Daphnia* about every three weeks.

Drosophila Fruit flies can be collected from fruit and vegetable markets or purchased from biological supply companies. Fruit flies with specific traits for use in genetics investigations must be ordered from a biological supply company far enough in advance to allow for the desired increase in the population size of the flies. Store flies in clear plastic or glass vials or jars with stoppers that allow for air exchanges. Stoppers must be escape-proof. Include in each vial a small piece of paper towel on which the flies can perch. Store the vials in a warm (18°–20°C) area away from bright light.

Fruit flies can be cultured on a few slices of overripe banana that have been sprinkled with a few grains of yeast. They can also be cultured on one of a large number of commercial or "home-made" media. The recipe for one particularly effective home-made medium is as follows.

- Banana-Agar Medium: Bring 625 mL water to a boil. Add 20 g agar powder and boil until thoroughly dissolved, stirring constantly. Add 25 mL white corn syrup and 250 mL mashed, very ripe bananas. Add 20 g dried brewer's yeast. Bring

this mixture to a boil. If desired, add 20 g of a commercial mold inhibitor at this point. Stir mixture until all ingredients are thoroughly mixed. Pour into sterile culture vials as needed.

Fill a culture bottle with 1 to 2 cm of medium. Insert a piece of crumpled paper toweling into the medium before it hardens. This provides a surface for egg-laying and pupation. Bottles may be stoppered with foam rubber or cotton wrapped in cheesecloth.

The life cycle of *Drosophila* takes about two weeks and varies with temperature. At 20°C, the life cycle usually takes 15 days. A magnifying glass is useful in sexing adult fruit flies. Males, which are slightly smaller than females, have a wide pigmented band that covers the posterior third of their rounded abdomen. Females have 5 to 8 thin bands on their slightly pointed abdomen.

Because female *Drosophila* store sperm within their body for some time after mating, virgin females must be obtained for genetic crosses. One way of ensuring that the females in a culture are virgin is to remove all the adult flies in a culture as pupae begin to form. The emerging female flies will be virgin for the first 10 hours.

Fruit flies must be anesthetized so that they can be examined. Traditionally, ether has been used; however, there are a number of commercial anesthetics available that are much less volatile. You can obtain anesthetizers from biological supply companies or construct them yourself.

To construct an anesthetizer, you will need a bottle whose mouth is the same size as that of the culture bottles, a cork stopper that fits the bottle, a nail about 3 cm long, cotton or gauze, and thread. Push the nail into the cork stopper so that the head of the nail is flush with the top of the stopper and the point of the nail protrudes from the bottom side of the stopper. Cover the nail with cotton; secure the cotton with thread. When ready to use the anesthetizer, put a few drops of anesthetic on the cotton.

To transfer flies from the culture bottle to the anesthetizer, tap the side of the culture bottle so that the flies fall to the bottom of the bottle. Quickly place the mouth of the anesthetizer over the mouth of the culture bottle. Invert the culture bottle and tap it so the flies (but not the medium or larvae) fall into the anesthetizer. Then quickly separate and stopper the bottles.

When the flies stop moving, spill them onto a sheet of white paper. Have on hand a petri dish cover that has a piece of filter paper taped to the inside. If the flies begin reviving too soon, put a drop or two of anesthetic on the filter paper and then cover the flies for a few seconds until they are reanesthetized.

Manipulate the flies using a small paintbrush. Transfer dead or unwanted flies to the "morgue"—a container of mineral oil. When transferring flies into a culture bottle, make sure that they fall on the paper toweling. If they fall on the medium, they will get stuck and die.

Duckweed Duckweed can be purchased from a biological supply company or collected from ponds and slow-moving streams in spring and early summer. A manure medium for duckweed can be prepared by adding 10 mL fresh or dried cow manure to 2 L tap water that has been allowed to stand at least 24 hours. Boil this mixture for 15 minutes and then allow it to cool. Pour the manure medium into several large jars. Add about 50 duckweed clusters to each jar. Duckweed can also be maintained on the surface of an established aquarium that contains snails and fish.

Earthworms Earthworms are readily collected when they come to the surface at night or after a heavy rain. They can also be obtained from a biological supply company. Food and habitats for worms are available commercially. You can also house worms in wooden containers such as cigar boxes. Fill the container with 5 to 15 centimeters of moist soil or peat moss. Keep the container covered and store it at a temperature of about 15°C. Make sure the soil remains moist. Twice a week, bury some lettuce and bits of bread soaked in milk in the soil.

Ferns Ferns may be grown in clay pots or terraria. The soil should be kept moist but not wet. Most ferns prefer medium light and relatively cool temperatures. Certain ferns, such as the bracken fern, should not be placed in direct or strong sunlight. Fern gametophytes take at least six weeks to grow from spores. The spores from crushed sori may be cultured in flowerpots, on the surface of an inverted flowerpot, or in sterile agar medium.

Frogs Live adult frogs can be maintained for short periods of time in plastic containers approximately 35 × 25 × 11 cm. Add enough tap water to half cover the frogs. At one end, insert an upside-down glass dish on which the frogs can rest out of the water. Provide hiding places by including broken pieces of clay pots. Cover the container to prevent escape. Clean the water every two to three days. Feed the frogs live insects or worms daily.

Eggs of *Xenopus* and *Rana pipiens* are recommended for hatching in the classroom. Use only tap water that has been allowed to stand at least 24 hours at room temperature to hatch the eggs and raise the tadpoles. Separate the eggs into clumps of about 10. Place the eggs in shallow containers of water. Maintain the eggs at room temperature and near a window where they can receive direct sunlight at least part of the day. Ten immature tadpoles can be maintained in a liter of water. Begin feeding tadpoles when strands of fecal matter appear in the water. Twice a week, feed tadpoles dry yeast or dry pea-soup powder. Clean the water as necessary. Larger tadpoles should be kept one each in a liter of water.

Goldfish The hardiest and least expensive type of goldfish are the wild-type fishes that are generally sold in pet stores as food for exotic fishes. Goldfish may also be obtained from biological supply companies.

Goldfish can be maintained in an aquarium or large glass container. Use tap water that has stood at room temperature at least 24 hours. If possible, use an aquarium with a corner or under-gravel filter to clean the water. Feed the goldfish daily, using commercial

food, crushed dog or cat food, or dry high-protein baby cereal. Approximately one-half teaspoon of food is adequate for five fish. Keep the water clean to avoid contamination by bacteria and fungi.

Grasshoppers Collect live grasshoppers from nearby fields. Maintain live grasshoppers in glass jars or aquariums with mesh or screen coverings. Provide twigs on which the grasshoppers can crawl and perch, water, and food such as leaves of lettuce and spinach.

Hydra Hydras are easily grown in a culture dish containing a 5-cm sprig of an aquatic plant and pasteurized spring water (pH 7). (See the section on *Amoeba* for directions on the preparation of pasteurized spring water.) Place 20 to 30 hydras in the culture dish. Place the dish near a fluorescent light where it will receive 16 hours of light per day. Hydras are active carnivorous feeders that will eat only live food. Providing an adequate food supply is the most difficult aspect of maintaining hydras in the classroom. Feed hydras the washed larvae of brine shrimp, *Daphnia,* or chopped *Tubifex* worms every other day. Hydras require clean water. About 30 minutes after each feeding, remove uneaten brine shrimp and other debris from the bottom of the dish with a medicine dropper. Remove half the water from the dish and replace it with pasteurized spring water. Replace the aquatic plant as it deteriorates. When the population reaches 50 hydras, begin a new culture with half of the individuals from the existing culture.

Lichens Lichens may be obtained from biological supply companies. Alternatively, you may collect lichens from the surfaces of rocks, buildings, and dead trees. Spraying the attached lichens with water softens them and loosens their hold. Use a sharp knife to gently remove the lichens and place them in a cardboard box. The lichens can be stored in loosely covered cardboard boxes in a cool dry location. Spraying the lichens with water before they are used in the investigation softens them somewhat and reduces their brittleness.

Mosses and liverworts Mosses and liverworts may be obtained from biological supply companies or collected in woodland areas. A moist, covered terrarium in medium light provides the best growing conditions. If molds start to grow in the terrarium, remove the cover and reduce the amount of water until the molds disappear. Sprinkling a small amount of powdered sulfur in the terrarium may also discourage molds.

Pillbugs Terrestrial isopods such as pillbugs, woodlice, and sowbugs can be raised in a terrarium that contains damp, rich humus with small rocks under which the isopods can hide. These isopods will eat small pieces of apples, raw potatoes, and lettuce.

Planarians Planarians such as *Dugesia* can be collected from the underside of logs and stones in bodies of cold, clear fresh water. They can also be obtained from biological supply companies. Planarians should be kept in black or opaque containers such as enameled pans at a temperature of about 23°C. The water should be changed frequently. Feed the planarians bits of raw liver, *Tubifex* worms, or egg yolk. Remove excess food with a medicine dropper or pipette after several hours to avoid fouling the water.

Plants Terrestrial plants such as *Coleus,* geraniums, and *Mimosa pudica* can be obtained from biological supply houses. Follow the supplier's directions regarding frequency of watering, exposure to light, and fertilizing. *Coleus* can be easily propagated from stem cuttings.

Protists Protists such as *Euglena, Amoeba, Stentor,* and *Paramecium* can be cultured in the classroom. Protists are easily cultured in stackable containers, such as finger bowls, Syracuse dishes, watch glasses, and petri dishes. The successful culturing of protists requires clean glassware. If possible, sterilize all glassware in an autoclave or pressure cooker. If sterilization is not possible, thoroughly wash all glassware in a solution of 10% nitric acid. Take care to avoid burns when working with nitric acid. Rinse the glassware several times with distilled water. Chemical and soap residues are harmful to protists and may prevent their successful culturing.

Pure stock cultures of protists can be purchased from a biological supply company. Mixed species of protists can be collected from ponds and slow-moving streams.

Cultures of protists can be successfully grown in pond water. Before using pond water, filter it through several layers of muslin or cheesecloth to remove debris. Protists can also be cultured in pasteurized spring water with a pH near 7. To pasteurize spring water, place 12 to 16 L spring water in a large enameled container. Heat the water to 65°C for 15 minutes. Pasteurized spring water can be stored up to two weeks in covered plastic containers. Longer storage requires repasteurization at two-week intervals to control the growth of hydrogen sulfide bacteria. Pond or pasteurized spring water should be used in the preparation of growth media. The following recipe for wheat medium is a good all-purpose growth medium for most protists.

- Wheat Medium: Collect wheat seeds that have not been sprayed with pesticides; obtain the seeds from farmers or order them from a biological supply company. Dried split peas or rice (not the quick-cooking variety) can be substituted for wheat seeds. Place 50 to 75 wheat seeds in a glass jar, seal the jar, and place it in an 82°C (180°F) oven for four hours. Or place 50 to 75 wheat seeds in a screw-top test tube filled with spring water. In an autoclave or pressure cooker, heat the test tubes for 15 minutes at 15 pounds pressure. In a culture dish, add three to five wheat seeds to pasteurized spring water. Add 3 to 4 mL stock protist culture to the dish. Loosely cover the culture dish and set it aside in a dimly lit area of the laboratory. Replenish evaporated water with distilled, pond, pasteurized spring, or tap water that has been allowed to stand uncovered at room temperature for at least 24 hours.

Amoeba Amoebas are easily grown in a special salt solution called Chalkley's solution mixed with rice or a population of small ciliates such as *Chilomonas.*

- Chalkley's Solution: To prepare 1 L of stock solution, mix 1 g sodium chloride (NaCl), 0.04 g potassium chloride (KCl), and 0.06 g calcium chloride (CaCl$_2$) to 1 L distilled water. Stir until dissolved. The salts in the solution closely resemble those found in pond water. To use Chalkley's solution, add 100 mL of the prepared stock solution to 900 mL distilled water. This diluted solution is called the working solution.
- Chalkley's Solution-Rice Medium: Place about 250 mL Chalkley's working solution into several finger bowls or similar containers. To each container, add four or five grains of polished rice (not the quick-cooking variety). Place 50 to 100 *Amoeba* in each dish. Stack the dishes and cover the top dish with a loosely fitting lid. Place the cultures in a dark location at room temperature for two to four weeks. Once the cultures are established, occasionally add a few rice grains or several drops of *Chilomonas* culture to replenish the food supply.

Amoeba will need to be subcultured about once every four to five weeks. To subculture *Amoeba,* drain off about half the liquid. Divide the remaining liquid containing the *Amoeba* into two new culture dishes containing Chalkley's solution-rice medium. Set the cultures aside in a dark location for two to four weeks until the cultures become clearly established.

Chlamydomonas *Chlamydomonas* does well in Chalkley's solution-rice medium and in wheat-grain medium. Like *Euglena* and other photosynthetic protists, *Chlamydomonas* requires light.

Diatoms Although commercial media for diatoms are available, diatoms usually do not survive for long in the classroom.

Euglena *Euglena* cultures thrive in water that contains relatively large amounts of organic matter. *Euglena* can be grown successfully in three different media.

- Manure-Wheat Medium: Bring to a boil 250 mL spring water containing three wheat grains and six rabbit or sheep pellets (or equivalent mass of fresh or dried horse or cow manure). Boil for 15 minutes. Pour the mixture into a deep container such as a mayonnaise jar or large beaker. Set the container aside at room temperature for two days. Add *Euglena* from a pure culture. Cover the culture and place it near a window with diffuse light. In about two weeks, a large population of *Euglena* will be present, indicated by a greenish tinge to the water.
- Wheat-Rice-Milk Medium: For five minutes, boil a mixture of 20 wheat grains, 15 rice grains (not the quick-cooking variety), 5 mL nonfat milk, and 500 mL pasteurized spring water. Set the mixture aside overnight before adding *Euglena* from a pure culture. Store the culture in dim light near a window for about two weeks or until the *Euglena* culture becomes established.

- Rice Medium: Boil seven or eight grains of rice (not the quick-cooking variety) in 475 mL distilled water or old aquarium water for about one minute. Pour the mixture into a shallow dish. Allow the dish to stand at room temperature until a bacterial scum forms on the surface, about one week. Add *Euglena* from a pure culture and cover. Place the infusion in dim light near a window for six to eight weeks to allow the *Euglena* culture to develop and grow. Replenish water as necessary, using distilled or old aquarium water.

Euglena cultures can be maintained up to a year before subculturing becomes necessary.

Paramecium Paramecia can be successfully cultured in an infusion of dried lettuce leaves. To prepare the infusion, remove several large outer leaves from a head of lettuce. Place the leaves in an oven at low temperature for several hours to dry. Remove the lettuce leaves when they have become crisp and brown. Discard any blackened or charred leaves. Grind the dried leaves with a mortar and pestle. The ground leaves can be stored almost indefinitely in a tightly sealed glass container. In an Erlenmeyer flask, add 1.5 g powdered lettuce leaves to 1 L boiling distilled water. Boil for five minutes. Filter the infusion into smaller Erlenmeyer flasks. Seal the flasks with cotton plugs. Sterilize the flasks for 15 minutes at 15 pounds pressure in an autoclave or pressure cooker. Allow the infusion to stand overnight. Using sterile pipettes and flasks, add two parts of the lettuce infusions to one part distilled water. Add several drops of pure concentrated *Paramecium* culture to each flask. Stopper the flasks with cotton plugs. Set the cultures in dim light at room temperature for one to two weeks.

Paramecia need to be subcultured every month. Place several drops of the existing culture into flasks of dilute lettuce infusion.

Physarum polycephalum Slime molds, such as *Physarum polycephalum,* can be cultured on filter paper and oatmeal. Wrap a small glass bowl with a piece of filter paper or a paper towel so the the mouth of the bowl is covered by a smooth flat paper surface. Place the covered bowl in a large container such as a battery jar so that the mouth of the bowl and the flat paper surface face upward. Partially fill the battery jar with water so that the water level is about three-quarters of the way up the sides of the bowl. Place the slime mold on the filter paper. Sprinkle about 0.2 g oatmeal or pulverized rolled oats into the paper. Feed the slime mold with oatmeal every one to two days. The slime mold can be stored in a dormant state by drying the filter paper at room temperature and placing it in sealed containers in a refrigerator. The slime mold will survive for a year or two under these conditions.

Stentor The easiest way to grow *Stentor* is in a medium made of Chalkley's solution, wheat, and *Chilomonas.*

- Chalkley's Solution-Wheat-*Chilomonas* Medium: Boil five to six wheat grains in distilled water for about one minute. Add the boiled wheat grains and 5 mL dense *Chilomonas* culture to 100 mL working Chalkley's solution. (See directions for the preparation of Chalkley's solution under *Amoeba*). Allow the medium to stand at room temperature for two days. Add 10 to 20 *Stentor* to the medium. Cover the culture and place it in a cool, even-temperature room for two to three weeks. Replenish evaporated water with distilled water or pasteurized spring water as necessary.

The *Stentor* culture should last about six months without subculturing. Add one additional boiled wheat grain per month to the culture to maintain the food supply.

Rodents Small rodents such as hamsters, gerbils, mice, and rats may be housed in cages that are available commercially or in glass aquaria with a screen top. If you choose to raise mice, make sure that the classroom is well-ventilated, as mice have an offensive odor. Separate males and females to avoid unwanted litters. Clean the rodents' habitat daily (except for the first two days after the birth of a litter). The rodents should be provided with an exercise wheel and chewing sticks; some may require a salt lick. Make sure that a supply of fresh water is available at all times. Use a glass or plastic water fountain rather than a water bowl; open bowls become fouled easily. Rodents can be fed commercial food pellets supplemented with pieces of fresh vegetables such as carrots.

Snails Freshwater snails will flourish in an established aquarium with aquatic plants provided for food. Remove dead snails immediately to prevent fouling of the water. Snails can help keep the glass in a freshwater aquarium relatively free of algae. Place two medium-sized snails in the aquarium for each gallon of water.

Vinegar eels Order *Anguilla aceti* or *Turbatrix aceti* from a biological supply company. These roundworms are harmless and nonparasitic, and are commonly found in bulk cider vinegar. Vinegar eels can also be obtained from local cider mills or vinegar manufacturers. Ask for pure bulk vinegar that contains "mother of vinegar." To culture vinegar eels, place about 200 mL unadulterated cider vinegar (from a grocery store) and 2 tablespoons of commercial vinegar eel medium into finger bowls or similar containers. A 2-cm cube of peeled raw apple can be substituted for commercial vinegar eel medium. Add vinegar eels. Cover containers loosely and place them in a dimly lit location. No further care is necessary. Subculture every three months if required.

Yeast To prepare an actively growing culture of yeast, dissolve 0.1 g dry yeast and 5 g sucrose in 75 mL distilled water. Mix thoroughly. The yeast culture should be used within two to four days. This culture should provide enough yeast for three classes of 30 students each.

Suppliers of Laboratory Materials and Equipment

Analytical Scientific, Ltd.
11049 Bandera Road
San Antonio, TX 78250
www.analyticalsci.com

Apple Computer, Inc.
1 Infinite Loop
Cupertino, CA 95014
www.apple.com

Arbor Scientific
P.O. Box 2750
Ann Arbor, MI 48106
www.arborsci.com

Bausch and Lomb
Scientific Optical Products Division
1400 North Goodman Street
Rochester, NY 14692-0450

Bio-Rad Laboratories
1000 Alfred Nobel Drive
Hercules, CA 94547
www.bio-rad.com

California Corporation of Biochemical Research
3625 Medford Street
Los Angeles, CA 90063

Carolina Biological Supply Company
2700 York Road
Burlington, NC 27215
www.carolina.com

CellServ
Foundation for Advanced Education in the Sciences,
   Inc.
One Cloister Court
Bethesda, MD 20814-1460
www.cellservkits.com

Chem Scientific, LLC
1250 Washington Street
Norwood, MA 02062
www.chemscientific.com

Connecticut Valley Biological Supply Company, Inc.
82 Valley Road
Southampton, MA 01073
www.ctvalleybio.com

Delta Biologicals
P.O. Box 26666
Tucson, AZ 85726-6666
www.deltabio.com

Edmund Scientifics
60 Pearce Avenue
Tonawanda, NY 14150-6711
www.scientificsonline.com

Edvotek
P.O. Box 1232
Bethesda, MD 20827-1232
www.edvotek.com

Fisher Science Education
4500 Turnberry
Hanover Park, IL 60133
www.fisheredu.com

Flinn Scientific
P.O. Box 219
Batavia, IL 60510
www.flinsci.com

Forestry Suppliers, Inc.
P.O. Box 8397
205 West Rankin Street
Jackson, MS 39204
www.forestry-suppliers.com

Frey Scientific Company
P.O. Box 8101
100 Paragon Parkway
Mansfield, OH 44903
www.freyscientific.com

Gourmet Mushrooms and Mushroom Products
P.O. Box 515 IP
Graton, CA 95444
gmushrooms.com

Grau-Hall Scientific Corporation
6401 Elvas Avenue
Sacramento, CA 95819
www.grauhall.com

Harvard Apparatus, Inc.
84 October Hill Road
Holliston, MA 01746
www.harvardapparatus.com

Hubbard Scott Scientific Resources
P.O. Box 2121
401 W. Hickory Street
Fort Collins, CO 80522
www.shnta.com

Lab-Aids, Inc.
17 Colt Court
Ronkonkoma, NY 11779
www.lab-aids.com

Learning Things, Inc.
P.O. Box 1112
Olean, NY 14760
www.learningthings.net

Ben Meadows Company
P.O. Box 5277
Janesville, WI 53547-5277
www.benmeadows.com

Nasco, Inc.
901 Janesville, Avenue
Fort Atkinson, WI 53538
www.nascofa.com

Niles Biological
9298 Elder Creek Road
Sacramento, CA 95829
www.nilesbio.com

Parco Scientific Company
P.O. Box 189
316 Youngstown-Kingsville Road
Vienna, OH 44473
www.parcoscientific.com

Phipps and Bird, Inc.
1519 Summit Avenue
Richmond, VA 23230
www.phippsbird.com

Sargent-Welch International
P.O. Box 5229
Buffalo Grove, IL 60089-5229
www.sargentwelch.com

Schoolmasters Science
P.O. Box 1941
745 State Circle
Ann Arbor, MI 48106
www.schoolmasters.com

Science Kit and Boreal Labs
P.O. Box 5003
777 East Park Drive
Tonawanda, NY 14150
www.sciencekit.com

Spectrum Educational Supplies
150 Pony Drive
Newmarket, Ontario, Canada L3Y 7B6
www.spectrumed.com

Ward's Natural Science
P.O. Box 92912
Rochester, NY 14692-9012
www.wardsci.com

Wildlife Supply Company
301 Cross Street
Saginaw, MI 48602
www.wildco.com

Wilkes-Anderson Company
4525 West Division Street
Chicago, IL 60651
www.waco-lab-supply.com

Guidelines for the Use of Live Organisms

Living organisms are an essential part of a biology curriculum. Few things are as interesting and motivating to students as animals. The judicious use of live or preserved animals can help students realize that biology is relevant, fascinating, and rewarding.

Although there are many advantages to providing biology students with opportunities to study real animals, it is important to be aware of and sensitive to ethical and practical concerns. The purpose of this section is to discuss some realistic guidelines for using animals in a secondary classroom. The final decision regarding the use of animals in your classroom should take into consideration these recommendations, the safety guidelines on pages Tviii–Tx, local and school guidelines, your personal views, and your assessment of your students' needs, interests, maturity, and ability to behave responsibly.

1. Whenever possible, live animals should be observed in their natural habitats or in zoos, parks, and aquaria.

2. Check the state and federal codes regarding animal welfare that apply in your area. The National Association of Biology Teachers (NABT) recommends the "Principles and Guidelines for the Use of Animals in Precollege Education" developed by the Institute of Laboratory Animal Resources. You can access the "Principles and Guidelines" at http://dels.nas.edu/ilar/prin_guide.asp. You may also wish to refer to guidelines published by the National Science Teachers' Association or the International Science Fair. Make students aware of all safety rules and regulations regarding animals.

3. Before bringing a live animal into the classroom, determine whether a proper habitat can be maintained in the classroom situation. Such a habitat includes temperature, space, and type of food. Students should have a clear understanding of the appropriate care needed by the live animals brought in the classroom. Do not allow students to tap on animal enclosures or otherwise disturb the animals.

4. No wild vertebrate animals should be brought into the classroom. Purchase animals from a reputable dealer only.

5. Live animals should be nonpoisonous and healthy. Any mammals used in the classroom should be vaccinated against rabies unless the animals were purchased recently from a reliable scientific supply company. Quarantine any animal to make sure it is disease-free before bringing it into the classroom.

6. Make sure that the living quarters of classroom animals are clean, located away from stressful situations, appropriately spacious, and secure enough to confine the animal. You may wish to lock cages to prevent the accidental release of animals; the small padlocks used on luggage are good for this purpose.

7. Remove wastes from animal living quarters daily. Thoroughly clean animal living quarters periodically to ensure that they are odor- and germ-free. Provide a daily supply of fresh water and any other need specific to the particular animal.

8. Provide for the care of the animals during weekends and school vacations. Inform the custodial staff of the presence of animals and warn them of any special requirements. For example, turning off the aquarium pump to save electricity or spraying the classroom for insects can be fatal to animal collections.

9. Students should be instructed as to how to handle each species brought into the classroom. For example, students can

receive painful wounds from the improper handling of some fishes, mollusks, and sea urchins.

10. Animals should be handled only if necessary. If an animal is frightened or excited, pregnant, feeding, or with its young, special handling is required.

11. Students should thoroughly clean their hands after handling animals or their cages.

12. Animals should be returned to their natural habitat after an observation period of not longer than 14 days. However, laboratory-bred animals or species that are not indigenous to an area should not be released into the environment.

13. If an animal must be euthanized, do not allow students to watch. Do the sacrificing humanely. Contact the local humane society for advice.

14. Before performing any experiment involving live animals, check local and state regulations. In some states, certification is required before a teacher is permitted to experiment with animals.

15. No animal studies involving anesthetic drugs, pathogenic organisms, toxicological products, carcinogens, or radiation should be performed.

16. Any experiment requiring live animals should have a clearly defined objective relating to the teaching/learning of some scientific principle.

17. No experimental procedures that will cause pain, discomfort, or harm to mammals, birds, reptiles, fishes, and amphibians should be done in the classroom or at home.

18. Surgical procedures should not be performed on live vertebrate animals.

19. If fertilized bird eggs are opened, the embryo should be destroyed humanely two days before it would have hatched, at the latest.

20. Whenever possible, substitute plants or invertebrate animals for vertebrates.

21. When working with preserved animals, make sure that students maintain a serious and respectful attitude toward the specimens.

Handling Ethical Issues

There is much controversy regarding the use of animals in science research. This controversy extends to preserved animals in dissections as well as live animals in experiments. Although the battle over what uses of animals are appropriate in a biology classroom can be frustrating and emotionally charged, it can also provide an opportunity for students to closely examine a current issue. You may wish to have students read current literature on the subject and contact groups and individuals with varying points of view.

Stress that it is important to make a rational, informed decision before taking a stand on any issue. Point out that it is vital to know and understand the arguments on both sides of an issue. Help students analyze the sources they find in terms of slant, bias, and the reliability and objectivity of the author(s). Teach them methods to distinguish between fact and opinion. Encourage them to question what they read and hear. Challenge them to discover the hidden assumptions and implications of different points of view.

If dissections are a part of your curriculum and a student chooses to avoid dissections because of ethical concerns, you should respect that student's opinion. Point out, however, that no simulation or videotape can replace hands-on, first-hand experience.

BIOLOGY
Exploring Life

Laboratory
Manual

Diane Sweeney
Biology Instructor
Prince of Peace Lutheran School
Fremont, California

Brad Williamson
Biology Instructor
Olathe School District
Olathe, Kansas

PEARSON

Prentice
Hall

Boston, Massachusetts
Upper Saddle River, New Jersey

ISBN 0-13-064266-5

8 9 10   10 09 08 07

CONTENTS

Safety in the Biology Laboratory

Working in the biology laboratory can be interesting, exciting, and rewarding. But it can also be quite dangerous if you are not serious and alert, and if proper safety precautions are not taken at all times. You are responsible for maintaining an instructional and safe environment in the biology laboratory. Unsafe practices endanger not only you but the people around you as well.

Read the following information about safety in the biology laboratory carefully. Review applicable safety information before you begin each Investigative Lab. This information is highlighted in two ways:

- Safety symbols placed near the **Procedure** heading will signal you to follow specific safety precautions for the entire lab. Safety symbols placed near a **Part** heading signal you to follow specific safety precautions for that part of the procedure. See the next page for a detailed explanation of the hazard represented by each safety symbol and ways to avoid them.

- Highlighted **CAUTION** statements within the steps of the lab procedure alert you to possible specific hazards and indicate how you can avoid accidents.

If you have any questions about safety or laboratory procedures, be sure to ask your teacher.

Safety Symbol Guide

All the investigations in this Laboratory Manual have been designed with safety in mind. If you follow the instructions, you should have a safe and interesting year in the laboratory. Before beginning any investigation, make sure you have read the general safety rules that follow this symbol guide.

The safety symbols shown on the next page are used to alert you to the need for special safety precautions throughout the Laboratory Manual. When safety symbols appear next to the **Procedure** heading, the symbols apply to all parts of the lab. Sometimes specific parts in the lab require special precautions. In these cases the symbols appear next to the appropriate part. The description of each symbol indicates the precaution(s) you should take whenever you see the symbol in an investigation.

Safety Symbols

These symbols alert you to possible dangers.

Safety Goggles Always wear safety goggles to protect your eyes in any activity involving chemicals, flames, or heating, or the possibility of broken glassware.

Laboratory Apron Wear a laboratory apron to protect your skin and clothing.

Breakage You are working with breakable materials, such as glassware. Handle breakable materials with care. Do not touch broken glassware.

Heat-resistant Gloves Use hand protection when handling hot materials. Hot equipment or hot water can cause burns. Do not touch hot objects with your bare hands.

Plastic Gloves Wear disposable plastic gloves to protect yourself from chemicals or organisms that could be harmful. Keep your hands away from your face. Dispose of the gloves according to your teacher's instructions.

Heating Use a clamp or tongs to pick up hot glassware. Do not touch hot objects with your bare hands.

Sharp Object Pointed-tip scissors, scalpels, knives, needles, pins, or tacks can cut or puncture your skin. Always direct a sharp point or edge away from yourself and others. Use sharp instruments only as directed.

Electric Shock Avoid the possibility of electric shock. Never use electrical equipment around water, or when equipment or your hands are wet. Be sure cords are untangled and cannot trip anyone. Disconnect the equipment when it is not in use.

Corrosive Chemical Avoid getting acids or other corrosive chemicals on your skin or clothing, or in your eyes. Do not inhale the vapors. Wash your hands when you are finished with the activity.

Poison Do not let any poisonous chemical come in contact with your skin, and do not inhale its vapors. Wash your hands when you are finished with the activity.

Physical Safety When an experiment involves physical activity, take precautions to avoid injuring yourself or others. Follow instructions from your teacher. Alert your teacher if there is any reason you should not participate in the activity.

Animal Safety Treat live animals with care to avoid harming the animals or yourself. Be aware of your surroundings during field investigations. Working with animal parts or preserved animals also may require caution. Wash your hands when you are finished.

Plant Safety Handle plants only as directed by your teacher. If you are allergic to certain plants, tell your teacher before doing an activity in which plants are used. Avoid touching poisonous plants or plants with thorns. Wash your hands when you are finished with the activity.

Flames When working with flames, tie back loose hair and clothing. Follow instructions from your teacher about lighting and extinguishing flames.

No Flames Flammable materials may be present. Make sure no flames, sparks, or exposed heat sources are present.

Fumes When poisonous or unpleasant vapors are used, work in a ventilated area. Avoid inhaling vapors directly. Only test an odor when directed to do so by your teacher, and use a wafting motion to direct the vapor toward your nose.

Disposal Chemicals, biohazardous materials, and other used materials must be disposed of safely. Follow the instructions from your teacher.

Hand Washing Wash your hands thoroughly with soap and warm water. Lather both sides of your hands and between your fingers. Rinse well.

General Safety Awareness You may see this symbol when none of the other symbols specifically apply, but some level of caution is needed. In this case, follow the specific instructions provided.

Science Safety Rules

One of the first things a scientist learns is that working in the laboratory can be an exciting experience. But the laboratory can also be quite dangerous if proper safety rules are not followed at all times. To prepare yourself for a safe year in the laboratory, read over the following safety rules. Then read them a second time. Make sure you understand each rule. If you do not, ask your teacher to explain any rules you are unsure of.

Dress Code

1. Many materials in the laboratory can cause eye injury. To protect yourself from possible injury, wear safety goggles whenever you are working with chemicals, flames, or any substance that might get into your eyes. Never wear contact lenses in the laboratory.

2. Wear a laboratory apron or coat whenever you are working with chemicals or heated substances.

3. Tie back long hair to keep your hair away from any chemicals, flames, or other laboratory equipment.

4. Remove or tie back any article of clothing or jewelry that can hang down and touch chemicals and flames. Do not wear sandals or open-toed shoes in the laboratory. Never walk around the laboratory barefoot or in stocking feet.

General Safety Rules

5. Be serious and alert when working in the laboratory. Never "horse around" in the laboratory.

6. Be prepared to work when you arrive in the laboratory. Be sure that you understand the procedure to be employed in any laboratory investigation and the possible hazards associated with it.

7. Read all directions for an investigation several times. Follow the directions exactly as they are written. If you are in doubt about any part of the investigation, ask your teacher for assistance.

8. Never perform activities that are not authorized by your teacher. Obtain permission before "experimenting" on your own.

9. Never handle any equipment unless you have specific permission.

10. Take extreme care not to spill any material in the laboratory. If spills occur, ask your teacher immediately about the proper cleanup procedure. Never simply pour chemicals or other substances into the sink or trash container.

11. Never apply cosmetics or eat or taste anything in the laboratory unless directed to do so. This includes not eating or drinking food, drinks, candy, or gum, as well as chemicals. Wash your hands before and after performing every investigation.

12. Know the location and proper use of safety equipment such as the fire extinguisher, fire blanket, first-aid kit, safety shower, and eyewash station.

13. Notify your teacher of any medical problems you may have, such as allergies or asthma.

14. Keep your laboratory area clean and free of unnecessary books, papers, and equipment.

First Aid

15. Immediately report all accidents, no matter how minor, to your teacher.

16. Learn what to do in case of specific accidents such as getting acids in your eyes or on your skin. (Rinse acids off your skin with lots of water.)

17. Become aware of the location of the first-aid kit. Your teacher should administer any required first aid due to injury. Or your teacher may send you to the school nurse or call a physician.

18. Know where and how to report an accident or fire. Find out the location of the fire extinguisher, phone, and fire alarm. Keep a list of important phone numbers such as the fire department and school nurse near the phone. Report any fires to your teacher at once.

Heating and Fire Safety

19. Never use a heat source such as a candle or burner without wearing safety goggles.

20. Never heat a chemical you are not instructed to heat. A chemical that is harmless when cool can be dangerous when heated.

21. Maintain a clean work area and keep all materials away from flames.

22. Never reach across a flame.

23. If using a Bunsen burner, be sure that you know how to light the burner. (Your teacher will demonstrate the proper procedure for lighting a burner.) If the flame leaps out of a burner toward you, turn the gas off immediately. Do not touch the burner. It may be hot. And never leave a lighted burner unattended.

24. Point a test tube or bottle that is being heated away from you and others. Chemicals can splash or boil out of a heated test tube.

25. Never heat a liquid in a closed container. The expanding gases produced may blow the container apart, injuring you or others.

26. Never pick up a container that has been heated without first holding the back of your hand near it. If you can feel the heat on the back of your hand, the container may be too hot to handle. Use a clamp, tongs, or heat-resistant gloves when handling hot containers.

Using Chemicals Safely

27. Never mix chemicals for the "fun of it." You might produce a dangerous, possibly explosive, substance.

28. Never touch, taste, or smell a chemical that you do not know is harmless. Many chemicals are poisonous. If you are instructed to note the fumes in an investigation, gently wave your hand over the opening of a container and direct the fumes toward your nose. Do not inhale the fumes directly from the container.

29. Use only those chemicals needed in the investigation. Keep all lids closed when a chemical is not being used. Notify your teacher of any chemical spills.

30. Dispose of all chemicals as instructed by your teacher. To avoid contamination, never return chemicals to their original containers.

31. Be extra careful when working with acids or bases. Pour such chemicals over the sink, not over your workbench.

32. When diluting an acid, pour the acid into water. Never pour water into the acid.

33. Rinse any acids off your skin or clothing with water. Immediately notify your teacher of any acid spill.

Using Glassware Safely

34. Never force glass tubing into a rubber stopper. A turning motion and lubricant will be helpful when inserting glass tubing into rubber stoppers or rubber tubing. Your teacher will demonstrate the proper way to insert glass tubing.

35. Never heat glassware that is not thoroughly dry. Use a wire screen to protect glassware from any flame.

36. Keep in mind that hot glassware will not appear hot. Never pick up glassware without first checking to see if it is hot.

37. If you are instructed to cut glass tubing, fire polish the ends immediately to remove sharp edges.

38. Never use broken or chipped glassware. If glassware breaks, notify your teacher and dispose of the glassware in the proper trash container.

39. Never eat or drink from laboratory glassware. Clean glassware thoroughly before putting it away.

Using Sharp Instruments

40. Handle scalpels or razor blades with extreme care. Never cut material toward you; cut away from you.

41. Be careful when handling sharp, pointed objects such as scissors, pins, and dissecting probes.

42. Notify your teacher immediately if you cut yourself or receive a cut.

Handling Live Organisms

43. No investigations that will cause pain, discomfort, or harm to mammals, birds, reptiles, fish, or amphibians should be done in the classroom or at home.

44. Treat all living things with care and respect. Do not touch any organism in the classroom or laboratory unless given permission to do so. Many plants are poisonous or have thorns, and even tame animals may bite or scratch if alarmed.

45. Animals should be handled only if necessary. If an animal is excited or frightened, pregnant, feeding, or with its young, special handling is required.

46. Your teacher will instruct you as to how to handle each species that may be brought into the classroom.

47. Treat all microorganisms as if they were harmful. Use antiseptic procedure, as directed by your teacher, when working with microbes. Dispose of microbes as your teacher directs.

48. Clean your hands thoroughly after handling animals or the cage containing animals.

49. Wear gloves when handling small mammals. Report animal bites or stings to your teacher at once.

End-of-Investigation Rules

50. When an investigation is completed, clean up your work area and return all equipment to its proper place.

51. Wash your hands after every investigation.

52. Turn off all burners before leaving the laboratory. Check that the gas line leading to the burner is off as well.

Safety Contract

Once you have read all of the safety information on the previous pages and are sure you understand all the rules, fill out the safety contract that follows. Signing this contract tells your teacher that you are aware of the rules of the laboratory. Turn in your signed contract to your teacher. You will not be allowed to work in the laboratory until you have returned your signed contract.

SAFETY CONTRACT

I, _____, have read the **Safety in the Biology Laboratory** section. I understand its contents completely, and agree to follow all the safety rules and guidelines that have been established in each of the following areas:

Dress Code   Using Glassware Safely

General Safety Rules   Using Sharp Instruments

First Aid   Handling Live Organisms

Heating and Fire Safety   End-of-Investigation Rules

Using Chemicals Safely

Signature _____ Date _____

Using Your Laboratory Manual

This is probably the most exciting time in history to study biology. Biology is directly related to many of today's most important news stories. Cloning, preventing and curing cancer, genetic fingerprinting, and efforts to save endangered species all involve biology.

In order to gain a working knowledge of biology and understand these issues, you need to learn about some of the processes that scientists use to find answers to questions. The Investigative Labs in the *Biology: Exploring Life Laboratory Manual* enable you to learn about and practice methods used by scientists.

In each Investigative Lab, your objective is to answer a question or questions using scientific methods. Each Investigative Lab follows a basic outline that will help you tackle this challenge in a systematic and organized manner.

Question(s) This section presents a problem in the form of a question or questions. Your job is to answer the question(s) based on your observations. In some labs you will see the heading **Inquiry Challenge** instead of Question. In these labs you will use the scientific process as you design your own experiments.

Lab Overview This section is a brief summary describing what you should accomplish in each Investigative Lab.

Introduction Included in most of the Investigative Labs, this section provides you with basic information to prepare you for the investigation.

Background The Background provides more detailed information you will need to complete the Prelab Activity and the investigation. The section also may tie the Prelab Activity and Investigative Lab to concepts discussed in the textbook. The Background corresponds to the first step in any scientific work—gathering information about the topic so that you can develop a hypothesis.

Prelab Activity and Prelab Questions Some Prelab Activities are designed to prepare you for particular steps in the Investigative Lab. Others demonstrate how the lab ties into concepts you are studying in your textbook. Prelab Questions may ask you to discuss information from the Background or Introduction or to identify the roles of certain materials or reasons for specific steps in the Procedure. The questions will prepare you for active understanding needed to take full advantage of the Investigative Lab.

Materials A list of all required materials appears at the beginning of the investigation. Before beginning the lab, you should make sure that you have all the required materials.

Procedure This section provides detailed step-by-step instructions. Diagrams are included where necessary. Make sure you read the entire Procedure carefully before you begin the investigation. Look for safety symbols and notes. If safety symbols appear next to the Procedure heading, you should follow the corresponding safety precaution(s) throughout the lab. If safety symbols appear next to a part in the Procedure, you should follow the corresponding safety precaution(s) for that part. **CAUTION** statements within the steps of the Procedure warn of possible hazards. **NOTES** in the Procedure provide other important directions or background information. You will record your data by filling in data tables, graphing data, labeling diagrams, drawing observed structures, and answering questions.

Analysis and Conclusions Two steps of the scientific method—analyzing data and forming a conclusion—are represented in this section. Here, you are asked to analyze and interpret your experimental results. This section may also challenge you to apply your conclusions to real-life situations or related experiments.

Extension This section suggests an additional activity for you to pursue on your own. Some of these are extensions of the Investigative Labs that you might perform with your teacher's permission. Others involve library research.

Units and Measurements

Measurement plays a critical role in science. Quantitative observations yield precise data that can be mathematically analyzed and easily communicated to others. To achieve this, measurements are associated with standard systems of units. For everyday measurements, you probably use many English units, such as the pound, inch, ounce, and degree Fahrenheit (° F). But in making scientific measurements, scientists around the world use the International System of Measurements, abbreviated as SI (from the French name, Système International d'Unités). SI is derived from the metric system. The metric system is based on powers of ten, making it easy to convert one unit to another. Latin prefixes indicate how units are related to one another (see Table 1 below).

Table 1: Unit Prefixes and Meanings

Prefix	Power of Ten	Prefix	Power of Ten
kilo-	10^3 (one thousand)	*milli-*	10^{-3} (one thousandth)
deci-	10^{-1} (one tenth)	*micro-*	10^{-6} (one millionth)
centi-	10^{-2} (one hundredth)	*nano-*	10^{-9} (one billionth)

There are several types of measurements that you will need to make in the laboratory. The most common are

- **Mass:** the amount of matter in an object
- **Length:** the distance from one point to another
- **Volume:** the space occupied by an object
- **Temperature:** the average energy of random motion of particles in an object

Table 2 below lists SI/metric units and their symbols for each of these types of measurements.

Table 2: Common SI/Metric Units

Measurement	Unit	Symbol	Useful Equivalents
Mass	kilogram	kg	1 kg = 1000 g
	gram	g	1 g = 0.001 kg
	milligram	mg	1000 mg = 1 g
	microgram	µg	1,000,000 µg = 1 g
Length	kilometer	km	1 km = 1000 m
	meter	m	1 m = 100 cm
	centimeter	cm	1 cm = 0.01 m
	millimeter	mm	10 mm = 1 cm
	micrometer	µm	1000 µm = 1 mm
	nanometer	nm	1000 nm = 1 um

(continued)

Table 2: Common SI/Metric Units (*continued*)

Measurement	Unit	Symbol	Useful Equivalents
Volume	liter	L	1 L = 1000 mL
	deciliter	dL	1 dL = 0.1 L
	milliliter	mL	1 mL = 0.001 L
	cubic centimeter (for measuring the volume of a solid object)	cm^3 or cc	1 L = 1000 mL
Temperature	degrees Celsius	°C	0°C = freezing point of water 100°C = boiling point of water

You will use different pieces of laboratory equipment to obtain these different kinds of measurements. Review the equipment and how to use it below.

Measuring Mass

Most likely you will measure the mass of objects in the laboratory using a *triple-beam balance*. A triple-beam balance is a scale with three horizontal bars (called beams), each marked with a different scale of measurement. On top of each beam is a weighted piece called a *rider.* You adjust the position of the riders until the balance's pointer is centered on the target mark of zero.

To measure an object's mass on a triple-beam balance, follow these steps:

1. First make sure that the balance is "zeroed"—that is, that it gives a zero reading when empty. To do this, be sure that all the riders are moved all the way to the left. The pointer should point at the zero mark on the post. If it does not, you may need to adjust the balance by turning the knob underneath the pan.

2. Place the object to be measured on the pan of the balance.

3. Move the rider on the middle beam one notch at a time until the pointer drops below zero. Then move it back one notch.

4. Move the rider on the back beam one notch at a time until the pointer again drops below zero. Then move it back one notch.

5. Slide the rider along the front beam one notch at a time until the pointer centers as close to zero as possible.

6. Read the mass of the object to the nearest tenth of a gram by adding together the readings on the three beams, then adding or subtracting the tenth of a gram markings above or below the zero mark on the post.

Measuring Length

In the lab you will measure the length of objects using either a *metric ruler* (for small objects) or a *meter stick* (for large objects).

To practice measuring the length of objects, follow these steps:

1. Place the object to be measured on a flat surface.

2. Align the left edge of the ruler or meter stick with the left edge of the object. Make sure to place the ruler or meter stick with the marked side facing up.

3. Read the measurement that is closest to the other end of the object. Note the units of the smallest markings.

Measuring Volume

In the lab you will measure the volume of liquids using a *beaker* (for rough measurements) or a *graduated cylinder* (for precise measurements). A graduated cylinder is a column-shaped container with markings (graduations) indicating measurements on its side.

To practice measuring the volume of a liquid, follow the steps below.

1. Pour the liquid into the graduated cylinder.

2. Inside the graduated cylinder, the surface of the liquid will be slightly curved. The curved surface is called a *meniscus*. Different liquids form a meniscus to different degrees depending on their properties. Lean down until your eye is at the same level as the bottom of the meniscus. Read the marking at the lowest point of the meniscus. (**NOTE:** *Do not hold the graduated cylinder up to eye level to read it. Place the cylinder on a flat surface and lean down to ensure an accurate reading.*)

To measure the **volume of an irregular solid,** such as an apple, follow the steps below (called the *displacement method*).

1. Find a graduated container that is large enough to hold the object, along with some water. If you cannot find a large enough graduated container, pour a known amount of water (such as 2 L) into a bucket or tub.

2. Record the initial water level, either by reading the marking on a graduated container, or by placing a piece of tape at the water level in an unmarked container.

3. Immerse the object in the water. Be sure your fingers do not remain underwater, or their volume will count in the measurement.

4. Record the new water level. If using a graduated container, subtract the starting water level from the ending water level. The difference represents the volume of the object. If using an unmarked container, remove the object. Add water in known amounts (for example, 25 mL at a time) until the new water level is reached. The amount of water you need to add to reach the ending water level represents the volume of the object. (**NOTE:** *Remember to use the unit cubic centimeters [cm³] instead of milliliters to record the volume of a solid object.*)

Measuring Temperature

In the lab you will measure temperature using a *thermometer*. To practice measuring temperature, follow the steps below.

1. Insert the bulb of the thermometer into the sample to be measured.

2. Give the thermometer some time to record the temperature of the sample (wait for the reading to stop changing).

3. Read the measurement from the markings on the thermometer. Be sure to note the units of the smallest marking you are reading.

Organizing Data and Graphing

An important step of the scientific process is to collect data through observations and experiments. It is important to record data precisely—even if you think the results are wrong or do not support your hypothesis. If you analyze your data correctly—even if the data are not perfect—you will be thinking like a scientist, which is an important learning goal of your study of biology this year.

Making Data Tables

When you conduct experiments and research, you may collect large amounts of information, including measurements, descriptions, and other observations. To analyze and communicate this information effectively, it is important to record it in an organized fashion. Data tables can help you keep good records of your data in the lab.

Each column in a data table should have a heading that indicates the type of information to be recorded in that column (see Data Table 1 below). If you are collecting quantitative measurements, the column heading should indicate the unit of measurement. The completed data table will help you interpret the information you collected and complete the Analysis and Conclusions questions at the end of each Investigative Lab.

A key step in analyzing data is often to find the average of several measurements from different trials or time periods. To **calculate an average,** add together the measurements in the group and then divide the total by the number of different measurements. For example, to find the average height of five seedlings measuring 4.0 cm, 5.2 cm, 4.6 cm, 4.9 cm, and 5.8 cm, you would first add the measurements together to get 24.5 cm. Then you would divide by 5 to get the average height: 4.95 cm.

Data Table 1: Effect of Radiation Exposure on Seedlings

Radiation exposure: _____ KR

Seedling	Height of Seedling (cm)	General Appearance, Color, and Leaf Shape
1		
2		
3		
4		
5		

Making Drawings

Scientific drawings can be made in several ways, depending on the subject you are observing. If you are looking through a microscope, you may want to make your drawing in a circle to represent the field of view. Always be sure to record the magnification at which you viewed the object for such a drawing.

Other drawings represent entire organisms or parts of organisms. Such drawings show the relative size, shape, and location of structures in the organism. You may also use colored pencils or other tools to indicate colors and markings you observe. When completing such drawings, try to make the structures as clear and as accurate as possible. It is often a good idea to sketch an overall outline first, then fill in the details.

Most scientific drawings should include labels and a title. To make your labels as clear as possible, follow these guidelines:

- Use a ruler to draw straight lines leading from labels to structures in the drawing.
- Leader lines should point to the center of the structure being labeled.
- Write all labels at the same angle (usually horizontal).
- Do not cross label lines.

Graphing

Recorded data can often be plotted on a graph. Graphs are one of the most useful ways to organize and analyze quantitative data. Graphs reveal patterns, communicate information, and allow scientists to make predictions. Different types of graphs are suited to different purposes. This section provides instructions for constructing and reading three frequently used types of graphs. For more information and practice, go online to the **Online Skills Activity: Graphing** on the *Biology: Exploring Life* Web site.

Line Graphs A line graph shows how changes in one variable are linked to changes in another variable. You may be able to make predictions based on patterns revealed by the graph.

To construct a line graph, start with a grid (provided in certain labs in this Laboratory Manual or a separate sheet of graph paper). Draw two lines at the left and bottom edges of the grid to form the vertical and horizontal axes. Next, divide each axis into equal units and label it with the name of the variable, the unit of measurement, and a range of values. Mark each data point on the graph grid. Draw a straight or curved line through the data points and add a title.

When you are graphing a continuous process, such as a change in temperature over time, it generally makes sense to connect all of the data points together. But in other cases, connecting each data point would produce a messy graph that yields little useful information. For such data, instead draw a line or curve that reflects the general trend (pattern) formed by the data. Such a line should run as close as possible to as many points as possible. This "best-fit" line enables you to make generalizations or predictions based on your data.

Bar Graphs A bar graph is useful for comparing data from two or more distinct categories. For example, you might use a bar graph to display the numbers of students with different eye colors in your class. Each bar would represent a distinct eye color category you define.

As with a line graph, construct a bar graph by first drawing the axes. On one axis (usually the horizontal), write the name of each category to be represented. Then label the vertical axis, and mark off a range of values. For each group, draw a short bar at the appropriate value. Then fill in the space from the bar to the horizontal axis. Include a title for your graph.

Circle Graphs Like a bar graph, a circle graph also compares data from several different categories. Circle graphs, sometimes called pie charts, display data as parts of a whole. To use a circle graph, you must have data that add up to 100 percent. Each sector of the graph represents a different group. The entire graph accounts for the total.

To construct a circle graph using percentages, first draw a circle and mark the center. Then draw a radius line from the center to the circle's edge. Next, determine the size of each sector by calculating the number of degrees that correspond to the percentage you wish to represent. For example, suppose one category of your data represents 10% of the total. Therefore,

$$360° \times 0.10 = 36°$$

With a protractor fixed at the center of the circle, measure an angle—in this case 36°—from the first radius, and draw a second radius at this point. Label the sector. Repeat for each of the other categories. For easier reading, color or shade each sector differently. Remember to include a title for the graph.

Acknowledgements

Thank you to all of the individuals and organizations that shared their knowledge and materials with us as we developed this Laboratory Manual.

Investigative Lab 2: Making a Rip-o-meter is adapted from "The Rip-ometer" by Donald Cronkite and Kathy Winnett-Murray, Hope College, Holland, MI. Used by permission.

Investigative Lab 9A: Meiosis Square Dance is adapted from "Turkeys in the Cell—The Meiosis Square Dance" developed by Donald Cronkite.

Investigative Lab 10: Family Reunion in a Dish is based on "Who's the Father?" developed by Sarah Lauffer, Dan Lauffer and Paul H. Williams at the University of Wisconsin. Used by permission.

Investigative Lab 12: You Are a Cytogeneticist is based on Kit 4 by Mark Nardone from CellServ, Foundation for Advanced Education in the Sciences, Inc. at the NIH, Bethesda, MD. Used by permission.

Investigative Lab 13: A Glowing Transformation is adapted from "pGLO Bacterial Transformation Kit Instructional Manual" by Ron Mardigian from BIOLOGY EXPLORER pGLO BACTERIAL TRANSFORMATION KIT. Used by permission of Bio-Rad Life Science Education.

Investigative Lab 15: Eat Your Greens is adapted from INVESTIGATING LIFE WITH THE WHITE CABBAGE BUTTERFLY AND BRASSICAS IN THE CLASSROOM developed by Dan Lauffer and Paul Williams at the University of Wisconsin. Used by permission.

Investigative Lab 22: How Do Plants Grow Up? is based on SPIRALING THROUGH LIFE WITH FAST PLANTS: AN INQUIRY-RICH MANUAL developed by Robin Greenler, John Greenler, Dan Lauffer and Paul Williams at the University of Wisconsin. Used by permission.

Investigative Lab 23A: Wanted Worms was adapted from "America's Most Wanted Invertebrates" (2001) by Lori Ihrig and Charles Drewes from www.eeob.iastate.edu/faculty/DrewesC/htdocs/. Used by permission.

Investigative Lab 24: The Life of WOWBugs was adapted from "Courtship Communication" by Robert Matthews from WOWBUGS: NEW LIFE FOR SCIENCE © 1996 by Riverview Press LLC. Used by permission.

Investigative Lab 24A: Crustacean Formation was adapted from "Stuck on Artermia" (1999) by Charles Drewes from www.eeob.iastate.edu/faculty/DrewesC/htdocs/.

Investigative Lab 31: Detecting Disease is adapted from "Using the ELISA Assay for Disease Detection" by Ken Kubo, PhD from http://biotech.biology.arizona.edu/labs/ELISA_assay_students.html.

Investigative Lab 34A: Diversity Discovery was adapted from "Leaf Mold Community" (2002) by Charles Drewes from www.eeob.iastate.edu/faculty/DrewesC/htdocs/. Used by permission.

Prelab Activity for **Investigative Lab 35: Dynamic Populations** was adapted from "Effects of a Catastrophic Flood and Debris Flow on the Brook Trout and Instream Habitat of the Staunton River" by Craig Roghair, Virginia Polytechnic and State University, Blacksburg, Virginia from filebox.vt.edu. Used by permission.

Special thanks from the authors to Tim Patterson of Crystal Springs Upland School in Hillsborough, California for his help with the development of **Investigative Lab 25: Voyagers and Acrobats.** And, also to Judy Brown for her assistance with **Investigative Lab 16: Sari Solution,** adapted from her inquiry-based workshop of the same name.

Note: *Every effort has been made to locate the copyright owner of material used in this textbook. Omission brought to our attention will be corrected in subsequent editions.*

Kingdom Exploration

Observing Organisms With a Microscope

Question How do microscopes help biologists explore the diversity of life?

Lab Overview In this investigation, you will use a microscope to observe representatives of each of the four kingdoms of organisms in domain Eukarya. You will sketch them as you observe them, then make a final drawing of each that indicates their relative sizes.

Introduction In this lab, you will observe one type of organism from each of the four kingdoms in domain Eukarya: plants, animals, protists, and fungi. Although these organisms are all very different, one characteristic they share is that they all consist of one or more eukaryotic cells. A eukaryotic cell contains a membrane-enclosed nucleus that separates genetic material from the rest of the cell. In contrast, prokaryotic cells do not contain a membrane-enclosed nucleus.

A microscope enables you to see cells and cell structures at different magnifications. To start your investigation, you will identify the basic parts of a microscope and learn how the different objective lenses are used to obtain focused images of various magnifications. You will also practice using the diameter of the microscope's field of view to estimate the general size of the objects you are looking at.

Prelab Activity Study the diagram below of the basic parts of a microscope, and then read about its parts on the next page.

Objective to use a microscope to make observations of a variety of cells and organisms of different sizes

Inquiry Skills
• observing
• measuring
• calculating

Time
• 15–20 min for Prelab Activity
• 10 min each for Parts A–E
• 15–20 min for Analysis and Conclusions

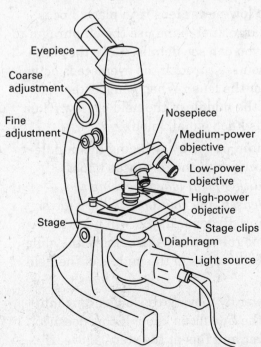

Eyepiece

Coarse adjustment

Fine adjustment

Stage

Nosepiece

Medium-power objective

Low-power objective

High-power objective

Stage clips

Diaphragm

Light source

The eyepiece of a microscope usually has a magnification of 10×. To calculate the total magnification of each power of a microscope, multiply the magnification of the eyepiece by the magnification of the objective lens. For example, if the medium-power objective lens is 10× and the eyepiece is 10×, the total medium-power magnification of the microscope is 100×. In Table 1, record the magnifications available on your microscope.

Data Table 1

Objective	Magnification of Objective	Magnification of Eyepiece	Total Magnification
Low power	4×	10×	40×
Medium power	10×	10×	100×
High power	40×	10×	400×
Other	100×	10×	1000×

When you look into the eyepiece of a microscope, the brightly lit circle you see is called the field of view. When you look through the high-power objective lens, the field of view has a much smaller diameter than the field of view when you look through the low-power objective lens. In the lab, you will measure or calculate the diameter of the field of view seen through each objective lens. This information will help you estimate the sizes of the objects you observe with the microscope. To observe organisms with a microscope, follow the basic steps described below for each objective lens. Always start with the low-power lens first.

Low Power   Make sure that the low-power lens is in place. Focus only with the coarse focus knob (large knob), and use the diaphragm to adjust the incoming light so that you can see details. Move the slide slightly to make sure that what you see through the eyepiece is actually on the slide (not just the glass of the lens). When you locate what you want to look at, position it in the middle of the field of view. Then adjust the focus with the fine focus knob (small knob).

Medium Power   Switch to medium power by swinging the middle-sized lens into place. Adjust the focus with the fine focus knob. **CAUTION:** *Never use the coarse adjustment when focusing the medium- or high-power objective lenses. You could break the slide or damage the lens.* Adjust the lighting. In general, you will need to let in more light as you increase magnification. Again, move the slide slightly until the object you are observing is in the middle of the field of view.

High Power   Switch to high power by moving the longer lens into place. Adjust the focus only with the fine focus knob. If this doesn't work, switch back to medium power and repeat the steps above. If you can't see the object on medium power, switch to low power and start over.

Estimating Field of View   To model the circular field of view you see when you look into a microscope, draw a circle with a diameter of 10 cm on a piece of white paper. Put a penny in the circle to represent a cell. By comparing the known size of the circle with the size of the penny, you can estimate the penny's diameter in centimeters. Write your first estimate in the space provided. Follow the steps below to make a second estimate and then answer the Prelab Questions.

Gather at least five pennies per lab group for the Prelab Activity.

First estimated diameter of a penny: _____ cm

1. How many pennies fit along the diameter of the circle?

   ___5___

2. Estimate the diameter of one penny again, based on what you know about the circle's diameter and your answer to Question 1. Record your estimate below.

   Second estimated diameter of a penny: ___2___ cm

3. Measure a penny with a ruler to check how close your estimates were. Record your measurement in the space below.

   Actual diameter of penny: ___1.8___ cm

Prelab Questions

1. When do you use the coarse focus knob on a microscope?

   Suggested answer: Only when focusing on an object while the low-power objective is in place.

   _____

2. Suppose you are looking at protists under the microscope and cannot see anything on low power. What adjustment could you make to the microscope that might help you see the protists, without switching to a higher magnification?

   Suggested answer: Use the diaphragm to adjust the amount of light coming through the microscope.

   _____

3. Suppose you focused on an organism using medium power, but then cannot see the organism after switching to high power. What should you do?

   Suggested answer: Go back to medium power. Find the organism again. Make sure it is centered in

   the field of view and is in focus. Switch back to high power and use the fine focus knob.

4. Which of your estimates of a penny's diameter was more accurate? Suggest an explanation.

   Sample answer: The second estimate was more accurate because it helped to know the number of

   pennies that fit across the circle.

Materials

- plant
- animal
- cultures of fungal and protist cells
- microscope
- transparent metric ruler
- microscope slides and cover slips
- well slides
- 6 transfer pipettes (one cut short)
- colored pencils

Procedure 🔲 🔲 🔲

Part A: Determining Size of Microscope Field of View

1. Place a transparent metric ruler on the microscope stage so that the millimeter marks fall across the diameter of the circular opening where the light comes through.

2. Look through the low-power lens. Focus on the millimeter marks. Move the ruler so that one mark lines up at one side of the field of view. Measure the diameter of the field of view. Write your measurement in the space provided.

   Diameter of low-power field of view = _____ mm

3. Calculate the diameter of the field of view for the medium-power objective lens using the formula below. Write the result of your calculation in the space provided. (*Hint:* To find the power of each objective lens, look at the number written on it, usually after a few letters. For example, a lens marked DIN40 has a power of 40×.)

$$\text{Diameter of medium-power field of view} = \frac{\text{(diameter of low-power field of view)} \times \text{(power of low-power objective)}}{\text{power of medium-power objective}}$$

   Diameter of medium-power field of view = _____ mm

4. Calculate the diameter of the field of view for the high-power objective lens using the formula below. Write the result of your calculation in the space provided.

$$\text{Diameter of high-power field of view} = \frac{\text{(diameter of low-power field of view)} \times \text{(power of low-power objective)}}{\text{power of high-power objective}}$$

   Diameter of high-power field of view = _____ mm

Advance Preparation

A couple of weeks before the lab Order cultures for delivery a few days before the lab. See the front of this Laboratory Manual Teacher's Edition for supplier information. When the cultures arrive, loosen the container lids to allow air inside. Keep the cultures at room temperature.

Suggested Samples
Plants: Elodea, parrot feather, or other thin-leafed water plants (the leaves should be thin enough that a whole leaf can be placed on a slide). The epidermis from spinach or succulent leaves can also be used if you use a razor blade to peel off the epidermis.
Animals: Rotifers, *Daphnia, Triops,* ostrocods, copepods, *Tubifex* (tropical fish store)
Protists: Paramecium multinucleatum or *caudatum, Blepharisma, Stentor,* or *Volvox*
Fungi: Bread mold or baker's yeast. To make a culture from baker's yeast, dissolve one packet in 100 mL warm water with a pinch of sugar. Students can dip a toothpick in the culture, then swirl the toothpick in water on their slide. You may want to have students stain the yeast with methylene blue. If stains are used, have students wear gloves and aprons.

If all the microscopes in your classroom are the same, you can post the diameters of the different objective lenses for students to reference the rest of the year.

Name _____ Class _____ Date_____

Part B: Observing a Plant

1. Write the name of the plant you will observe in the space below.

Plant name: _____

2. Measure the length of the plant with a metric ruler, and record the length below.

Length of plant: _____ cm

3. As directed by your teacher, place a leaf or a portion of a leaf on a microscope slide. Add a drop of water. Slowly place a cover slip over the leaf and the drop of water, making sure that no air bubbles are trapped between the cover slip and the leaf. The type of slide you just made is called a *wet mount*.

4. Place the slide on the slide stage. Focus on the plant cells at low power, then switch to medium power to get a closer look inside the cells. Use the space below to draw a sketch of what the plant cells look like through the microscope. On the lines provided, write a description of the cells. Label your sketch with the plant name and the magnification.

Sketch and Description of Plant Cells

_____

_____

_____

Part C: Observing an Animal

1. Write the name of the animal you will observe in the space below.

Name of animal: _____

2. With the short transfer pipette, draw up the animal (or one drop of a culture) and place it on the indented area of a well slide. Add water to fill the well and cover with a cover slip.

3. Measure or estimate the length of one animal. Use a metric ruler if the animal is large enough. If not, focus on the animal at low power and estimate its size based on the diameter of the low-power field of view determined in Part A. Write your measurement, or estimate, in the space below.

Size of animal: _____ mm

4. Use the space below to draw a sketch of the animal as seen through the microscope. On the lines provided, write a description of the animal. Label your sketch with the name of the animal and the magnification.

Sketch and Description of Animal

_____

_____

_____

Part D: Observing a Protist

1. Write the name of the protist you will observe in the space below.

Name of protist: _____

2. As directed by your teacher, add one drop of protist-slowing solution (or a bit of cotton fibers) to the slide.

3. With a transfer pipette, draw up one drop of protist culture, making sure to draw the liquid from the bottom of the culture container where there is visible debris. Place one drop of the culture in the well of a clean well slide. Add water to fill the well, if needed. Cover with a cover slip.

4. Focus on one protist at low or medium power. Estimate its size based on the diameter of the appropriate field of view (see Part A). Write your estimate in the space below.

Approximate size of protist: _____ mm

5. Use the space on the next page to draw a sketch of the protist as seen through the microscope. On the rules provided, write a description of the protist. Label the sketch with the name of the protist and the magnification you are using.

Sketch and Description of Protist

◯

_____
_____
_____

Part E: Observing Fungi

1. You will observe one of the many species of fungi known as yeasts. If available, write the scientific name of the yeast you will observe in the space below.

   Name of fungi: _____

2. With a transfer pipette, draw up one drop of yeast culture. Place the drop on a clean flat slide. Cover with a cover slip.

3. Observe the yeast cells at low and medium power. In order to estimate the size of a yeast cell, you will need to switch to high power. Focus on one individual yeast cell at high power. Estimate its size based on the diameter of the high-power field of view (see Part A). Write your estimate in the space below.

   Approximate size of yeast cell: _____ mm

4. Use the space below to draw a sketch of the fungi as seen through the microscope. On the rules provided, write a description of the fungi. Label the sketch with the name of the fungi and the magnification.

Sketch and Description of Fungi

◯

_____
_____
_____

Analysis and Conclusions

1. Which of the organisms you observed were unicellular (consist of only one cell)? On what observations do you base your answer?

Sample answer: I think the yeasts were unicellular because they looked like individual spheres

attached to each other. I think that the protist (*Paramecium*) was unicellular because I didn't

see individual cells in the slipper-shaped structure.

2. Which of the organisms you observed were multicellular? On what observations do you base your answer?

Sample answer: I think the animal is multicellular because it had many kinds of different structures

that were most likely made from different kinds of cells. I think that the plant was unicellular

because I observed that each plant cell was surrounded by neighboring cells.

3. List the organisms that you observed according to their relative size from largest to smallest.

Student answers will vary based on the organisms observed.

4. Although the organisms you observed all look very different, each is classified in a kingdom that is part of domain Eukarya. What evidence suggests that these diverse organisms belong to the same domain?

Suggested answer: Each cell in these organisms contains a membrane-enclosed nucleus.

Extension

Make a mini-mural comparing the organisms you observed representing the four kingdoms in domain Eukarya. On one sheet of paper, sketch all four organisms you observed to scale, indicating their relative sizes. Draw a scale bar at the bottom of the mural to show the relative size of a millimeter in your mural.

Extension
As a class, discuss how the plant should be depicted in the mini-mural, as it is much larger than the other organisms. For example, students could depict just one leaf to scale, placed next to a small-boxed sketch of the plant (not to scale). A blowup arrow could connect the two, indicating that the leaf shown is just one small part of the entire plant.

Investigative Lab 1A

Window to Inquiry

Using the Scientific Method to Answer Questions

Question Is a Mexican jumping bean alive? If so, what type of organism is it?

Lab Overview In this investigation you will study Mexican jumping beans. After making your observations, you will design an experiment to answer questions about your observations.

Introduction Most biological discoveries are the result of a scientist asking a question and designing an experiment to answer the question. Often, during the hunt for an answer to one question, several more questions will arise, leading to more experiments. As you observe the Mexican jumping beans, record further questions in your notebook as they arise. See how many discoveries you can make along the way.

Prelab Activity Before you begin your investigation, observe a Mexican jumping bean. Then answer the Prelab Questions.

Objective to practice developing scientific questions and designing experiments

Inquiry Skills
- asking questions
- observing
- designing experiments
- controlling variables
- communicating conclusions

Time
- 15 min for Prelab Activity
- 20–30 min for Part A
- 20 min to design experiment (Time to do the experiment will vary.)
- 15 min for Analysis and Conclusions

1. Hold the jumping bean in your hand for several minutes. Record your observations below.

   See Part A, Step 5 for information on Mexican jumping beans.
   _____

   _____

2. Use a hand lens or stereomicroscope to look closely at the outside of the jumping bean's shell. Record your observations below.

   _____

   _____

Prelab Questions

1. Do you think the jumping bean is alive? Explain your reasoning.

   Students' answers will vary, but they will most likely answer that it is alive because it moves.
   _____

   _____

2. What characteristics of a Mexican jumping bean are similar to those of a plant? What characteristics of a Mexican jumping bean are similar to those of an animal?

   Suggested answer: The outside looks like a seed, which is produced by a plant. The bean also moves

   from one place to another like an animal.
   _____

   _____

3. After making your observations, what are some additional questions you have about Mexican jumping beans?

Students' responses will vary.

_____

_____

_____

Materials

- Mexican jumping beans
- clear mailing tape
- metric ruler
- scissors
- slide
- transfer pipette
- microscope
- cover slip

Procedure

Part A: Taking a Closer Look

1. Use scissors to cut a 1-cm square of clear mailing tape. Trim the square to make a half circle. The half circle should be slightly larger than one of the flat sides of your jumping bean.

2. Hold the bean between the index finger and thumb of one hand so that one of the flat sides of the bean is facing out. Use the scissors to carefully shave off this flat section. **CAUTION:** *Handle sharp objects with care to avoid injury.* Do not shave more off the jumping bean than can be covered with the piece of mailing tape. Put the shaving to the side. Later you will view it under a microscope.

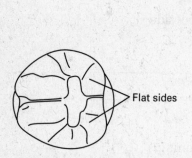

Mexican jumping bean

Flat sides

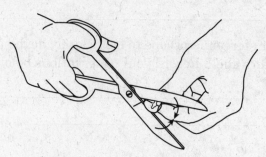

Hold the scissors on an angle as shown.
Slice off only enough to see the inside of
the jumping bean.

3. Place the tape over the open side of the bean and press down to seal it. Look closely at the interior of the bean. Record your observations below.

_____

_____

_____

Advance Preparation
Order Mexican jumping beans from a biological supplier such as Connecticut Valley Biological Supply Company. See the front of this Laboratory Manual Teacher's Edition for contact information.

Mexican jumping beans can be purchased from late August through November. To store the jumping beans for up to several months, place the opened container of jumping beans and a crumpled wet paper towel inside a larger container. Cover the large container and place it in a refrigerator (preferably the crisper). Keep the paper towel moist.

Safety and Disposal
Students should wash their hands after handling the jumping beans. Remind students of the guidelines of working with live organisms. Place the larvae in the freezer overnight before disposing of them in the trash.

To prevent the larvae from dehydrating, students can use a toothpick to apply a thin layer of caulk to the tape edge.

4. Notice the paper-thin layer that was the inside layer of the jumping bean. Place the shaving on a microscope slide with the paper-
thin layer facing up. Use a transfer pipette to place one drop of
water on the shaving. Cover the shaving with a cover slip. This
type of slide is called a wet mount.

5. Place the slide on the microscope stage and view it with the high-
power objective in place. In the space below, sketch what you see.

A type of female moth found in the Sonoran Desert and Baja California lays its eggs on the ovary of one type
of shrub, *Sebastiana pavoniana.* The moth is known by many names including *Laspeyresia saltitans, Cydia
saltitans,* and *Cydia deshaisiana,* but is commonly referred to as the Mexican jumping bean (MJB) moth. After
hatching, the larvae chew through the ovaries and feed on the developing seeds. Three pods (carpels) form
the woody fruit of the shrub. When the dry pods fall to the ground in late summer and separate into single
pods, many of them contain MJB larva.

After the larva has consumed the materials inside the pod, it spins a silk lining on the inner wall of the pod. As
it spins, the larva causes the pod to jerk. A benefit of this movement may be that it enables the larva to move
out of the hot sun. MJB larvae move more frequently in higher temperatures. It has also been suggested that
this movement may deter seed-eating birds.

Before the larva becomes a pupa, it chews a circular "trap door" in the pod. The cut does not go all the way
through. The adult moth pushes through the "trap door" to emerge from the pod.

6. Now make a wet mount of a small piece of paper and view it with
the high-power objective. Compare it to the shaving from the
jumping bean. Can you draw any conclusions about the material
that makes up the outside of the jumping bean?

Sample answer: The fibers of the piece of paper and the fibers of the shell look very similar.

Since paper is made of wood, perhaps the shell is also made of wood.

Part B: Designing an Experiment

In the Prelab Activity you identified additional questions about Mexican jumping beans. Choose a question and design an experiment to try
to answer it. (**NOTE:** *In a scientific investigation it is important to
study only one question at a time.*) In your experiment, use as many
jumping beans as are available. Describe your experiment below.

You could have stu-
dents with similar
questions design an
experiment together.

Question:

Some questions that students might ask: Why do the beans jump? Do they jump toward or away

from light? Do they jump toward or away from warmer temperatures? Do they jump more often

at certain times of day than others? Do they jump more often or less often as the days pass?

Hypothesis: (This should be a statement that describes what you
think the answer to your question is and why.)

Students' responses will vary depending on their questions.

Prediction:

Students' responses will vary depending on their hypothesis.

Procedure: (Include a list of the materials you will use.)

Sample procedures: Students can detect the pattern of movement of a jumping bean by placing it in

fine sand spread evenly in a shoe box. To discover how or if the bean responds to light, cover half the

box with aluminum foil and place the bean in the center. To test its reaction to temperature, place a

heating pad on a low setting under one side of the box.

Observations:

Students' responses will vary.

Analysis and Conclusions

1. Based on your observations in Part A, what kind of organism do you conclude that a Mexican jumping bean is? Explain.

   Sample answer: The "bean" part of the jumping bean is a plant. An animal (a small caterpillar) lives

   inside the "bean" and causes its movement. (The amount of detail you provide your students

   about the Mexican jumping bean moth and shrub will influence this answer.)

2. Did the results of your experiment in Part B support your hypothesis or not? Explain.

   Students' responses will vary based on their experiments.

3. Based on the results of your experiment, suggest a new question about Mexican jumping beans.

   Students' responses will vary.

Extension

For the next couple of weeks, continue to observe the jumping bean from which you cut part of the covering. How long does it continue to move? What changes occur inside the covering? Keep a record of your observations. Record any additional questions that you think of.

Extension
Students should note that the larva continues to move for several weeks before it pupates.

Making a Rip-o-meter

Design an Experiment to Measure Leaf Toughness

Inquiry Challenge How can you use measurements of leaf toughness to test a hypothesis? What factors may contribute to leaf toughness?

Lab Overview In this inquiry investigation you will make a "rip-o-meter"—a simple device used to measure leaf toughness. You will consider how to use leaf toughness measurements to test one or more hypotheses, then design and carry out an experiment of your own.

Introduction Making a leaf rip-o-meter like the one shown below provides a simple way to quantitatively measure the "toughness" of a leaf. First you will hang a paper cup from a leaf by a paper clip. Then you will add pennies to the cup until the paper clip rips through the leaf. The number of pennies required to rip completely through the leaf is a measurement of leaf toughness. To start your investigation, you will study an example of an experiment that one student designed and carried out using a leaf rip-o-meter. You will analyze the results of this student's experiment and answer questions based on the data. Then you'll design your own experiment using a rip-o-meter.

Objective to practice making hypotheses and designing experiments

Inquiry Skills
- predicting
- observing
- making measurements
- collecting data
- asking questions
- formulating testable hypotheses
- designing experiments
- controlling variables
- communicating conclusions

Time
- 15–20 min for Prelab Activity
- 15 min for Part A
- 15 min for Part B
- 15 min for Part C
- 15–20 min for Analysis and Conclusions

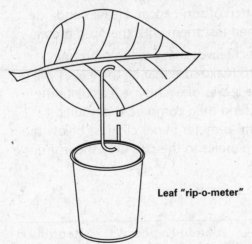

Leaf "rip-o-meter"

Background A leaf's toughness depends on certain substances in its cells. Plant cells are surrounded by cell walls made of a fibrous material called cellulose. Some plant cell walls also contain a tougher fiber called lignin. Cellulose and lignin add strength and rigidity to leaves and other plant structures, helping plants stand upright and withstand the forces of wind and rain. Leaves of some plants have much tougher cell walls than others. For example, the leaves of palm trees are much tougher than the leaves of lettuce plants.

To design an experiment that gives meaningful results, it is important to make sure that the experiment tests only one variable at a time. For your rip-o-meter experiment, this means that the two types of leaves you choose to test should vary in only one way. If you test leaves that vary in several ways, such as leaves from different plants that have been exposed to different amounts of sun and wind and grown in different soils, you will not be able to conclude which variable is connected to any measured differences in leaf toughness. In your experiment you will test leaves from a single type of plant. In the experiment you will read about in the Prelab Activity below, notice how the student designed the experiment to control as many variables as possible.

Prelab Activity Study the description below of one student's leaf rip-o-meter experiment. Consider the experimental design and the results. Then, answer the Prelab Questions.

Sample Experiment

Observation: Leaves that grow on the same jasmine plant are exposed to different amounts of sun.

Question: Are jasmine leaves that are exposed to the sun for most of the daytime tougher than leaves of the same plant that are in constant shade?

Hypothesis: Jasmine leaves exposed to sun for most of the daytime are tougher because they need to withstand the heat.

Prediction: If jasmine leaves exposed mostly to sun are tougher, then leaves exposed mostly to shade will tear more easily.

Experiment: I will gather one batch of sun-exposed leaves and one batch of shade-exposed leaves, then test them with the rip-o-meter.

To control variables: I will collect leaves that are the sixth one inward from the tip of a branch, to make sure that all the leaves will be about the same age. I will test five leaves of each type, calculate the average toughness of each batch, and then compare the results.

I will pierce each leaf with the rip-o-meter paper clip just below the middle vein of the leaf. I will add pennies to the cup until the leaf rips completely through.

Rip-o-meter Test Data

Sun-Exposed Leaf	Pennies Added	Shade-Exposed Leaf	Pennies Added
1	89	1	73
2	70	2	94
3	77	3	88
4	80	4	83
5	89	5	72
Average for sun	81	**Average for shade**	82

To save time and to require fewer pennies, students could choose a different ripping point, such as 3 mm. What is important is that the ripping point be consistent in all of the samples.

Prelab Questions

1. Which variable is the student's experiment described in the Prelab Activity designed to test?

Suggested answer: The effect of sun exposure on leaf toughness.

_____

_____

2. List three other possible variables in this experiment and explain what the student did to control each one.

Suggested answer: One variable is the age of the leaf. To control this variable, the student collected

leaves that are the sixth one inward from the tip of a branch. Another variable is the range of toughness

in leaves grown in the same conditions. To control this variable, the student tested five leaves of each

type, calculated the average toughness, and then compared the results. The third variable is the point

at which the paper clip pierces the leaf. To control this variable, the student pierced each leaf below the

middle vein.

3. Which of the following conclusions is best supported by the data the student collected? Explain.
   a. Jasmine leaves exposed mostly to shade are tougher than those grown in the sun.
   b. Jasmine leaves exposed mostly to sun are tougher than those grown in the shade.
   c. The amount of sun exposure does not seem to affect the toughness of jasmine leaves.

Suggested answer: Conclusion c is best supported by the data. The average toughness measurements

of leaves grown in the shade and leaves grown in the sun are very close. Also, the data for each type of

leaf vary widely in a similar range.

4. If the student had tested only one leaf grown in the sun and one leaf grown mostly in the shade, might that data have supported a different conclusion? Explain.

Suggested answer: Yes. For example, from just the first leaf of each type, it appears that the

sun-exposed leaf is tougher. However, as more leaves are tested, it became clear that sun-exposed

leaves are not always tougher. In fact, the toughest leaf was a shade-exposed leaf.

Materials
- paper cup
- paper clip
- approximately 150 pennies
- 2 plastic sandwich bags
- masking tape
- marker
- leaves

Advance Preparation

Week of the lab
Decide on a source of leaves. If you plan to provide your students with leaves, good plants to use are ficus, coleus, and ivy. If you decide to have students collect their own leaves, tell students they must obtain permission from the property owner before collecting leaves on private property. If you or students will collect leaves on school property, obtain permission from the grounds manager.
   Obtain paper cups, paper clips, and pennies. Each lab group will need at least 150 pennies.

Procedure

Part A: Developing Your Hypothesis

1. Your teacher will discuss with you the sources of leaves you will use for this lab. Based on this information, observe the possible leaves and brainstorm questions you could explore with the leaf rip-o-meter. Choose one and write it in the space below.

   Question:

   Student questions will vary.
   _____

   _____

2. Form a testable hypothesis and record it below. (Hint: Write your hypothesis in the form of a statement.)

   Hypothesis:

   Student hypotheses will vary.
   _____

   _____

3. Predict what will happen when you test your hypothesis. Write your predictions in the space below, and explain them.

   Predictions:

   Student predictions will vary.
   _____

   _____

   _____

Part B: Designing Your Experiment

1. Devise an experiment to test your hypothesis, and describe it below. Describe the two groups of leaves you will collect and test. Remember that the best experiments test only one variable. List possible variables and explain how you plan to control each one. (Attach another piece of paper if necessary.)

   Student responses will vary.

2. List the steps of the procedure for your planned experiment.

Proposed Procedure:

Student procedures will vary.

3. Have your teacher approve your procedure before you start. If you need to revise your procedure, write the new procedure below.

Revised Procedure:

Student procedures will vary.

Part C: Collecting and Testing Leaves

1. Follow your teacher's instructions about collecting leaves. Collect two batches of leaves. Place each batch in a separate plastic sandwich bag. Use masking tape and a marker to label each bag with the date, your group's name, and a description of the leaf type. If you collect the leaves the day before the lab, place a moist paper towel in the bag so that the leaves do not wilt.

2. After collecting your leaves, observe them closely. Note any differences between the batches. For example, you may observe differences in leaf size, shape, color, or thickness.

3. Build your rip-o-meter, following the description and illustration in the Introduction.

4. Test the leaves with the rip-o-meter. Record your results in Data Table 1 on the next page.

Data Table 1

Batch 1 Leaves	Pennies Added	Batch 2 Leaves	Pennies Added
Student data will vary.			
Average Batch 1		**Average Batch 2**	

Analysis and Conclusions

1. What variable did you test in your experiment?

Responses will vary based on student experiments.

2. How did you control other variables in your experiment?

Responses will vary based on student experiments.

3. Based on your data, do you think that the variable you tested had any effect on leaf toughness? Why or why not?

Responses will vary based on student experiments.

4. Based on the results of your experiment, could you now say your hypothesis is a theory? Why or why not?

Suggested answer: No. A theory is a well-tested explanation that ties together a great variety of scientific observations, not just the results of one experiment.

Extension

Design a second experiment that uses the leaf rip-o-meter to test a different variable. Carry out the second experiment. Then compare your data with the results of your first experiment. (**NOTE:** *Always obtain permission from your teacher before carrying out any experiments.*)

Extension
Check student procedures before giving permission to perform a second experiment. Remind students to obtain permission from the property owner before collecting leaves from plants on private property.

Squash Statistics

Learning How to Make Scientific Measurements

Questions What features of a pumpkin can be measured scientific-ally? What patterns exist in the physical features of a pumpkin?

Lab Overview In this investigation you will use a variety of methods to measure various physical characteristics of a pumpkin. You will learn how to measure the volume of a solid object as well as how to make accurate estimates. Finally, you will compare and analyze class data to look for patterns and relationships.

Introduction Accurate measurements are important in scientific investigations. Four basic types of measurements you will use are mass, length, volume, and temperature. In everyday life you may use the English system of measurement, which includes units such as the ounce, inch, pint, and degree Fahrenheit. But in the laboratory, you will almost always use the International System of Units (SI units), such as the gram, centimeter, liter, and degree Celsius.

In this investigation, some of your measurements will be exact, while others will be estimates. As you take measurements, note connections between the measurements. For example, you may observe that larger pumpkins have thicker flesh than smaller pumpkins. New questions can spring from such observations.

Prelab Activity The following activities will help familiarize you with two activities you will perform in this lab and in future labs— measuring volume by displacement and estimating numbers.

1. Volume of an Object In the lab you will have to measure the volume of a pumpkin. You can measure the volume of a liquid using a container with measurement indicators. But how do you measure the volume of an irregularly shaped object?

The volume of an object can be measured by submerging the object in a known volume of water. When the object is submerged, the water will be displaced, and the water line will rise. The difference between the new water line and the original water line is the volume of the object. Note, however, that although the volume of a liquid is expressed in mL, the volume of a solid is expressed in cm^3 (1 mL = 1 cm^3). For example, if a pencil were placed in a graduated cylinder with 80 mL of water and the water level rose to 90 mL, what would the volume of the pencil be?

$$\begin{array}{r} 90 \text{ mL} \\ -80 \text{ mL} \\ \hline 10 \text{ mL} = 10 \text{ cm}^3 \end{array}$$

Volume of pencil: _10 cm³_

2. Estimating Numbers

Many scientific investigations involve counting. In certain situations it is possible to count exact numbers. However, scientists often use estimates. Sometimes a small sample can be used to estimate the number of objects in a larger sample. For example, think about the number of leaves inside a large bag. How could you estimate the number of leaves in the bag without counting each leaf? One way would be to measure the mass of all of the leaves and the mass of a small sample containing a known number of leaves. Then perform a calculation like the one shown below. Study the formula below and then complete the calculation with the information provided.

$$\frac{\text{number of objects in small sample}}{\text{mass of small sample}} = \frac{\text{total number of objects}}{\text{total mass}}$$

The fraction on each side of the equation is called a *ratio*. To solve the equation, you begin by cross-multiplying as follows:

number of objects in small sample $\times$ total mass = total number of objects $\times$ mass of small sample

Then, solve for the variable (in this case, "total number of objects").

$$\frac{\text{number of objects in small sample} \times \text{total mass}}{\text{mass of small sample}} = \frac{\text{total number of objects} \times \cancel{\text{mass of small sample}}}{\cancel{\text{mass of small sample}}}$$

$$\frac{\text{number of objects in small sample} \times \text{total mass}}{\text{mass of small sample}} = \text{total number of objects}$$

Use the formula above and the following information to estimate how many total leaves are in the larger sample.

Total mass of leaves = 250 g

Mass of 10 leaves = 5 g

$$\frac{10 \text{ leaves}}{5 \text{ g}} = \frac{\text{total number of leaves}}{250 \text{ g}}$$

$$\frac{10 \text{ leaves} \times 250 \text{ g}}{5 \text{ g}} = 500 \text{ leaves}$$

Total number of leaves: ___500___

Name _____ Class _____ Date_____

Prelab Questions

1. What are three types of measurements you would be likely to use to describe your pumpkin?

Suggested answer: Types of measurements are mass, length, and volume.

_____

2. A local store is having a contest to see if anyone can guess how many jelly beans are in a 10-L (10,000-mL) container. You decide to use your estimating skills to try to win the contest. You discover that a 100-mL container holds 200 jelly beans. Based on this information, estimate how many jelly beans can fit in a 10-L container.

$$\frac{200 \text{ jelly beans}}{100 \text{ mL}} = \frac{\text{total number of jelly beans}}{10,000 \text{ mL}}$$

$$\frac{200 \text{ jelly beans} \times 10,000 \text{ mL}}{100 \text{ mL}} = 20,000 \text{ jelly beans}$$

Total "population" size: ___20,000 jelly beans___

3. Explain how you could determine the volume of a golf ball. What unit of measurement would you use to express the volume?

Suggested answer: Fill a container with a known volume of water and mark the water line. Submerge

the golf ball. Calculate the difference between the new water line and the original water line. The unit

of measurement that should be used is cm^3.

Materials
- pumpkin   (about 5–8 lbs)
- colored pencils
- laboratory balance
- bucket   (5-gallon)
- knife
- spoon
- paper towels
- metric ruler
- metric measuring tape
- strainer
- 1-L graduated container
- 100-mL graduated cylinder

You could have students cut the pumpkins in half to remove the seeds in Part B. Or, you could have students cut out only the top. Then they could take the pumpkin home to carve.

Alternate Materials
Rather than using measuring tape to measure the circumference of the pumpkin, students could wrap a piece of string around the pumpkin. Then they can measure the length of the string. If you do not have a balance that can measure several kg, bring in or borrow a bathroom scale. One student from each lab group should weigh himself or herself, then step on the scale with the pumpkin. (Note that the student does not need to reveal his or her own weight, just note the difference without and with the pumpkin.) If the scale is not calibrated for kg, remind students that they need to convert lb to kg.

Safety and Disposal
Remind students to use caution when cutting into the pumpkins, or cut the pumpkins for them. Students may wish to wear aprons and gloves when scooping out and washing off the seeds. Students with allergic skin conditions should also wear gloves when handling the pumpkins. Place all pumpkin parts in double plastic bags for disposal. Do not allow the used pumpkins to remain in the building overnight.

Procedure

Part A: Observing the Exterior of the Pumpkin

1. Describe the color of the pumpkin skin. Compared to the other pumpkins in the room, is it darker or lighter?

   _____

   _____

2. Describe the shape of your pumpkin compared to other pumpkins in the room. Is it tall and narrow, or short and wide? Does it have any flattened spots?

   _____

   _____

3. Sketch your pumpkin with colored pencils in the space below. Include the pumpkin's imperfections, such as scrapes, bruises, and rotting or discolored spots.

Part B: Making Measurements of the Pumpkin

1. Use the metric ruler to measure the height of the pumpkin from the bottom to the base of the stem. Be sure to include the proper unit of measurement.

   Height of pumpkin: _____

2. Measure the circumference (the length around its widest point) of the pumpkin with the measuring tape.

   Circumference of pumpkin: _____

3. Use a balance or scale provided by your teacher to obtain the mass of the pumpkin. Record the mass below.

   Mass of pumpkin: _____

4. Use the bucket and water to measure the volume of the pumpkin.

   Volume of pumpkin: _____

Alternate Methods
One method of measuring the pumpkins' volumes is to fill a 5-gallon bucket half full of water. Mark the starting level of water with a permanent marker. One group at a time should dunk its pumpkin, dry off the area on the bucket just above the water line, and mark the new level with a permanent marker. Label the marks so that groups can identify their marks later. Then add 1 L of water to the bucket at a time, counting the number of liters you add until you get to each marked line.

Another method is to calibrate the bucket before placing a pumpkin in it. Fill the bucket halfway. Add 1 L of water at a time and draw a line with a permanent marker to indicate each liter-mark.

5. Carefully cut the pumpkin open with a knife. **CAUTION:** *Use extreme caution with sharp objects to avoid injury.* Use a spoon to scoop the seeds onto a paper towel. Measure the thickness of the flesh around the center of the pumpkin (at its widest point).

   Thickness of pumpkin: _____

6. Bring the pile of pumpkin seeds to the sink. Place them in a strainer and rinse off as much pulp as you can.

7. Use a balance to measure the mass of the total pile of seeds. Then measure the mass of just 10 seeds.

   Mass of all seeds: _____   Mass of 10 seeds: _____

   a. Estimate the total number of seeds based on the mass of all the seeds and the mass of 10 seeds.

   Total number of seeds: _____

   b. Estimate the average mass of one seed based on the mass of 10 seeds.

   Mass of one seed: _____

Part C: Gathering Class Data

Gather data from the whole class so you can look for relationships or patterns in the measurements. Record the data (including your group's) in the data table below. In the parentheses, indicate the unit of each measurement.

When calculating the number of seeds, students often record a number exactly as it appears on their calculators. Remind them that they are estimating and that rounding to the nearest whole number will give them an appropriate answer. Students also often make mistakes when they compare statistics. They may observe that a pumpkin with a larger circumference than other pumpkins, also has thicker flesh. They may mistakenly conclude that all pumpkins with larger circumferences have thicker flesh. It is important to emphasize that in order to make a conclusion about a relationship between two measurements, that many pumpkins need to be measured and compared.

Data Table

Group	1	2						
Shape	oblong	circle						
Color	light orange	dark orange						
Health	some bruises	a few scrapes						
Mass (g)	14	14						
Volume (cm³)	4.2	5.0						
Thickness (cm)	2.5	2.7						
Height (cm)	16	24						
Circumference (cm)	64	61						
Number of seeds	490	530						
Average mass of 1 seed (g)	0.18 g	0.15 g						

Analysis and Conclusions

1. Look for patterns and relationships among the class data. For example, does the total number of seeds seem to be related to the total mass of the pumpkin? Record your findings in the space below.

Sample answers: Heavier pumpkins have larger volumes. Taller pumpkins have thicker flesh.

Wider pumpkins have more seeds.

2. Which of the types of measurements were the most exact? Explain.

Sample answers: The measurements that were the most exact were the thickness of the flesh and

the mass of the pumpkin seeds. The thickness of the flesh could easily be measured with a ruler

and a balance can be trusted to give accurate measurements.

3. Which of the types of measurements were probably the least exact? Explain.

Sample answers: The measurements that were least exact were the height of the pumpkin

and the mass of one seed. We had to estimate the height by "eyeing" the top of the ruler and the

top of the pumpkin. The mass of one seed was an estimate based on the mass of 10 seeds.

4. Which measurements varied the most among pumpkins? Which measurements were the most similar among the pumpkins?

Sample answers: Volume and number of seeds varied the most among the pumpkins.

Thickness of flesh and mass of a single seed varied the least.

5. A pumpkin farmer has learned that she makes a greater profit on her pumpkin crop when she grows pumpkins with thicker flesh. Pumpkins with thicker flesh are less likely to crack open and rot. Look at your class data. Is there an external characteristic of pumpkins that the farmer could use to identify the pumpkins with the thickest flesh?

Sample answer: From the data it seems that in most cases the dark orange pumpkins had the

thickest flesh. Also, many of the tall pumpkins had thicker flesh.

Extension

The density of a substance is calculated by dividing the substance's mass by its volume. A liquid's density is usually expressed with the units g/mL. A solid's density is usually expressed with the units g/cm^3. Based on the measurements you made in Part B of the lab, calculate the density of the whole pumpkin. How would you calculate the density of the stem or the pumpkin flesh? With your teacher's permission, carry out your plan. Compare the density of the whole pumpkin to just the stem or pumpkin flesh. Describe your results.

Extension
Students should cut a chunk from the pumpkin's stem and a cube from the pumpkin flesh to measure the mass and volume of each. You could also have students compare the density of flesh from smaller, younger pumpkins to larger, older pumpkins. Younger pumpkins will most likely have denser flesh since they contain more water.

Termite Tracking

Learning About Termite Behavior

Inquiry Challenge How do termites navigate in their environment?

Lab Overview In this inquiry investigation you will discover how worker termites find their way in their environment and how they signal other worker termites to follow them.

Background Termites are insects that build large colonies either underground (subterranean termites) or inside wood (drywood termites). Most termites eat dead wood, although some species feed on living trees. Termites are able to digest certain plant fibers found in wood with the help of protists that live in the termites' digestive system. The protists produce a chemical that breaks down plant fibers into compounds the termites can absorb.

The termites you will observe in this investigation are worker termites, one of several types, or castes, of termites that make up a subterranean termite colony. Each caste carries out specific jobs in the colony.

The Queen and King The queen termite produces eggs. The queen has a large abdomen that is adapted for laying thousands of eggs every year or even thousands of eggs each day in some species. The king termite fertilizes the eggs. The queen and king cannot leave the nest's "royal chamber" because their bodies are too large to fit through the passageways. Termites that hatch from the fertilized eggs develop into one of three castes—soldiers, workers, or winged termites.

Soldiers The soldier termites defend the colony. If a soldier spots an invader, it signals other soldiers to fight. Some soldier termites also stay at the entrances to the "royal chamber" to protect the queen and king. Soldier termites have large pinching mouthparts that help them fight. These termites cannot reproduce.

Workers The worker termites build the tunnels and chambers in the nest, search for food, and feed the other termites. For example, workers must feed the soldier termites. Workers also bring food to the queen and king, and feed young termites. When foraging, workers often travel more than 70 meters from the nest. Worker termites have light-colored, relatively soft bodies and cannot reproduce. You will study worker termites in this investigation.

Winged Termites The winged termites fly away and start new colonies. These termites have hardened bodies and two pairs of wings of equal size. When winged termites find a new place to start a colony,

Objective to learn about scientific observation and experimental design while observing termite behavior

Inquiry Skills
- predicting
- observing
- asking questions
- designing experiments
- controlling variables
- drawing conclusions

Time
- 15 min for Prelab Activity
- 15 min for Part A
- 10 min for Part B
- 15–20 min for Part C
- 15 min for Analysis and Conclusions

Worker termites will not cause a pest problem in the school building because they are not capable of reproducing.

they find a mate, remove their wings, and mature into queens and kings. When a queen matures, she produces a chemical that prevents other nearby winged termites from developing into queens.

Prelab Activity Examine the termite nest shown below. Identify the queen, the king, soldier termites, worker termites, and winged termites. Then, answer the Prelab Questions.

Additional Resources

For students: Telford, C. and R. Theodoru. *Through a Termite City.* Heinemann Library, 1998.

Professional reference: Pearce, M. J.*Termites: Biology and Pest Management.* CABI Publishing, 1998.

Termite inspectors often will have hand-outs explaining the life cycle of termites. You could also go to termite extermination company Web sites for information.

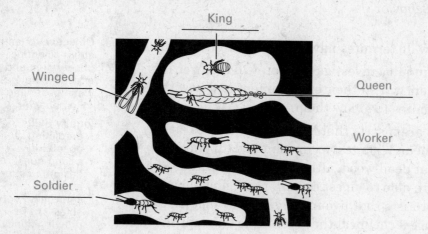

Prelab Questions

1. What tasks do the worker termites perform in a termite colony?

Suggested answer: Worker termites dig tunnels, search for food, and feed other termites.

2. In a mature colony, which castes of termites can reproduce?

Suggested answer: queens and kings

3. Would you expect worker termites to have keen eyesight? Explain. (Worker termites do not have eyes.)

Sample answers: No, because they live underground their whole lives. OR Yes, because they need to be able to see in the dark.

4. How could you test the ability of a worker termite to see?

Sample answers: Place a barrier in front of the termite to see if it changes direction before walking into the barrier. Test if it is attracted to or repulsed by light.

5. How could you test whether a worker termite can smell?

Sample answers: Observe if a termite is attracted to or repulsed by certain strong smells. Place strong-smelling chemicals such as perfume or vanilla, etc., on cotton swabs near the termite.

6. Why do you think you will use worker termites in this experiment?

Suggested answer: Worker termites do not reproduce; therefore, there is no worry about a pest problem in the school if they escape. Since worker termites must travel from the nest in search of food, they must have a way to navigate in their environment.

Materials

- worker termite
- white paper
- assorted ballpoint pens
- small paintbrush
- stereomicroscope or hand lens (optional)
- plastic petri dish (optional)

Advance Preparation

Two weeks before lab

- Order the worker termites from a biological supply company. Order extra termites and ask to receive them the day you plan to do the lab. It is difficult to keep them alive even overnight. When they arrive, keep the wood pulp moist, but not soggy.
- Collect ballpoint and felt-tip pens of various brands and colors. Termites respond the most to Paper-mate® ballpoint pens. They do not respond to felt-tip pens, nor generally to green ballpoint pens.

Procedure

Part A: Observing Termite Behavior

1. Use a small paintbrush to gently transfer a termite to a piece of white paper. Practice moving the termite with the brush. How does the termite react to being touched?

_____

2. Develop a list of questions about how a termite finds food or locates other termites. Write your questions in the space provided.

Questions:

_____

_____

_____

Part B: Testing an Ink Trail

Safety and Disposal
It is recommended that students wear plastic gloves. After the lab, have all students wash their hands thoroughly with soap. Freeze insects overnight in a plastic bag before disposal in the trash.

1. Using one of the ballpoint pens provided by your teacher, slowly draw a line in front of your termite. Change the direction of the line. Record your observations below.

Observations:

_____

_____

2. Which of the following hypotheses, if any, explains your observations? You may want to write your own hypothesis.
   a. Termites deposit a chemical trail they follow by smell.
   b. Termites deposit a chemical trail they follow by sight.
   c. Wood produces a chemical smell that termites migrate toward. This ink contains the same chemical smell.
   d. Other hypothesis:

Have students start the lab using a blue Papermate® ballpoint pen to draw a line on the paper. The termites will follow the pen line in any direction. Students should ask what attracts the termites to the ink. They should experiment to find answers by using different colors and types of ink.

_____

_____

Part C: Designing Your Own Ink Trail Experiments

1. Develop a hypothesis to answer the question, "How do termites navigate in their environment?" Then write a prediction in the form of an "If . . . then" statement, based on your hypothesis. Design an experiment using ink trails to test this hypothesis. Describe your experiment and results on a separate piece of paper. If you are unable to answer the question based on the results of your first experiment, revise your hypothesis and design a new experiment.

   Question: How do termites navigate in their environment?

   Hypothesis:

   _____

   _____

   Prediction:

   _____

   _____

Examples of experiments:
- Use the same brand of ink, different color.
- Use a different brand of ink, same color.
- Use a different brand of ink, different color.
- Use a pencil.
- Examine the termite with a stereomicroscope to see if it has eyes.
- Draw two circles with different brands of ink and see if a termite will go around one circle more times than another circle.

2. When you are finished with your experiments, return the termite to the original container as directed by your teacher.

Expected Results
Termites will follow any color ink from a Papermate® ballpoint pen except for green. Possibly a molecule in the ink is similar to pheromones that termites release to lead other termites to a food source.

Analysis and Conclusions

1. What have you learned about how termites navigate in their environment?

   Answers will vary, but should contain the idea that termites follow some kind of scent trail.

   _____

   _____

2. Explain how your observations support your conclusions about termite navigation behavior.

   Answers will vary based on observations.

   _____

   _____

3. What new questions do you have based on your observations? How might you test them?

   Answers will vary.

   _____

   _____

Extension

Place two or three termites together in a petri dish and observe their interactions. Make a list of questions you have about how they interact with each other. Design a hypothetical experiment to answer one of the questions. (**NOTE:** *Do not carry out any investigations without permission from your teacher.*)

Extension
As needed, review guidelines for the use of live animals in the classroom. Have students return all termites to the original container after making their observations.

Name _____ Class _____ Date _____

Wildlife Watching

Observing Vertebrate Behavior

Question What can you discover about animal behavior through observations?

Lab Overview In this investigation you will observe one type of vertebrate animal interacting with its environment and with other animals. Your observations could occur at a zoo, via a Web cam, in a park, at a birdfeeder, on a farm, or other setting. You will act as an animal behaviorist as you make initial observations, pose questions, and then observe the animal more closely to try to answer the questions you have raised. In particular, look for the types of behaviors identified in Chapter 3 of your textbook.

Introduction Discovery science often depends on being patient and recording in detail everything you observe. Even if a behavior that you observe at first seems unimportant, it may end up being important later to help you answer a question. Some of the questions you raise may be answerable with more observations, while others may require a controlled experiment. You may not be able to answer some of the "how" and "why" questions you raise in this investigation, but perhaps someone else (such as a zookeeper or a wildlife biologist) can. Careful observation is often the first step to major discoveries.

Prelab Activity An animal behaviorist returns from a trip to the Midway Islands (1,900 km northwest of Hawaii) with sketches of albatrosses displaying interesting behaviors. Practice making observations and asking questions by examining the sketches below. Then answer the Prelab Questions that follow.

Objective to make detailed observations of an animal's behavior and to explore the challenges of an animal behaviorist's work

Inquiry Skills
• observing
• asking questions
• making inferences

Time
• 15 min for Prelab Activity
• 30 min for Part A (for observations)
• 40 min for Part B
• 20 min for Analysis and Conclusions

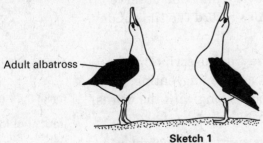

Adult albatross

Sketch 1

The albatrosses in Sketch 1 are performing part of a courtship ritual. In Sketch 2, an adult albatross is feeding a chick.

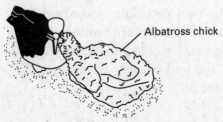

Albatross chick

Sketch 2

Prelab Questions

1. Describe the behaviors you observe in each sketch.

Sample answer: In the first sketch, two adult albatrosses are standing chest to chest. Both birds'

necks are extended and their beaks are pointing toward the sky. In the second sketch, an albatross

chick's beak is inside the beak of an adult albatross.

2. List two questions you have about the birds' behavior in each sketch.

Students' questions will vary.

3. Do you think that you could answer your questions through further observations of the actual birds? Explain.

Students' responses will vary depending on their questions.

Materials
- notebook
- pencil
- watch
- binoculars (optional)

Procedure

Part A: Making an Ethogram

1. Discuss with your teacher a plan for observing an animal.

2. For 15 min make careful observations of what the animal is doing. Note how it is interacting with its environment and with other animals. Record in your notebook everything you observe and any questions the behaviors raise. Also record the time of day of your observations.

3. Look over your observations. Think of one-word descriptions for the types of behavior you observed (such as sleeping, eating, playing, etc.) and record them in your notebook. Along with the words, write a short description of each behavior.

4. The sample chart on the next page shows six types of behavior an animal behaviorist observed in a hamster. This type of chart is called an *ethogram*—a catalogue of an animal's behaviors. On a separate sheet of paper, make a similar chart based on your one-word descriptions from Step 3. You will observe the animal for 30 min, so your chart should have 30 rows.

Advance Preparation

A couple of weeks before the lab
Work with students to develop a plan for observations. If a trip to the zoo is possible, monkeys, apes, birds, meerkats, and otters are good subjects to observe. Some zoos even offer Web cams with streaming video, enabling observations to be made online. Students could also observe behavior at a birdfeeder; in a field or forest with squirrels or birds; in a farmyard with chickens; in a park or plaza with pigeons; or at the shore with seagulls. You can also do this activity in your classroom if you have active animals. Anoles are a good choice, especially if you have both sexes of anoles.

Safety and Disposal
Tell students to be cautious of poisonous or biting animals, such as insects or spiders, and dangerous plants, such as poison ivy or plants with thorns, as they make their observations. No observations should be performed on private property without the consent of the owner. Remind students to be respectful of the animals that they observe. No disposal required.

Name _____ Class _____ Date _____

Sample Ethogram

Minute	Behavior					
	Sleeping	Grooming	Eating	Burrowing	Scratching	Drinking
1	✓					
2		✓		✓		
3					✓	
4			✓			
5						✓

Part B: Observing the Animal for the Second Time

1. Observe the same animal or same type of animal again for 30 min. If possible, this second observation period should occur at the same time of day as the first observation period. At the very beginning of the first minute, place a check mark in the column of the behavior that the animal is exhibiting. Do not record any observations for the rest of the minute. Because most animals tend to repeat behaviors often, recording everything an animal does for 30 min is not necessary for the sake of this lab. At the start of the next minute, observe the animal again and place a check mark in the appropriate behavior column. If you notice behaviors that you did not notice during your first observations, add additional columns. Continue this process for 30 min. Stay focused or you will miss some of your observation times!

An ethogram is a description of the behavioral patterns of an animal. Ethograms are generally produced by cataloging all the typical behaviors and then determining the duration, frequency, and sequence of these behaviors. The method that students use to construct the ethogram is called a behavioral scan—snapshots of an animal's behavior taken over time.

2. On a separate sheet of paper, construct a bar graph showing the percentage of time the animal spent performing each type of behavior included in the ethogram.

3. Chapter 3 in your textbook describes many types of animal behavior. Examine the list in the data table below for the types of behavior you observed. Describe any ways in which the animal you observed displayed these behaviors.

Data Table

Type of Behavior	Description of Behavior
Aggressive behavior	
Territorial behavior	
Courtship	
Communication	
Cooperation	

Analysis and Conclusions

1. Identify the type of animal you observed. If possible, find its genus and species names. Also, describe the area in which you observed the animal and if the animal interacted with other animals of the same or a different species.

Students' responses will vary based on their observations.

_____

_____

_____

2. Which of the behaviors in your ethogram did the animal perform the most and the least often? Explain.

Students' responses will vary based on their observations.

_____

_____

3. Which, if any, of the behaviors you observed do you think might be related to environmental cues such as time of day or season? Explain.

Students' responses will vary based on their observations.

_____

_____

_____

4. Choose a behavior listed in your ethogram and hypothesize the possible immediate and ultimate causes of the behavior.

Students' responses will vary based on their observations.

_____

_____

_____

Extension

Review your questions about the animal's behavior. Design an experiment to answer one of the questions. Review the procedure with your teacher before performing the experiment. Always obtain permission from your teacher before carrying out any investigations.

Extension
For example, a student could make further observations of the animal at a different time of day to study whether any behaviors may be due to natural rhythms.

Soil Solutions

Exploring Ions Found in Soil

Questions Which ions will be dissolved when soil is mixed with water? How do the amounts of these ions vary in soils from different locations?

Lab Overview In this investigation you will collect and test soil from two locations. One sample will be soil you predict to be high in nutrients important to plants, and the other will be soil you predict to be low in these nutrients. You will use a soil testing kit to find out if your predictions were correct.

Introduction In this lab you will compare levels of certain plant nutrients in soils from different areas near your home or school. You will collect two samples of local soil and use a soil testing kit to identify and determine the amounts of plant nutrients available as dissolved ions in each "soil solution."

Background Soil is made up of weathered rock particles, clay, and decaying organic material called humus. As you'll observe in this lab, when you place soil and water in a cup, the rock and clay particles sink and the humus floats. Meanwhile, ionic compounds dissolve in the water and form a solution. Some of these dissolved ions contain elements that are required for a plant to be healthy. For example, plants need nitrogen (N) to make chlorophyll, a molecule that plays an important role during photosynthesis. Without nitrogen and certain other elements from soil, such as phosphorus (P) and potassium (K), plants cannot survive. Plants obtain these elements by absorbing the ions NH_4^+ (ammonium), PO_4^{3-} (phosphate), and K^+ (potassium) from the soil.

The type of particles that make up the soil affects the soil's ion levels. For example, humus and clay particles are negatively charged. These negatively charged particles attract positive NH_4^+ and K^+ ions, but repel negative ions such as PO_4^{3-}. As a result, soils that are particularly high in humus and clay particles compared to rock particles tend to have high levels of NH_4^+ and K^+ ions.

Prelab Activity A farmer has several fields of corn planted in different areas. Most of the farmer's cornfields contain healthy plants, but three have sickly plants. The farmer had the soil tested in these three fields as well as in a field with healthy plants. The results of the soil

Objectives to look at how plants are affected by the availability of ions containing certain elements that are plant nutrients, to make inferences about soils that may contain low or high levels of plant nutrients, and to measure and compare the levels of plant nutrients in soil samples from different locations

Inquiry Skills
- predicting
- making inferences
- making measurements
- analyzing data
- drawing conclusions

Time
- 20–25 min for the Prelab Activity
- 30 min for Parts A and B
- 20–30 min for Part C
- 20 min for Analysis and Conclusions

tests are summarized in Table 1. Use the test results to help guide you in choosing sites where you might find soil with high or low levels of N, P, and K for your own investigation.

Table 1: Farmer's Soil Testing Results

Field #	Level of N	Level of P	Level of K	Description of Plants
1	high	high	high	This field contains a good crop: tall, strong plants with dark green leaves.
2	low	high	high	Older leaves are yellowish.
3	high	low	high	Older leaves are purplish in color, especially at the outer edges.
4	high	high	low	Leaves are yellowed at the outer edges. Some of the leaf tips appear burned.

Plants need nitrogen to produce proteins. Many proteins (enzymes) are needed to build chlorophyll molecules; therefore, lack of chlorophyll is often a sign of nitrogen deficiency.

Plants low in phosphate produce an increased amount of a purple compound called anthocyanin.

Potassium deficiency results in the inability of plants to regulate water uptake. Without enough potassium, water does not reach the outer margins of leaves, causing them to wither and turn brown.

Prelab Questions

1. Fill in the chart below about plant nutrients found in soil.

Plant Nutrients in Soil

Element Name	Symbol for Element	Chemical Formula of Ion	Name of Ion
a. Nitrogen	b. N	NH_4^+	c. Ammonium
Phosphorus	d. P	e. PO_4^{3-}	f. Phosphate
g. Potassium	h. K	i. K^+	Potassium

2. Your goal in choosing the sites to sample is to find soil that is high in N, P, and K and soil that is likely to be low (deficient) in at least one of these plant nutrients. How might you use the information you learned in the Background and the Prelab Activity as clues to finding nutrient-deficient soil?

Collect samples from areas where plants show signs of nutrient deficiencies such

as leaves that have turned yellow or purplish or appear burned.

3. Based on the information you read in the Background, explain how you will separate the ions from the soil during your investigation.

Mix the soil with water. The rock/clay particles will sink, the humus will float, and the ionic

compounds will dissolve in the water.

Materials

- ruler
- garden trowel or small shovel
- 2 small self-sealing plastic bags
- marker
- masking tape or labels
- soil testing kit (rapitest® Soil Kit or LaMotte Soil Testing Kit)
- cups
- bottled or distilled water

Procedure

Part A: Choosing Your Soil Collection Sites

1. You will need to collect two soil samples. One soil sample should come from a site that you think may be high in the plant nutrients nitrogen (N), phosphorus (P), and potassium (K). The other soil sample should come from an area that you think may be low in N, P, and K. Follow your teacher's instructions about where to find soil collection sites—around your school, near your home, or in a nearby park, wooded area, or other open space. (**NOTE:** *Do not collect soil from private property unless you have specific permission from the property owner.*)

When choosing your soil collection sites, consider the following questions:

- What are some clues that might indicate that a site has high levels of these plant nutrients? (*Hint:* Would you look near lush plant growth, areas where crops are grown, sandy soil, soil rich in humus, soil near water, or rocky soil?)
- What are some clues that might indicate that a site has low levels of these plant nutrients? (*Hint:* Remember what you learned about the appearance of plant leaves.)

Advance Preparation

More than two weeks before the lab Purchase soil testing kits directly from Flinn Scientific or Lamotte, or purchase at a hardware/garden supply store. Kits should be less than one year old.

Three days before the lab Locate nearby sites for collecting soil. Take a class trip to collect samples or remind students to choose their sites and obtain permission from property owners if necessary. Review the correct procedure for collecting samples.

One day before the lab Remind students to bring in their samples.

The day of the lab Have extra samples available for students without their own to test.

Safety and Disposal Remind students to wash hands after handling soil. Goggles and aprons may be worn while working with the soil testing kits to prevent contact with chemicals or clothing damage. If any solutions get into a student's eye, flush with water for 15 min and seek medical attention. Consult the kit instructions for disposal information.

Record observations about your sites in Data Table 1 below.

Data Table 1

	Site A	Site B
Name of site	Student observations will vary.	
Description of site		
Do you think this site is high or low in plant nutrients? Explain your hypothesis.		

2. After you have chosen your sites, obtain a garden trowel or small shovel, marker, and two self-sealing plastic bags. Then prepare to collect samples following the directions in Part B.

Part B: Collecting Your Soil Samples

1. To collect a soil sample at your first collection site, begin by scraping off the top layer of soil with a garden trowel to remove any sticks, leaves, or other debris.

2. Dig an 8-cm-deep hole into the soil and collect your sample. Fill a self-sealing plastic bag about half-full. Label the bag with the site name. **CAUTION:** *Soil can contain disease-causing microorganisms. Wash your hands thoroughly with soap after handling soil.*

3. Go to the second collection site. Repeat Part B, steps 1 and 2.

4. Bring the two labeled bags with your soil samples to your classroom lab.

Part C: Testing Your Soil Samples

1. To test your soil samples, read the directions in the soil testing kit. Then use the kit to test your soil samples. **CAUTION:** *Handle test kit solutions carefully to avoid getting any on your skin or clothing. These solutions may be acidic and/or contain permanent dyes.*

Expected Results
Samples of fertile soils such as flowerbeds or agricultural fields (made up largely of potting soil and/or compost) will give high readings for N, P, and K with the rapitest® kits. Soil samples from a vacant lot or a typical backyard may test lower in N, P, and K. The Lamotte soil testing kits are somewhat more sensitive and may give higher readings.

2. After testing each sample, record the levels of N, P, and K in Data Table 2.

Data Table 2

Site Name	N Level	P Level	K Level
	Student results will vary.		

Analysis and Conclusions

1. Compare the results from your two sites. Did they support your hypotheses about which site was likely to be high in nutrients and which was likely to be low?

Students should compare their results and relate them to their original predictions.

2. Plant roots can only absorb dissolved ions. For example, plant roots cannot absorb the compound KNO_3 (potassium nitrate). However, when this compound dissolves in water, the ions K^+ and NO_3^- (nitrate) form. Plants can absorb these ions. What property of water is most important for plants to obtain these ions?
 a. It takes a lot of heat to change the temperature of water.
 b. Water is less dense when it is frozen than when it is liquid.
 c. Hydrogen bonding of water creates surface tension.
 d. Water molecules are polar with partial negative and partial positive charges.

Explain.

The negatively charged portion of the water molecule attracts K^+ ions, while the positively charged portion will attract the NO_3^- ions. Because water molecules pull apart KNO_3 in this way, plants are able to obtain the nutrients in ion form.

3. Collaborate with your classmates to determine which locations were the source of the soil samples with the highest and lowest levels of N, P, and K.
 a. Describe any patterns that you observe for sites with high and low levels of the nutrients.

Patterns will depend on class results.

b. Develop hypotheses that could explain why these areas have high or low levels of the nutrients.

Hypotheses will depend on class results, but should relate ion levels to soil makeup.

4. Table 2 below provides a list of some organic fertilizers that contain N, P, and K. Based on your soil testing results, which fertilizer (or combination of fertilizers) do you think would be best to add to your soil in order to provide adequate amounts of N, P, and K? Explain why you think this is the best choice.

Answers will vary. Blood meal and alfalfa meal would be good fertilizers to add to soil with low

levels of N and K, but high levels of P. Bone meal would be a good addition to a soil with low levels

of P, high levels of K, and moderate levels of N.

Table 2: Percentages of Nutrients in Various Fertilizers

Fertilizer	N	P	K
Alfalfa meal	2	0.5	2
Bat guano (droppings)	10	3	1
Cotton seed meal	6	2	1
Kelp meal	1	0.1	2
Blood meal	13	0	0
Bone meal	3	15	0

Organic fertilizers such as those listed in this table tend to be better choices than inorganic fertilizers because organic fertilizers release needed ions slowly. Many inorganic fertilizers are salts. Unless they are formulated to dissolve slowly, they may wash away before the plant receives any nutritional benefits.

Extension

The pH of soil affects how easily plants can obtain nutrients from soil. If the pH is too high or too low, the ionic compounds do not dissolve as easily in water and are less available to plants. Most plants require the soil pH to be between 6 and 7. Design an experiment to determine whether adjusting the pH of your soil samples could increase their levels of dissolved nutrients. You can alter the pH of the soil by adding an acid such as vinegar, or a base such as limestone. (**NOTE:** *Be sure to check with your teacher before carrying out any investigations.*)

Extension
Make sure that students follow all safety guidelines as they test additional soil samples for the Extension activities. Student results will vary.

Where to Turn for Heartburn

Evaluating the Effectiveness of Antacids

Question Which antacid is the most effective in neutralizing acid?

Lab Overview In this investigation, you will compare the effectiveness of two different antacid medications. To do this, you will measure the amount of vinegar (a weak acid) needed to change the pH of solutions containing each antacid from pH 7 to pH 4.

Introduction You will start your investigation of antacid effectiveness by taking a closer look at how acids and bases interact. To begin, you will construct models of hydrogen ions (H^+) and hydroxide ions (OH^-). You will use these models as you take part in a class role-play to discover what happens to H^+ ions and OH^- ions when an acid is neutralized. You will also make models of buffer molecules and explore what happens when acid is added to a buffer solution.

Background The lining of your stomach secretes hydrochloric acid (HCl) that aids digestion. This strong acid normally remains in the stomach, which is protected from acid burns by a mucous layer. However, stomach acid can sometimes flow into the esophagus, the tube that connects the mouth to the stomach. If stomach acid comes into contact with the lining of the esophagus, a burning pain known as heartburn occurs.

Antacid medications are used to treat heartburn and other medical problems caused by stomach acid. In an aqueous solution, HCl breaks apart completely into H^+ and Cl^- ions. Antacids contain bases, compounds that can remove H^+ ions from aqueous solutions. Some bases found in antacids, such as aluminum hydroxide, $Al(OH)_3$, do this by adding OH^- ions to the solution. The OH^- ions combine with H^+ ions and form molecules of water (H_2O). Removing the H^+ makes the solution less acidic (raises its pH). Other antacids, such as calcium carbonate ($CaCO_3$) and sodium bicarbonate ($NaHCO_3$), act as buffers when dissolved in water. These buffers regulate pH by removing H^+ ions from the solution when their levels increase and donating H^+ ions to the solution when their levels decrease.

Objective to observe the interaction between acids and bases with the aid of a pH indicator and learn about the role of buffers in maintaining homéostasis

Inquiry Skills
- making measurements
- collecting data
- analyzing data
- drawing conclusions

Time
- 10–25 min for the Prelab Activity
- 10 min for Part A
- 20 min for Part B
- 20–30 min for Analysis and Conclusions

The active ingredient in Tums® is calcium carbonate ($CaCO_3$). When calcium carbonate dissolves in water, carbonate ions (CO_3^{2-}) are formed. Carbonate is a base and can accept one or two hydrogen ions, forming bicarbonate (HCO_3^-) or carbonic acid (H_2CO_3), depending on how much acid is added. Bicarbonate is a buffer because it can either accept H^+ ions or donate H^+ ions depending on whether acid or base is added.

Prelab Activity Your teacher will assign you a role in each of the following class role-plays. Follow the instructions below.

Role-Play 1: Neutralization of an Acid With a Base If you are assigned the role of an acid, you will be given a marshmallow, which you will use to represent a H^+ ion. If you are assigned the role of a base, your teacher will give you materials to construct a model of an OH^- ion like the one shown below. The free end of the paper clip represents a negatively charged region where a H^+ ion can bind.

Obtain marshmallows, gummy ring candy, and paper clips for Prelab Activity. Remind students to handle the pointed ends of the opened paper clips with care.

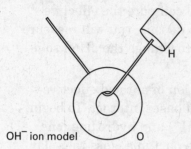

OH$^-$ ion model   O

To begin the role-play, students with H^+ ions will gather in a designated area. Students with models of OH^- ions will move about randomly in another part of the room. Your teacher will "add" two H^+ ions at a time to the "solution." How do you think these ions will interact? How can you and your classmates represent this interaction?

An H^+ ion will bind to the negatively-charged end of an OH^- ion, forming a molecule of water.

Students with marshmallows (representing H^+ ions) can stick them on the end of paper clips

(representing the free end of an OH^- ion).

Role-Play 2: Interaction Between Acids and Buffers If you are assigned the role of an "acid" you will be given a marshmallow, which you will use to represent an H^+ ion. If you are assigned the role of a "buffer," you will construct a model of a buffer molecule like the one shown below. Straighten three paper clips and twist them around each other. Put three marshmallows on three of the six ends to represent H atoms. The three free ends represent negatively charged regions where H^+ ions can bind.

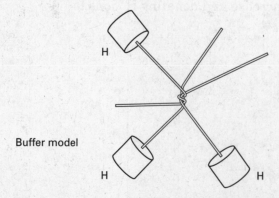

Buffer model

The active ingredients in Alka-Seltzer® Heartburn Relief are citric acid and sodium bicarbonate. Citric acid is an organic acid with a molecular formula of HOC(COOH)(CH$_2$COOH)$_2$. The three carboxyl groups (COOH) can donate or receive H^+ depending on the pH of the solution. When sodium bicarbonate dissolves in water, it forms bicarbonate ions.

To begin the role-play, students with ions will gather in a designated area. Students with buffer molecules will move about randomly in another area of the classroom. Your teacher will "add" one H^+ at a time to the "solution." How do you think the H^+ ion and buffer molecule will interact? How can you and your classmates represent this interaction with your models?

H⁺ ions will bind to the three free ends of the buffer molecule. Students with marshmallows will

stick them onto the free ends of the buffer molecules.

Prelab Questions

1. How did your class use the models to represent the interaction between H^+ ions from an acid and OH^- ions from a base?

Each marshmallow (H⁺ ion) was stuck onto the end of a paper clip representing an OH⁻ ion to

show how H⁺ ions from an acid bond to OH⁻ ions from a base.

2. What molecule was formed from H^+ and OH^-?

Water (H₂O)

3. How did your class use the models to represent the interaction between H^+ ions and buffer molecules?

Marshmallows (H⁺ ions) were stuck onto the free ends on the paperclip model of a buffer

molecule to show how a buffer molecule can take up H⁺ from an acid.

4. Based on the role-plays, what do you predict will happen to the pH of a buffer solution when a small amount of acid is added? Explain.

The pH of the buffer solution will not change when a small amount of acid is added because

the H⁺ ions from the acid will bind to buffer molecules.

5. If you keep adding more and more acid to the buffer solution described in Question 4, what do you predict will happen to the pH over time? Explain.

The pH of the buffer solution will eventually become more acidic because the "free ends" of

the buffer molecule will fill up, leaving excess H⁺ ions in the solution.

Materials

- antacid medications (2 types)
- self-sealing plastic sandwich bag
- hammer
- clear plastic cups or beakers
- marker
- masking tape
- graduated cylinder
- water
- 2 plastic spoons
- transfer pipette
- universal pH indicator solution
- vinegar (weak acid)

Procedure

Part A: Preparing Antacid Solutions

1. Read the dosage information on the antacid bottle or package. Determine how much of each product is used for one dose.

2. If the antacids you are using are both liquids or powders, continue to Step 3. If you are assigned a tablet antacid, you will need to crush the tablet into a powder. To do this, place the antacid tablet inside a self-sealing plastic bag, seal the bag, then tap (do not pound) the tablet firmly with a hammer. **CAUTION:** *Use hammer carefully to prevent injury.*

3. Label one plastic cup or beaker "Antacid 1" and add the name of the product you are testing. Repeat for "Antacid 2."

4. Place one dose of each antacid in the appropriately labeled cup.

5. Add 100 mL of water to each cup. Mix each solution thoroughly with a plastic spoon until the antacid is completely dissolved in the water.

6. Add approximately 1–2 mL of universal pH indicator to each cup. Add more if needed to give the solution an obvious color.

7. Your teacher will have a color chart available that you can use to determine the pH of each solution. Using the color chart as a key, determine the initial pH of each antacid solution and record it in Data Table 1 below.

Alternate Materials
Bromothymol blue could be used in place of universal pH indicator, although there will be fewer color changes. Another option would be to use pH paper at set time intervals.

Advance Preparation
- Order universal pH indicator if needed.
- Purchase several brands of antacids at a grocery store or pharmacy so that different lab groups can try different brands. Tums® and Alka-Seltzer® Heartburn Relief provide good data.

Safety and Disposal
Remind students not to consume anything that is or has been in the laboratory. Have students wear goggles whenever they are working with solutions. Monitor proper student use of hammers. Remind students to handle glassware with care to avoid breakage. Pour solutions down the drain and flush with excess water.

Part B: Adding Acid to Antacid Solutions

1. Add 0.5 mL of vinegar to each cup and stir with a plastic spoon. Use a separate spoon for each solution.

2. Observe the color of each antacid solution and determine the pH with the color chart. Record the pH of each solution in Data Table 1.

3. Continue adding 0.5 mL of acid to each solution, stirring each one, and recording the pH you determine in Data Table 1. Keep going until both solutions have reached pH 4. If you have added 5 mL of acid and the solution or solutions still have not reached pH 4, begin adding 1 mL of acid at a time.

Data Table 1: Total Amount of Acid Added

	Initial pH	0.5 mL	1 mL	1.5 mL	2 mL	2.5 mL	3 mL	3.5 mL	4 mL	4.5 mL	5 mL	6 mL	7 mL	8 mL
Antacid 1	7.5	7.5	7.5	7.5	7.5	7.5	7.5	7.5	7.5	7.5	7.5	7.5	7.5	7.5
Antacid 2	7.5	7.5	5	5	4									

	9 mL	10 mL	11 mL	12 mL	13 mL	14 mL	15 mL	16 mL	17 mL	18 mL	19 mL	20 mL	mL	mL
Antacid 1	6.5	6.5	6.5	6.5	5	5	5	5	5	5	5	4		
Antacid 2														

Analysis and Conclusions

1. On the grid below, make a line graph showing the data you collected for both antacids. The x-axis of your graph should show the variable you changed during the experiment (amount of acid added). The y-axis of your graph should show the dependent variable (pH). Be sure to label the axes and include a title.

Using Probeware to Plot Neutralization
If you have electronic probeware, it is interesting to gather the data when adding the antacid to a known amount of acid. Equilibrate the probe in 100 mL of vinegar, then add one dosage of a particular antacid all at once. The neutralization will plot automatically and students can compare the rate at which neutralization takes place.

If you have enough pH meters for the class, you can use these to obtain more precise quantitative results for the titration of acid into antacid.

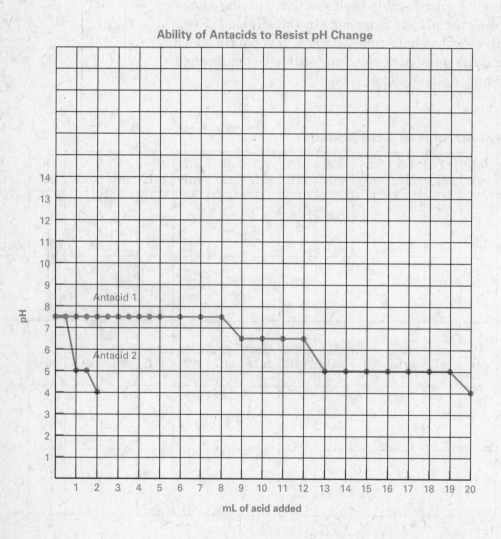

Ability of Antacids to Resist pH Change

2. Which of the two antacids you tested was more effective at neutralizing acid? Explain how your results support this conclusion.

Student answers will vary based on the antacids they tested. Students should answer that the

antacid solution that accepted the most acid before reaching pH 4 was the most effective at

neutralizing acid.

3. Collect data from four other lab teams that tested different antacids. Record their data in Data Table 2, along with the data you collected.

Data Table 2

Name of Antacid	mL of Acid Added to Reach pH 4
Student data will vary.	

4. Of all the antacids tested by your class, which one was the most effective? Explain.

Student answers will vary based on the antacids they tested. Students should answer that

the antacid solution that accepted the most acid before reaching pH 4 was the most effective

at neutralizing acid.

5. Acids add H^+ to a solution. Antacids contain bases and/or buffers. Write in your own words how antacids neutralize acid. (You may wish to review the section in Concept 4.4 in your text that discusses acids, bases, and buffers.)

Antacids contain chemicals (bases or buffers) that bind free H^+ ions in solutions. When

antacids take H^+ ions out of solution, the solution becomes less acidic.

6. Some antacids worked better than others, but all of them eventually lost their effectiveness and allowed the solution to become acidic. What do you think was happening in the antacid solution when the pH started to become acidic?

Eventually, the antacid bound all the H^+ ions that it could. Excess H^+ ions remained in the

solution and made it more acidic.

7. Suggest a reason why some antacids might be more effective than others.

Sample answers: Whether the buffer contains both bases and buffers, how many H^+ ions the

particular compounds of the antacid can accept.

Extension

Which antacid you tested is most *cost effective*? Research the prices of the antacids you tested. Calculate the cost per dose of each antacid by dividing the cost of the bottle or package by the number of doses it contains. To determine which antacid is most effective per dollar, do the following calculation for each antacid tested:

$$\frac{\text{mL acid added to reach pH 4}}{\text{the cost of one dose}} = \underline{\qquad}$$

Extension
The larger the fraction, the more cost-effective the product is. Larger fractions indicate that the product handles more acid for less money.

Way to Go, Indigo!

Biological Molecules and Denim Processing

Question How does the enzyme cellulase affect denim fabric?

Lab Overview In this investigation you will take on the role of an industrial scientist as you examine a process used by jeans manufacturers to soften and lighten denim fabric. You will identify problems with one industrial process, and investigate a possible solution by using your understanding of biological molecules.

Introduction In this lab you will start with three swatches (pieces) of denim fabric. You will treat one swatch with the enzyme cellulase, soak it in water, and then scrub it. You will soak a second untreated swatch in water and then scrub it. The third swatch will not be treated, soaked, or scrubbed. You will then compare the three swatches to determine the effects of cellulase on denim. How might these results be applied to make comfortable jeans?

Background Denim jeans were designed in the 1840s to be tough outdoor clothing for farmers, miners, and cattle ranchers. These jeans were stiff and uncomfortable until they had been worn or washed many times. Eventually, jeans became fashionable, but consumers wanted to buy jeans that were already comfortable. Manufacturers had to develop methods to provide new jeans that felt and looked "worn in."

To understand denim you should be familiar with some properties of cotton. Cotton plants produce seed-bearing capsules called bolls (BOHLZ). The bolls contain white balls of fuzzy fibers surrounding cottonseeds.

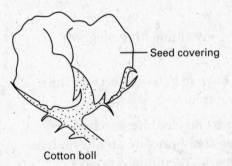

Seed covering

Cotton boll

The fibers are actually the cell walls of dead cells. These cell walls are made of a carbohydrate called cellulose. Cellulose is a long chain of glucose monomers. Multiple cellulose chains are linked together by

Objective to treat denim fabric with cellulase, observe any changes that occur, and draw conclusions about the effectiveness of cellulase treatment in denim processing

Inquiry Skills
• making inferences
• predicting
• controlling variables
• drawing conclusions
• communicating conclusions

Time
• 10–15 min for the Prelab Activity
• 20–25 min for Part A (swatches are left to soak for 2 days)
• 10–15 min for Part B, Steps 1–3; 10–15 min for Step 4 (swatches must dry overnight)
• 20–30 min for Analysis and Conclusions

You could add a fourth swatch to the experiment that the students treat with cellulase, but do not wash or scrub. Without scrubbing or washing there will be no visible effects of the cellulase treatment. This would demonstrate to the students that washing and scrubbing is an essential step for successful use of the enzyme.

hydrogen bonds. The chains wrap around each other, forming larger and larger strands.

To make denim cloth, manufacturers spin the cotton fibers into threads. The naturally white threads are woven together with threads that have been dyed blue. When the threads are dyed, molecules of the dye (called indigo) become trapped between the cellulose fibers, making the threads appear dark blue.

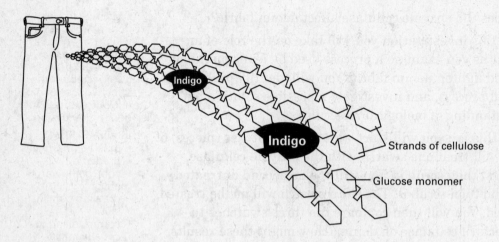

Strands of cellulose

Glucose monomer

As denim is worn and washed several times, the cellulose fibers start to break and wear thin. As the fibers break, the indigo dye is released and the fabric softens and becomes more flexible.

Manufacturers discovered that washing jeans with pumice stones sped up the softening process. However, stonewashing caused several problems:

1. The pumice stones took a toll on the industrial washing machines, which had to be replaced frequently.

2. Additional employees were needed to pick the pumice stones out of the pockets of the jeans.

3. Many jeans had to be destroyed because the pumice stones caused too much damage.

4. The pumice stones wore down to a sandy sludge that clogged drains and sewer lines.

5. Pumice has to be mined, which can have negative effects on the landscape and wildlife habitats in an area.

A better method of preparing denim was needed! Researchers have discovered that the enzyme cellulase could provide an alternative method of breaking down the cellulose fibers. As cellulase breaks down the fibers, the trapped indigo dye is released. The fabric surface becomes fuzzy as the threads fray. Some sort of agitation (shaking, scrubbing, or abrasion) is important to complete the breakage of the weakened fibers.

Indigo is a natural dye found in the leaves of the legume *Indigofera tinctoria*. The leaves contain a colorless compound that turns blue when the leaves are crushed in water. Today, synthetic indigo dye is used to color denim.

Prelab demonstration ideas: Tie wrapped peppermint candies together with dental floss to create a model for cellulose ("chain of sugars"). Use several strands of white yarn to represent cellulose strands. String indigo-colored beads on the strands to represent an "indigo-dyed thread." Indicate using scissors how cellulase breaks the cellulose strands and releases the indigo dye (beads).

Stonewashing jeans with pumice stones was introduced in the 1980s. Pumice is a porous, lightweight volcanic rock, with a rough, abrasive texture.

Enzymes called cellulases break the bonds between the glucose monomers that make up cellulose. IndiAge®, produced by Genencor International, is a cellulase designed for denim washing. The source of the enzyme is *Trichoderma*, a fungus that decomposes plant material.

Prelab Activity After reading the Introduction and Background sections, check your understanding by answering the Prelab Questions.

Prelab Questions

1. Match each action of cellulase with its effect on denim fabric.

   c   As the strands of cellulose break apart, dye is released.   a. softer-textured denim

   a   The fraying of the cellulose strands makes the cotton fibers in the thread fuzzy.   b. more flexible, less stiff denim

   b   The fraying of the cellulose strands reduces the thread's strength and thickness.   c. lighter-colored denim

2. Do you think denim treated with cellulase for 1 hour would look or feel different than denim treated for 24 hours? Explain your answer.

Fabric treated with cellulase for 24 hours would probably look lighter in color and feel softer when

compared with fabric treated for one hour. Since enzymes are not used up in reactions, the longer

the fabric is exposed, the more bonds will be broken in the cellulose fibers.

3. The enzyme cellulase is produced by a type of fungus called a mold. Why might people be interested in determining the environmental conditions, such as temperature and pH, that are best for the growth of this mold?

The enzyme would most likely function best at temperature and pH conditions in which the

mold thrives.

Materials

- three dark blue denim fabric swatches (about 7 cm by 7 cm)
- scissors
- masking tape
- marker
- two 500-mL beakers or large cups
- one pH 5 buffer capsule
- 500 mL water
- graduated cylinder
- 2 g IndiAge® cellulase
- transfer pipette
- large plastic bowl or bucket
- hot tap water
- paper towels
- magnifying glass

Advance Preparation

More than two weeks before the lab Order IndiAge® cellulase from Flinn Scientific (order #I0063). Order buffer capsules, or citric acid and sodium citrate, for the pH 5 buffer solution.

Three days before the lab Purchase 1 yard or more of dark indigo-colored denim at a fabric store. Obtain buckets or large plastic bowls.

Procedure

Part A: Treating Denim With Cellulase

1. You will be given three denim swatches. To distinguish the denim fabric swatch you will treat with cellulase, cut off one of the corners. With a marker, write "Control 1" on the back of a second denim fabric swatch and set it aside. Leave the third swatch unmarked—this swatch will be Control 2.

2. With masking tape and a marker, label one beaker or large cup "Buffer With Cellulase." Label the other beaker or cup "Buffer."

3. In the beaker labeled "Buffer," dissolve the contents of a pH 5 buffer capsule in 500 mL of water to make a buffer solution with the best pH for the cellulase.

4. Carefully pour 250 mL of the buffer solution you have prepared into the beaker labeled "Buffer With Cellulase." Add 2 g of IndiAge® cellulase.

5. Place the denim swatch with the cut corner in the beaker labeled "Buffer With Cellulase." Place the Control 1 swatch in the beaker labeled "Buffer."

6. Allow the two denim swatches to soak at room temperature for two days or over a weekend. The third denim swatch, Control 2, should not be treated or soaked in water.

Part B: Scrubbing Denim Swatches

1. After soaking the denim swatches for two days, remove the swatch with the cut corner from the beaker labeled "Buffer With Cellulase." Rinse the swatch well with warm water to wash away the cellulase. Then remove Control 1 from the other beaker, and rinse it separately.

2. In denim processing facilities, jeans are placed in industrial washers. The actions of the washers break the weakened cellulose fibers and release indigo molecules. Now you will handwash your samples to simulate this step. Put both denim swatches together in a container of hot water. **CAUTION:** *Use hot tap water, but at a comfortable temperature—take care to avoid scalding your hands.* Scrub the two pieces against each other in the water, and lift them out and squeeze them repeatedly. Continue scrubbing the swatches for at least 10 minutes. Change the water whenever it gets blue.

3. When no more blue dye is released, wring out the swatches and lay them flat on a paper towel to dry. Allow them to dry at least overnight.

One day before the lab
Cut denim fabric into 7-cm (3-inch) squares (three squares for each group). You could also make pH 5 buffer from citric acid and sodium citrate: First, prepare 0.1 M citric acid stock solution by dissolving 21 g citric acid in 1 L water. Next, prepare 0.1 M sodium citrate stock solution by dissolving 29.4 g sodium citrate in 1 L water. To make 1 L of pH 5 buffer, mix 205 mL of the citric acid stock solution with 295 mL sodium citrate stock solution, and add 500 mL water.

Safety and Disposal
To avoid scalding, adjust hot tap water to a suitable temperature. To avoid possible allergic responses to cellulase, caution students to wash their hands after any contact with the solution. You may want to have students wear gloves to avoid staining their hands. Tell students not to agitate cellulase solutions, as this produces droplets that can be inhaled. Remind students to wear goggles. If any solutions get into a student's eye, flush with water for 15 minutes and seek medical attention. No special disposal is required.

4. When the swatches are dry, compare all three denim swatches. Look for any differences in color, texture, and flexibility. Use a magnifying glass to look for differences in the fibers. Record your observations in Data Table 1.

Expected Results
Both Control 1 and the enzyme-treated denim swatches will get lighter in color and softer than Control 2. The enzyme-treated denim will be lighter and softer than Control 1, and the edges will be more frayed. Depending on how much abrasion the students apply, they may or may not be able to detect a difference when they compare the treated fabric and the controls with a magnifying glass.

Data Table 1

Observations	Color	Texture	Flexibility
Denim swatch soaked in buffer with cellulase, then washed			
Control 1: denim swatch soaked in buffer, then washed			
Control 2: untreated, unwashed denim swatch			

Analysis and Conclusions

1. From the results of your experiment, would you say that cellulase treatment is an effective method for softening and lightening denim? Explain your response.

   Cellulase treatment was an effective way to soften and lighten denim. The swatch treated

   with cellulase is much softer and lighter in color than Control 1 and Control 2.

2. Explain the purpose of the Control 1 swatch and the Control 2 swatch in the experiment.

   Two variables were used in this experiment—cellulase treatment and washing/scrubbing.

   Control 1 (not treated with cellulase, but washed) was needed to demonstrate the effect

   of cellulase compared to no cellulase. Control 2 (unwashed and untreated) was needed to show

   the overall change in the flexibility, color, and texture of the denim after treating it with cellulase

   and washing.

3. What economic and environmental concerns do you think denim manufacturers might have about using enzymes to soften jeans instead of pumice stones?

Cellulase may end up costing much more than pumice. The enzyme may also damage the

fibers too much. It may be too difficult to make conditions perfect for the enzyme. There may

be concerns about the environmental impact of releasing cellulase into wastewater.

Extension

Using enzymes in the jeans manufacturing process costs money. Design a series of experiments to determine the most cost-effective way to get the greatest softening effect on denim fabric using enzyme washing. In other words, how could manufacturers alter conditions so that they will need less of the enzyme? Use your understanding of enzymes and how cellulase works on denim. Remember to only change one variable at a time. For example, if you change the temperature of the buffer solution, you may not also change the amount of enzyme added. You could also experiment with alternative methods of scrubbing. Describe your experimental designs in detail and explain your plans. Make sure that your experiments include appropriate controls. (**NOTE:** *Be sure to check with your teacher before carrying out any experiments.*)

Extension
Students' experimental designs should include a plan for controlling variables other than the study variable. Make sure that students identify and follow appropriate safety guidelines as needed if they carry out their experiments.
- Temperature: Indi-Age® cellulase works best at 55°C.
- pH: Optimal pH is 5.
- Concentration: 2 g/250 mL is a very high concentration of cellulase. Students should be able to decrease this concentration without losing much effect. Help students to relate changes in concentration to their understanding of enzyme function.
- Abrasion: The more friction is applied, the greater difference will be seen. For example, brushes could be used to increase abrasion.

Name _____ Class _____ Date_____

'Zyme Time

Pectinase and Apple Juice Production

Question How does the enzyme pectinase affect apple juice production?

Lab Overview In this investigation, you will perform an experiment to discover how pectinase affects the amount of apple juice that can be obtained from a sample of applesauce. You will also measure the effects of pectinase on the rate of apple juice production. Then you will design and carry out your own pectinase efficiency experiment by altering one variable such as pH or temperature.

Introduction To start your investigation, you will take a closer look at apple cells and learn about the source of apple juice. You will also learn about the structure and function of pectin, a polysaccharide found in large quantities in soft, non-woody plant parts such as fruits.

Prelab Activity The cells inside an apple, like other plant cells, are surrounded by a plasma membrane and a rigid cell wall that helps the cell maintain its shape. Apple juice is made up mostly of the liquid found inside apple cells. To release the apple juice, the cell walls and plasma membranes must be crushed and broken apart. The more cells are broken apart, the more apple juice is released.

   A polysaccharide called pectin is found in apple cell walls. It is also found in the space between cells where it is one material that connects apple cells together.

Objective to investigate an industrial application of an enzyme by measuring the rate of enzyme action and to design and carry out an experiment to test the effect of temperature or pH on enzyme activity

Inquiry Skills
• making measurements
• calculating
• collecting data
• designing experiments
• controlling variables
• analyzing data
• drawing conclusions
• communicating conclusions

Time
• 10–15 min for the Prelab Activity
• 20–25 min for Part A
• 30 min for Part B
• 20 min for Analysis and Conclusions

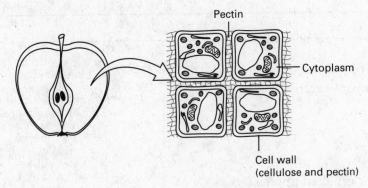

Apple cells

Each pectin molecule is made up of sugar monomers linked together in a long chain, with other chains that branch off from it. As apples ripen, they naturally produce enzymes called pectinases that break down pectin in a ripening apple, making the apple softer and juicier. Study the shape of a pectin molecule, then answer the Prelab questions.

Sugar monomer —

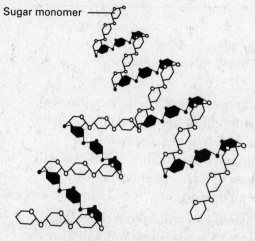

Pectin molecule

Prelab Questions

1. What do you predict would happen to apple cells if the pectin were broken down?

The cell walls and the connections between cells would weaken.

2. Based on what you know about the structure of pectin, how might breaking down pectin affect the taste of apple juice? Explain.

Pectin is a polysaccharide. Breaking down pectin into its sugar monomers may sweeten

the juice.

Materials

- 2 cheesecloth squares (2 layers each)
- 2 funnels
- 2 plastic cups
- 2 plastic spoons
- laboratory balance
- unsweetened applesauce or crushed apples (80 g)
- masking tape
- marker
- 2 graduated cylinders (25 or 50 mL)
- transfer pipette
- pectinase
- paper towels
- stopwatch or clock with second hand

Name _____ Class _____ Date_____

Procedure

Part A: Measuring the Effects of Pectinase on Apple Juice Production

1. Place the cheesecloth inside the funnel, then place the funnel into the graduated cylinder as shown below to make an apple juice filtration system. Repeat to make a second filtration system.

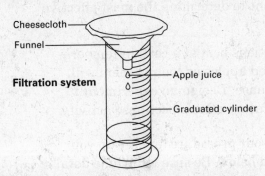

Cheesecloth

Funnel

Filtration system

Apple juice

Graduated cylinder

2. Using the laboratory balance and a plastic cup, measure 40 g of applesauce. Repeat with a second plastic cup.

3. Label the graduated cylinder of one filtration system "With Pectinase." Label the graduated cylinder of the other filtration system "Without Pectinase."

4. To one sample of applesauce, add 0.5 mL of pectinase. Stir well. Transfer the pectinase-treated applesauce into the filtration system labeled "With Pectinase." Put the used spoon aside on a paper towel. With the second, unused spoon, transfer the sample of applesauce in the second plastic cup to the filtration system labeled "Without Pectinase."

5. Start timing the experiment. Record the starting time in Data Table 1.

6. Use the markings on the graduated cylinder to measure how much juice is produced in each filtration system after 30 sec, 1 min, 2 min, 4 min, and 6 min. Record your measurements in Data Table 1.

Data Table 1

Time	Total Amount of Juice Produced (mL)	
	With Pectinase	**Without Pectinase**
Start time		
30 sec		
1 min		
2 min		
4 min		
6 min		

Alternate Materials/ Methods
• To avoid weighing the applesauce, you could have students use a standard medicine cup or condiment cup to measure the applesauce by volume. They should use 1 level cup in each experiment.
• If you don't have enough graduated cylinders, students could also use graduated test tubes or small beakers.

Advance Preparation
• Order pectinase from a biological supply company.
• Obtain applesauce, plastic spoons, cups, and cheesecloth at a market.
• Cut cheesecloth into squares. Each square should have two thin layers.

Safety and Disposal
Remind students not to consume any food that has been in the laboratory. Some students may have an allergy to pectinase. Students should wash their hands after the lab. No special disposal required.

Remind students if they use a spoon for their control applesauce that has come in contact at all with pectinase, it will affect their results.

Expected Results
Using 0.5 mL of pectinase with 40 g of applesauce will produce dramatic results. Typically 6 mL of apple juice are produced in the first 30 seconds. The control only produces about 1 mL of juice.

Part B: Designing a Pectinase Efficiency Experiment

1. You can use the same filtration systems to find out how pH or temperature affects the rate of apple juice production by pectinase. Read the information below and select one of the variables to study.

   pH: Every enzyme functions best at a certain pH. Perhaps pectinase functions better at a pH that is different from the pH of the applesauce. Design an experiment to determine the most effective pH for pectinase.

   Temperature: An enzyme functions best at a certain temperature. Perhaps heating the crushed apples or cooling them will increase the activity of the pectinase. Design an experiment to determine how changing temperature affects pectinase activity.

2. Design your experiment. Write your procedure and set up your data table in the spaces provided below. Be sure to include details such as how much pectinase or other materials you will need, the number of filtration systems needed, and so on. Explain how you plan to adjust the pH or temperature and how you will measure the rate of juice production. Check your experimental design with your teacher before you proceed.

Alternate Methods
- You can reduce the amount of pectinase to 0.1 mL for Part B.
- To reduce the amount of applesauce required, you may wish to put students in larger groups for Part B.

Note that the optimal temperature for pectinase is 37°C and the optimal pH is 5.0.

Procedure

_____

_____

_____

_____

_____

_____

Data Table 2

Name _____ Class _____ Date_____

Analysis and Conclusions

After the lab you could discuss how pectinase is produced in industrial settings. Certain fungi naturally produce pectinase. Industrial enzyme producers grow these fungi in fermentation tanks to produce the enzyme in large quantities. Many times, the fungi are mutated and screened for increased pectinase production.

1. Use the grid below to graph your data from Part A of the investigation. Your graph will have two lines, one for the "With Pectinase" sample and one for the "Without Pectinase" sample (control). Set up your graph to show time (in minutes) on the *x*-axis and the amount of juice produced (in mL) on the *y*-axis. After completing the graph, use it to answer parts a–e below.

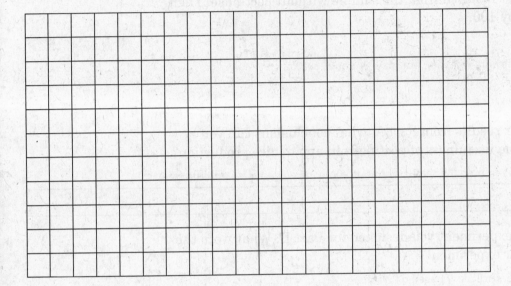

a. Calculate the rate of juice produced by the "With Pectinase" sample in the time period between 30 and 60 sec (0.5 min). (*Hint:* The rate is the amount produced in mL/time.)

Students' answers will vary based on data. Make sure that students express answers as a rate (mL/min).

b. Calculate the rate of juice produced by the "Without Pectinase" sample in the time period between 30 and 60 sec (0.5 min).

Students' answers will vary based on data, but will likely be lower than their answers in **a**.

c. Compare the rates of apple juice production in both samples. Which sample produced apple juice at a faster rate? How much faster?

Students will most likely answer that the sample with pectinase produced juice at a

faster rate—usually about six times faster.

d. Compare the amounts of juice produced by both samples after 6 min. Which produced more apple juice?

Students will likely answer that the sample with pectinase produced more juice.

e. How much more apple juice was released in the sample treated with pectinase than in the sample without pectinase? Give your answer as a percentage. To calculate the percentage, divide the amount released from the sample with pectinase by the amount released from the sample without pectinase. Then multiply by 100.

Students' answers will vary, but may be about 300%.

2. Based on your results from Part A, what conclusions can you draw about the usefulness of pectinase in apple juice production?

Pectinase increased both the total amount of apple juice produced, and the rate of production.

3. Describe the experiment you designed for Part B. What were the results of your experiment?

Students' answers will vary based on data.

4. What can you conclude about pectinase efficiency from these results?

Students' answers will vary based on data.

Extension

Design an experiment to test the variable you did not choose for Part B. Have your procedure approved by your teacher. If time and materials are available, perform the experiment. Compare your results with those of other students who tested this variable.

Extension
Check students' experimental designs. Make sure that students identify and follow appropriate safety guidelines as needed, if they carry out their experiments.

Name _____ Class _____ Date_____

Design a Cell

Comparing the Effects of Cell Shape on Diffusion Rate

Question What cell shapes are the most efficient at bringing in substances by diffusion?

Lab Overview In this investigation you will design your own cell shapes, carve model cells from gel cubes, and test how rapidly a substance can diffuse throughout each model cell. Your team will then design and make a model cell for a class "diffusion race," in which the cell with the largest ratio of mass to diffusion time wins.

Introduction You will use what you have learned about cell shapes and diffusion to design a cell best suited for rapid diffusion. You will carve your design from a blue agar cube. The agar cube is blue because it contains the pH indicator bromothymol blue. When you place your model cell into vinegar solution (a weak acid), acid will slowly diffuse into the agar and change its color from blue to yellow. You will observe the color change and record how long it takes the acid to reach the middle of your cell model—when your model turns yellow all the way through. This change will tell you how long it would take for nutrients to travel all the way through your "cell" by diffusion.

After designing and testing your first model cell, you will revise your design and make a second model cell for the class "diffusion race." Your goal is to give your model cell a shape that will allow it to change color quickly, while still having significant mass. The models that change color fastest are those that have the largest surface area/volume ratio. To win, your cell design must be the one that has the greatest mass and changes color the fastest, measured as the greatest value for mass per unit time (g/min). The winning cell also must be in one piece and cannot have any holes that reach from one side to the other.

Prelab Activity To prepare to design your own cell, first you will calculate surface area and volume for three different-sized agar cubes. Record your calculations in Data Table 1 on the next page. Then you will observe which cube changes color the fastest when placed in vinegar.

Objective to discover how cell size and shape affect the rate of diffusion into a cell

Inquiry Skills
- observing
- making measurements
- calculating
- formulating testable hypotheses
- evaluating and revising hypotheses

Time
- 45 min for Prelab Activity
- 15–20 min for Part A
- 15–20 min for Part B
- 20 min for Analysis and Conclusions

Bromothymol blue (also called bromthymol blue) is a pH indicator that is blue at a pH higher than 7, and yellow at a pH lower than 6. When students place their agar "cells" containing bromothymol blue into vinegar, they will see the blue change to yellow as the acid changes the pH of the indicator. This allows students to time the rate of diffusion.

Students should place the blue cubes in clear plastic cups, then pour in enough vinegar solution to cover them. After about 10 minutes it should be obvious which cubes will change color the fastest. See **Alternative Materials** and **Advance Preparation** to help you prepare for the Prelab Activity.

Data Table 1

Length of Cube Side	Surface Area*	Volume**	Surface Area to Volume Ratio***
Cube 1: 0.5 cm	1.5 cm²	0.125 cm³	12
Cube 2: 1.0 cm	6 cm²	1 cm³	6
Cube 3: 2.0 cm	24 cm²	8 cm³	3

*Surface area = length of a side × width of a side × number of sides
**Volume = length × width × height
***Surface area to volume ratio = surface area ÷ volume

1. Which cube changed color the fastest? The slowest?

Cube 1; Cube 3

2. From the results of the Prelab Activity, what characteristic of cell shape do you think is most important in enabling cells to obtain nutrients and eliminate wastes efficiently?

having a high surface area/volume ratio

3. From this activity, what factor(s) do you think might limit cell size?

Cell size is limited by how fast diffusion can occur. In a very large cell it would take too long

for nutrients to diffuse in and wastes to diffuse out.

4. What happens to the surface area/volume ratio if you increase the volume of a cell? If you decrease the cell surface area? Would either of these approaches increase the rate of diffusion? Explain.

If you increase the volume of a cell or decrease the surface area, the surface area to volume

ratio decreases; therefore neither of these approaches would increase the rate of diffusion.

The ratio must become greater for the rate of diffusion to increase.

5. Consider other shapes for a cell besides a cube. What cell shape might increase the surface area and decrease the volume? Explain.

Sample answers: Cell shapes could be flat, wavy, or have ridges carved into them.

Name _____ Class _____ Date _____

Materials

- agar cubes containing bromothymol blue (about 2 cm on each side)
- plastic knife
- paper or plastic plate
- plastic cup or beaker
- vinegar solution
- stopwatch or clock with second hand
- laboratory balance

Alternate Materials
Instead of bromothymol blue, you can use phenol red, which starts out red and turns yellow in acid. Instead of agar, you can use gelatin (diffusion times will be twice as long). See the online Teaching Guide for Chapter 6 for the gelatin recipe.

Procedure

Part A: Making and Testing a Model Cell

1. Work with your team to plan and sketch your cell design. Explain why you designed it as you did. Give the design a name so you can identify it in the data table.

Student explanations will vary.

_____

_____

_____

2. Obtain a blue agar cube from your teacher. **CAUTION:** *Wear safety goggles, plastic gloves, and lab aprons while working with the agar cubes.*

3. Using the plastic knife, carefully carve the agar cube into the shape you have decided on for your model cell. **CAUTION:** *Handle all sharp and/or pointed instruments carefully.*

4. Using a laboratory balance, determine the mass of your model cell. Record the mass in Data Table 2 on the next page.

5. Place your model cell into an empty cup or beaker.

6. Cover your model cell completely with the vinegar solution and start the stopwatch. Or, if you are using a clock with a second hand, record the start time in Data Table 2.

7. Watch your model cell closely. When it has turned completely yellow, record the time in Data Table 2. Enter the elapsed time in the data table.

8. Calculate the mass/time ratio (g/min) by dividing the mass of your model cell by the time it took to turn completely yellow. Compare this value with those of other groups in your class.

Advance Preparation

One day to 5 days before the prelab or lab
Make agar cubes. Turn to the end of the lab for instructions to make the agar cubes.

Safety and Disposal
Remind students to handle sharp instruments with care. Remind students not to eat or drink in the laboratory. Remind students to wear gloves as the indicator may stain skin. Have students wash their hands thoroughly after the lab. Pour leftover vinegar solution down a laboratory drain and flush with excess water. Agar cubes may be bagged and disposed of in the trash.

Data Table 2

Model Cell Design Name	Mass (g)	Start Time (If Using a Clock)	End Time (If Using a Clock)	Elapsed Time (min)	Mass/Time (g/min)
"Squishy"	1.4 g	8:30 A.M.	8:38 A.M.	8 min	0.175 g/min

Part B: Making Redesigned Model Cells for the "Diffusion Race"

While your model cell is changing color, part of the team can work on one or more revised cell designs that you think could have faster diffusion times. Repeat steps 1–8 of Part A to experiment with different shapes until you find a design that will give you the greatest value for mass/time.

When all the teams have tested their redesigned model cells, compare mass/time data to find the winner of the class diffusion race.

Expected Results
The thinnest cells change color the fastest. Thin cells with convolutions are often the winners.

Analysis and Conclusions

1. How did your team's best model-cell design differ from others you designed?

   Student answers will vary.

   _____

   _____

2. What were the characteristics of the model cell with the highest mass/time ratio in the class?

   Student answers will vary, but students will probably indicate that flat and curvy models

   were usually the winners.

   _____

3. Why do you think most cells are microscopic? What do you think limits cell size?

   Cells need to obtain nutrients and rid themselves of wastes at a fast rate. The speed at which

   nutrients and wastes can enter and leave the cell must be enough to sustain life.

   _____

   _____

4. All of the cells shown below have approximately the same volume. Circle the letter of the one with the largest surface area.

a.

b.

c.

5. Which one of the cells shown in Question 4 would change color most quickly in the experiment you just performed? Explain.

b. It has the largest surface area-to-volume ratio.

_____

6. Some of the cells in your body (such as the walls of small blood vessels and the linings of air sacs in your lungs) are designed to allow the quick passage of nutrients and gases. Which of the following shapes would you expect those cells to be? Explain.

a.

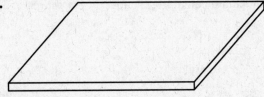

b.

c.

a. Nutrients and gases could quickly pass in and out of the cell because it is thin and flat.

_____

7. When a cell is very thin, flat, or narrow, it can obtain nutrients more quickly. What possible disadvantages might there be to such a cell shape? (*Hint:* Think about how you handled the cells you designed.)

Sample answer: If cells become too thin, they may be too fragile.

Extension

An organism's surface area to volume ratio also affects its ability to retain heat. To determine how, design a simple experiment with the following materials: three thermometers, a watch or clock, hot tap water (about 50°C), and three square or rectangular plastic food-storage containers with covers. The containers represent organisms with different surface area-to-volume ratios. The containers should be of different sizes, but made of similar materials. Discuss your hypothesis and experiment design with your teacher before carrying out any investigations. Write a report to explain your conclusions.

To make agar cubes:
- Mix 15 g agar in 1 L of water.
- Boil slowly in microwave or hot water bath until agar is melted (granules will disappear). Watch for and avoid boil over.
- Remove from heat. Add 0.1 g of bromothymol blue solid or several drops of bromothymol blue solution and mix.
- If the mixture is not deep blue, add more bromothymol blue. If the mixture is green or yellow, you will need to stir in dilute NaOH until it turns blue. Wear safety goggles and gloves when handling NaOH solutions.
- Pour the agar into ice cube trays or a flat rectangular or square container. Let agar harden at room temperature or in refrigerator.

Extension
Experiments should involve calculating surface area to volume ratio, recording the room temperature and water, then recording the water temperature in steady time intervals. Students should discover that organisms with the greatest surface to volume ratio lose heat the fastest. Ask students why it was important that their containers were made of the same type of material (using containers made of different materials could be an additional variable that would affect results).

Mystery Cell

Distinguishing Plant Cells and Animal Cells

Question How can you determine whether a cell is from a plant or an animal?

Lab Overview In this investigation, you first will learn about some distinguishing characteristics of plant cells and animal cells. Then you will use a microscope to observe plant cells and animal cells. You will make sketches of the cells and identify some structures and organelles. Next, you will be given unlabeled microscope slides with several "mystery cells" that you will identify as plant cells or animal cells.

Background Under the light microscope, plant cells usually appear boxy or angular due to their rigid cell walls. Many plant cells look green because they contain chloroplasts. These organelles contain a green pigment called chlorophyll. Within plant cells, you will often see a large, membrane-bound sac called the central vacuole. In contrast, animal cells do not contain chloroplasts or a central vacuole. Animal cells usually have rounded plasma membranes and a nucleus that is more visible than the nucleus of a plant cell.

Prelab Activity Study the features of a generalized plant cell and animal cell, and compare them with a sample mystery cell. Then, answer the Prelab Questions.

Objective to observe a variety of different types and diverse shapes of plant and animal cells and learn how to distinguish them

Inquiry Skills
- observing
- making inferences
- classifying
- predicting

Time
- 15–20 min for Prelab Activity
- 30 min for Lab Activity
- 20 min for Analysis and Conclusions

Plant Cell

Nucleus

Chloroplasts

Central vacuole

Cell wall

Animal Cell

Nucleus

Plasma membrane

Sample Mystery Cells

Nuclei

The "mystery cell" art depicts human muscle cells. Wait until students complete the lab activity to tell them the identity of the Prelab mystery cell.

Prelab Questions

1. Based on your observations, do you think the sample mystery cells are plant cells or animal cells?

Animal cells

2. Which cell structures helped you classify the sample mystery cell?

Sample answer: The cells do not appear to have cell walls or central vacuoles.

Materials

- slide with plant cells
- slide with animal cells
- slide(s) with mystery cells (coded by number)
- unlined paper for sketching
- microscope
- colored pencils

Despite the general guidelines presented in the Introduction, sometimes it is difficult for students to distinguish plant and animal cells. For example, many plant cells don't have chloroplasts and therefore do not appear green. Cell walls aren't always thick and the edges aren't always angular (leaf epidermis cells are an example of plant cells that are hard to identify).

Give students a variety of cells, some of which are easy to distinguish and some of which are more challenging. Cells from the water plant *Elodea* and cells from onion skins are easy to identify as plant cells. Human cheek cells and blood cells are easy to identify as animal cells. Muscle cells or nerve cells may pose more of a challenge because of their odd shapes.

Procedure

1. Make sure that the low-power lens is in place, then put the plant cell or animal cell slide on the microscope stage. Adjust the light coming into the microscope and focus with the coarse focus knob. Move the slide as needed to locate a cell to observe, then refocus.

2. Switch to the highest magnification available on your microscope and focus with the fine focus knob only. When in focus, make your observations. Draw a sketch of the cell on the unlined paper, and label any structures that you recognize. Beneath your sketch, write descriptions of any additional cell features you see.

3. Repeat steps 1 and 2 for the other known slide (plant cell or animal cell).

4. Once you are confident that you can distinguish plants cells and animal cells, ask your teacher for a number-coded slide which will be your assigned "mystery cell."

5. Repeat steps 1 and 2 as needed to make observations and draw a sketch of your mystery cell.

Safety and Disposal
Tell students to handle the microscope and microscope slides with care. Tell students to alert you immediately if a slide is broken, and not to touch the broken glass. If the microscopes have lamps, review electrical safety rules and make sure that all electrical cords are out of the way of foot traffic. Follow school guidelines for cleanup and disposal of broken glass.

Name _____ Class _____ Date_____

6. Use your descriptions and clues from your plant and animal sketches to determine whether your mystery cell is a plant cell or an animal cell. Record your slide number, descriptions about the mystery cell, and your identification of the cell in the Data Table below.

7. Repeat steps 1 and 2 as needed to make observations and draw sketches of any additional mystery cells provided by your teacher. Record additional numbers, descriptions, and identifications in the Data Table.

8. After the lab, your teacher will identify the mystery cells.

Data Table

Code Number on Slide	Observations/ Description	Identification
	Student responses will vary.	

Analysis and Conclusions

1. In your own words, summarize the differences you observed between plant cells and animal cells.

Student answers will vary based on the samples they observed.

_____

_____

_____

Advance Preparation

Several weeks before the lab
If needed, order prepared slides from a supply company. If you do have prepared slides, check them to make sure the tissues have not dried and cracked.

A couple of days before the lab
• If you plan to make your own plant cell slides, obtain a sprig of *Elodea* from a pet store. It is also easy to make slides from onion skin.
• Determine which will be the "known" cells and which will be the "mystery cells." Cover the labels for the mystery cells. Place a small square of paper over the label and tape around it. Label the slide with a number code. Create a key for the code so that you will be able to compare students' inferences with the identities of the "mystery cells."

The day of the lab
Make several slides of *Elodea* and cheek cells just before class.

2. Describe the mystery cell(s) you observed. What cell characteristics led you to make the identification(s) you did? Explain your reasoning.

Student answers will vary based on the samples they observed.

3. Your teacher will reveal the identities of your mystery cells. Were your identifications correct? If not, look at the slides again to find additional clues you may have missed. Describe your findings.

Student answers will vary.

4. Go back to the Prelab Activity and review your identification of the sample mystery cell. Do you still agree with your conclusion? Explain.

Student answers will vary depending on their original response to the Prelab Activity questions.

Extension

Unlike the eukaryotic cells of plants and animals, bacterial cells are prokaryotic cells. Your teacher will provide slides of bacterial cells or help you create your own wet-mount slides. Make a sketch of one of the bacterial cells you observe and write a description. How could you distinguish a bacterial cell from a plant or animal cell? Observe the bacteria under the microscope using high power. Be sure to use the diaphragm on the microscope to adjust the incoming light. Too much light will make it difficult to see the bacteria on the slide.

Extension
Provide students with prepared slides of bacteria, or show students how to make wet mount slides out of bacterial cultures from yogurt. Make sure students set their microscopes on high power and use the diaphragm to adjust incoming light. Students should observe that the prokaryotic cells do not contain nuclei.

Name _____ Class _____ Date_____

Food as Fuel

Measuring the Chemical Energy Stored in Food

Question How can you measure the calorie content of a peanut?

Lab Overview In this investigation, you will construct and use a simple calorimeter to measure the approximate number of calories in a peanut. You will compare the number of calories in a peanut with the calorie content of other foods. **CAUTION:** *This investigative lab includes peanuts and other food products as materials. If you are allergic to peanuts or any other food products, alert your teacher.*

Introduction Have you ever roasted marshmallows and accidentally set one on fire? You may have been amazed by the size of the flame that the marshmallow fueled! All food contains stored energy that can be released when the food is burned. To investigate the chemical energy stored in food, you need a calorimeter—an apparatus that measures the calorie content of food samples. Recall that a calorie is defined as the amount of energy required to raise the temperature of 1 g of water by 1°C. (Note that the "calorie" counts listed on food packaging labels are given in kilocalories [kcal]. One kilocalorie is equal to 1000 calories.) It is also useful to know that different types of molecules can store different amounts of energy. While proteins and carbohydrates contain 4 kcal/g, fats contain 9 kcal/g.

Prelab Activity Study the diagrams of two calorimeters below. The diagram on the left shows a commercial calorimeter used in laboratories. The diagram on the right shows the calorimeter you will construct and use in this investigation. Compare the features of both calorimeters, then answer the questions.

Objective to discover how energy stored in chemical compounds can be released and measured

Inquiry Skills
• observing
• making measurements
• analyzing data
• drawing conclusions

Time
• 15–20 min for Prelab Activity
• 20–30 min to construct the calorimeter
• 20–30 min to test food samples
• 15–20 min for Analysis and Conclusions

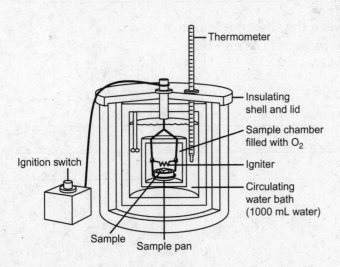

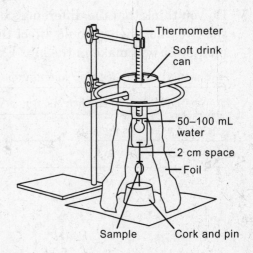

Prelab Questions

1. Which part of a calorimeter enables you to make measurements? In what units are the measurements?

   Thermometer, degrees Celsius

2. A food sample burned in the commercial calorimeter raised the temperature of the water surrounding the sample chamber by 4°C. Note that 1 g water = 1 mL water. To calculate the number of calories in the sample, multiply the amount of water in the chamber by the change in temperature in degrees Celsius (°C).

   Temperature change of __4__ °C × 1000 mL = __4000__ calories ÷ 1000 = __4__ kcal

3. Suppose you place a food sample in the chamber of the commercial calorimeter. This time, you put only 500 mL of water in the calorimeter. When you burn the sample, the water temperature increases by 2°C. How many kcal were in the food sample?

   2°C × 500 = 1000 calories ÷ 1000 = 1 kcal

4. Compare the features of the commercial calorimeter with those of the calorimeter you will construct in the lab. What features do both calorimeters have? How are these shared features different between the two calorimeters?

   Suggested answers: Both calorimeters have a container that holds water, both are insulated, and both have a place to burn a sample. Water circulates in the commercial calorimeter. The insulation in the commercial calorimeter is most likely more reliable than aluminum foil. In the commercial calorimeter, the sample is ignited within the enclosed device.

5. Do you think that the differences between the shared features of the two calorimeters could affect the accuracy of the measurements you will make in the lab? Explain.

   Suggested answer: Yes. The water temperature may not change as much as it would in a commercial calorimeter since it is not as well insulated and the sample is not completely enclosed when it is ignited.

Name _____ Class _____ Date_____

Materials

- hammer
- nail
- soft-drink can
- ring stand (10-cm or 4-inch ring)
- wooden dowel (3 mm or 1/8 inch in diameter)
- aluminum foil (heavy-duty type)
- water
- graduated cylinder
- samples of foods, including peanuts
- laboratory balance
- thermometer or temperature probe
- cork
- pin to hold food sample (dissecting pins work well)
- safety matches
- calculator (optional)

Advance Preparation
- Have students bring in soft-drink cans.
- Gather food samples, including peanuts (oil-roasted peanuts burn the best). Encourage students to bring in solid food samples, such as walnuts or sweet cereal.

Safety and Disposal
Remind students to wear safety goggles. Review laboratory fire safety rules and make sure that there is adequate ventilation. Have students tie back long hair. Have students place used matches in water and have a fire extinguisher available. Remind students not to eat or drink in the laboratory. Advise students to notify you immediately if they have allergies to peanuts or any other foods. Ashes can be thrown away. Soft-drink cans can be recycled.

Procedure

1. Before you begin the construction of your calorimeter, predict which food sample will burn the longest. Explain your prediction.

_____

_____

_____

2. Use a nail to poke two holes in the opposite sides of the soft drink can as shown. Carefully push the dowel through the can. **CAUTION:** *Be careful not to touch the sharp edges of the holes.*

3. Rest each end of the dowel on the ring on the ring stand.

4. Wrap the foil around the bottom of the soft drink can, creating a tent-like structure. Leave an opening that will allow you to easily place the cork with the food to be tested beneath the can.

5. Measure 75 mL of cool water with a graduated cylinder, and pour it into the soft drink can. (1 mL of water weighs 1 gram; therefore 75 mL = 75 grams.)

6. Record the mass of the peanut to be tested in Data Table 1 on the next page as **Beginning mass of food**.

7. Measure the starting temperature of the water and record it in Data Table 1 as **Initial water temperature**.

8. Gently, but firmly, push the blunt end of the pin into the cork. Hold the sides of the pin rather than pushing on the sharp point. **CAUTION:** *Be careful to avoid injuring yourself with the protruding sharp end of the pin.* Place the food sample to be tested on the sharp end of the pin.

Alternate Methods
You can wrap the cork in foil to protect it from the flame. You can substitute a jumbo paperclip for the cork and pin. Use the big outer loop as a base. Bend the smaller inner loop up and make a circle from its end to hold the food. Tape the "base" to the ring stand, and cover the paper clip "base" and ring stand base with aluminum foil.

9. Place the cork, pin, and food sample under the soft drink can. Make sure there is approximately a 2-cm space between the soft drink can and the food sample by raising or lowering the ring as needed. **CAUTION:** *Tie back loose hair and make sure your safety goggles are in place before proceeding.*

10. Place the cork with the food sample under the soft drink can, and light the food sample with a safety match. One person should use a clock or watch to time for how long the sample burns and record the time at the bottom of Data Table 1.

11. When the food is burning, determine the highest water temperature reached and record it in Data Table 1 as **Highest water temperature.**

12. When the food sample has finished burning, weigh any remaining ash. Record your results in Data Table 1 as **Final mass of food.**

13. Repeat steps 6 through 12 two more times—one for each additional food sample. Remember to use fresh, cool water for each sample. Record the results in Data Table 1.

14. Use the formulas in Data Table 1 to help you determine the number of kilocalories per gram in each food sample.

Data Table 1

	Peanut	Sample 2	Sample 3
Beginning mass of food sample (g)	Student responses will vary.		
Final mass of food sample (g)			
Mass of food burned (g) (Beginning mass − final mass)			
Beginning water temperature (°C)			
Highest water temperature (°C)			
Water temperature change (°C) (Highest temperature − beginning temperature)			
Mass of water used (1 mL = 1 g)			
Total calories (water mass in g × temperature change in °C)			
Total kilocalories (calories/1000)			
Kilocalories per gram (kcal/g) (total kcal/mass of food burned)			
Time sample burned			

Name _____ Class _____ Date_____

Analysis and Conclusions

1. Compare your results from the three food samples. Suggest why different foods might produce different results.

Different foods will produce different results based on the type of molecules they contain.

Molecules of fat contain more kcal/g than molecules of protein or carbohydrate.

_____

2. Do your results agree or disagree with the data below? If your results disagree, suggest two possible reasons why.

Food	kcal/g
Peanuts	5.81 kcal/g

Students may agree with the results or they may cite some of the following as sources of

error: misreading the thermometer, the food was not placed directly under the soft-drink can,

calorimeter not well insulated, different brands of peanuts were used, the food fell off the

needle, calculation errors.

_____

3. What happened to the heat that was not "captured" by the water?

The heat escaped to the surrounding environment (air).

_____

_____

4. Which sample burned the longest? Did this agree with your prediction?

Answers will vary based on student data and predictions.

_____

5. Look at your data. Is there any relationship between how long a sample burned and its calorie content? Explain.

Generally the samples with the highest calorie content will burn the longest because there is more

stored energy to fuel the fire.

_____

_____

6. Compare and contrast the burning of food in a calorimeter to the burning of food in your body.

Suggested answer: Cells "burn" food at a more gradual rate. Cells convert some of the

energy from food into useful work, while a calorimeter converts most of the energy in the

food to thermal energy.

Extension

Obtain and analyze the data collected by the other students in your class for each type of food sample tested. Then, write a summary comparing the class data with the information in Question 2. Suggest a new experiment to test your hypothesis explaining differences in the data. (**NOTE:** *Be sure to check with your teacher before carrying out any investigations.*)

Extension
Student summaries should include a discussion of class data and possible explanations for differences in data among the lab groups.

Fermentation Sensation

Observing Lactic Acid Fermentation

Question What changes occur in milk during lactic acid fermentation?

Lab Overview In this investigation, you will observe the changes that occur in milk during lactic acid fermentation as you make yogurt. You will also measure how the pH of the fermenting milk changes over time.

Introduction To start your investigation, you will learn how lactic acid fermentation is used to make yogurt and other foods. You will explore the process of lactic acid fermentation by modeling how bacteria break down lactose, the primary sugar found in milk.

Background People in many parts of the world have been consuming yogurt, sour cream, and other foods made from fermented milk for thousands of years. Although they did not understand the process, people observed that when milk was kept under certain conditions, it thickened, developed a sour flavor, and could be stored for a long period of time without spoiling.

People now know that milk fermentation occurs because of a group of bacteria, called lactic acid bacteria, that live in milk. Fermentation is a process by which some cells break down sugar for energy without the use of oxygen. For example, both human muscle cells and lactic acid bacteria can carry out fermentation. However, in the presence of oxygen, human muscle cells perform cellular respiration, while lactic acid bacteria always perform fermentation. The bacteria release an enzyme called lactase, which breaks down lactose, the main sugar in milk. Lactose is a disaccharide made of glucose and galactose. During fermentation, glucose is further broken down into lactic acid. As the quickly reproducing bacteria continue to feed, more lactic acid is produced.

Lactic acid helps prevent the growth of harmful bacteria and fungi in the food product and also denatures (changes the structure of) the proteins in the milk. Lactic acid also gives fermented milk products such as yogurt and sour cream their characteristic sour, tangy taste.

Objective to observe the changes that occur in fermenting milk and the bacteria whose processes cause these changes

Inquiry Skills
• observing
• measuring
• drawing conclusions

Time
• 15 min for Prelab Activity
• 40–45 min for Part A
• 30 min for Part B
• 15–20 min for Part C
• 20 min for Analysis and Conclusions

In various parts of the world, milk from horses, camels, sheep, goats, and cows is fermented into alcohol-containing drinks or yogurt. Some lactic acid bacteria produce lactic acid, ethanol, and carbon dioxide. Kumiss and kefir are two drinks made this way.

The bacteria typically used in commercially produced yogurt are *Lactobacillus bulgaricus*, *Lactobacillus acidophilus*, and *Streptococcus thermophilus*. *Lactobacilli* are rod-shaped and can be found in chains. They are non-motile, gram-positive, and "aerotolerant" anaerobes (they tolerate oxygen, but their metabolism is fermentative).

Prelab Activity

Lactose is a disaccharide made of two 6-carbon monosaccharides, glucose and galactose. Study the structural formula of lactose. Then, follow the directions to construct a model of a lactose molecule and find out how lactic acid bacteria convert lactose into lactic acid.

Lactose

1. Link 6 paper clips of one color together to represent glucose. Connect the first and sixth paper clips together to form a ring. Each paper clip represents one of the 6 carbon atoms in the glucose ring.

2. Repeat Step 1 with 6 paper clips of a second color to represent a galactose ring.

3. Link the two rings together to represent lactose.

4. Lactic acid bacteria, which use lactose as a source of glucose, produce an enzyme called lactase that breaks down lactose into glucose and galactose. Model the action of lactase by breaking apart the two rings of your lactose model.

5. Lactic acid bacteria do not use oxygen, and so do not carry out the last two stages of cellular respiration—the Krebs cycle and the electron transport chain. Instead, these bacteria obtain energy from glucose by using fermentation enzymes. Model the action of these fermentation enzymes by breaking the glucose ring apart into two 3-carbon straight chains. When this happens, the bacteria gain two ATP as shown in the diagram below.

Glucose   **Lactic acid**

Streptococcus thermophilus are spherical cells and are often found in chains. They are also gram-positive and aerotolerant anaerobes. If you look at a drop of yogurt under a microscope it is sometimes difficult to distinguish the bacilli from the cocci because the cocci elongate before dividing and therefore look like short rods.

In humans, lactase is secreted into the small intestine. As a person ages, lactase production may slow or stop and the person becomes less able to digest lactose. Someone who is lactose-intolerant may experience nausea, cramping, or diarrhea after consuming milk or ice cream. However, often a lactose-intolerant person can eat yogurt because lactic acid bacteria have already broken down much of the lactose for them.

Name _____ Class _____ Date_____

Prelab Questions

1. Describe the structure of lactose.

Lactose is a disaccharide consisting of galactose and glucose.

_____

_____

2. Explain what happens when lactic acid bacteria break
down lactose.

Lactic acid bacteria secrete lactase. Lactase is an enzyme that breaks the bond between

galactose and glucose.

_____

3. Do you think that someone who is lactose-intolerant and cannot
digest the lactose in products like milk or ice cream could digest
frozen yogurt? Explain. (*Hint:* Consider the action of lactic acid
bacteria in yogurt.)

The person may be able to eat frozen yogurt, because the lactic acid bacteria will have

broken down the lactose.

_____

Materials (per group)

- large saucepan for heating milk
- 2% milk (about 1 pint)
- plain yogurt or yogurt culture
- plastic spoon
- measuring cups
- large spoon for stirring
- hot plate
- thermometer
- 3 plastic foam cups with lids
  or aluminum foil covers
- foam ice chest
- small test tubes for taking samples
  (microcentrifuge tubes)
- transfer pipettes
- pH paper   (range of pH 3–7)
- microscope slides and cover slips
- plastic loops
- methylene blue stain (optional)
- calculator (optional)
- fine thread (optional)

Advance Preparation

A week or two before the lab
- Determine if your students
  will make the yogurt in
  class. If you opt to prepare
  it ahead of time, you may
  want to describe the steps
  you took to your students.
- The most reliable method
  to make yogurt is to use a
  yogurt maker. If you do not
  have a yogurt maker, you
  could borrow one from
  parents or another teacher.
  The foam ice chest incubator works, but it is difficult
  to keep the temperature
  constant.

**A couple of days before
the lab**
Obtain your yogurt culture.
Any plain yogurt labeled as
containing "active yogurt cultures" will work. Yogurt sets
very quickly if you use freeze-
dried starter culture. This can
be purchased at most health
food stores.

Procedure

Part A: Yogurt-making/Milk Fermentation

(**Note:** *If your teacher has prepared the yogurt samples in advance, go to Part B.*)

1. Heat milk to boiling on a hot plate or in a microwave. This kills any unwanted bacteria and concentrates the milk solids a bit. Stir occasionally. After it is boiling, remove the milk from the heat to let it cool. **CAUTION:** *Do not eat or taste yogurt prepared in the laboratory or with the use of any laboratory equipment.*

2. Let the milk cool until it reaches 40°C. Stir occasionally.

3. Add the lactic acid bacteria to the milk as follows:
   a. Pour one cup of warm milk into a cup.
   b. Add a spoonful of prepared yogurt or half a packet of yogurt culture to the milk and stir until it is well mixed.
   c. Add this mixture back to the rest of the warm milk and stir well.
   d. Fill plastic foam cups with the milk mixture.

4. Designate one cup as the cup that you will take samples from. Label the cup with your initials and class section. With a transfer pipette, measure out a 1-mL milk sample from this cup, place it in a separate microcentrifuge tube, and label it with the fermentation start time. Store the sample in a refrigerator as directed by your teacher. The cold temperature of the refrigerator slows the reproduction of lactic acid bacteria and the activity of the enzyme lactase, causing fermentation to slow dramatically.

5. Cover the warm milk-filled cups with lids or aluminum foil. Place in an incubator made from a foam chest partially filled with warm water (about 40°C). Keep the foam chest covered. Replace the water in the foam chest with more 40°C water as needed.

6. Take a final sample when the yogurt is done and label it with the time. Store all samples and the remaining yogurt in the refrigerator until needed for Part B.

Part B: Observing Milk Proteins and Lactic Acid Bacteria

1. Dip a plastic loop into water. Use the loop to smear a small amount of water onto the center of a microscope slide.

2. Dip a second plastic loop into the methylene blue stain. Use this loop to smear methylene blue over the wet area of the slide. **CAUTION:** *Handle methylene blue carefully to avoid staining skin and clothing.*

Safety and Disposal

Remind students to wear safety goggles. Aprons should be worn if methylene blue is used. Check with students regarding allergies to milk products. Remind students not to eat food that has been in contact with laboratory equipment or surfaces. Tell students to handle the slides with care and to notify you immediately of breakage. Review electrical safety rules and make sure that all electrical cords are out of the way of foot traffic. Slides, microcentrifuge tubes, and loops can be washed and reused. Double-wrap all food products before placing in trash. Do not allow trash to remain in building overnight. Methylene blue can be flushed down the drain with large quantities of water.

After the lab, if there are extra yogurt samples in foam cups that have not been in contact with lab equipment, you may choose to have students taste the uncontaminated samples. Remind students that they should never eat or drink in the laboratory itself.

When students use droppers, they often flood slides. Using loops to measure the yogurt and stain reduces the amount of liquid on the slides. Typical plastic disposable loops hold 10 µL.

3. Dip a third plastic loop into the first sample, labeled with the fermentation start time. Use the loop to smear a small amount of the sample on the area covered with methylene blue.

4. A piece of thread can help you focus. Place the thread in the center of the smeared yogurt sample, then cover with a cover slip. Rotate the smallest lens on your microscope into place and put the slide on the stage. Move the slide so that the thread is directly in your field of view, and focus on the thread using the fine focus knob. Adjust the amount of light coming into the microscope until you can see contrasts in the thread.

5. Switch to the next larger lens on your microscope. Use the fine focus knob again to focus on the thread. You will start to see milk proteins. Adjust the incoming light again if needed.

6. Switch to the 40× lens (overall magnification is now 400×). Make adjustments with the fine focus knob, until the thread is in focus. You should be able to see the milk proteins and fat droplets in the liquid. The milk proteins are ball-shaped.

7. If your microscope does not have a 100× lens, go to Step 8. If your microscope has a 100× lens, move it over so that the slide is between the 40× and 100× lenses. Place a drop of immersion oil on top of the lit-up portion of the cover slip. Rotate the 100× lens so that the tip goes down into the oil. Focus with the fine adjustment knob.

8. Observe the milk and record your observations in Data Table 1.

9. Repeat steps 1–8 above to prepare a microscope slide and make observations of the finished yogurt under the same magnification. Notice what has happened to the milk. Write your observations in Data Table 1.

The methylene blue makes it easier to see the bacteria in Step 10, but it is not necessary. The bacteria are quite obvious under 400×.

Placing a single strand of fine thread on the slide makes it a lot easier for students to focus on the right plane. A strand of hair could also be used (bacteria contribution would be negligible). Most of the problems students have with seeing bacteria is that since the bacteria are not visible under 40×, they don't know what to focus on.

Provide students with immersion oil if you'd like them to complete Step 7.

Data Table 1

Fermentation Time	Observations
Start time (0)	
Finish time (____)	

10. On the same slide used in Step 9, look carefully at the fluid surrounding the milk proteins. Adjust the incoming light as needed to increase the contrast. You should be able to see some of the bacteria whose processes have caused the changes you observed in the milk proteins.

11. In the space below, describe the bacteria you see. How many different types do you see in the sample? Describe their overall shape and appearance. Are the bacteria moving? In the space provided, draw a sketch based on your observations.

Observations of Lactic Acid Bacteria

Student responses will vary, but students should note that the milk has clumped together
_____
and that bacteria are visible.
_____

_____

Sketch

Student sketches will vary, but should include illustrations of the clumps in the milk and bacteria.

12. At 400× power, estimate the number of bacteria you can see in the field of view. Write this number in the space provided. You will use this number later to calculate the number of bacteria in a spoonful of yogurt.

A = approximate number of bacteria in field of view = ___500___

Student answers may vary greatly, but the approximate number of bacteria is 500.

Part C: Measuring Changes in pH

1. To determine the pH of the start time sample, use a clean loop or pipette to place a drop of the sample on the pH paper. Immediately compare the color of the paper with the chart on the pH paper container. Record the pH in Data Table 2.

2. Determine the pH of the other yogurt sample as described in Step 1. Record the pH in Data Table 2.

If you want students to observe a gradual pH change, you could take an additional sample 1–3 hours after fermentation begins. In a yogurt maker, it takes about 4 hr to get to pH 5. At 10 hr, it is usually sour and pH 4.

Data Table 2

Fermentation Time	pH
Start time (0)	pH 6
Finish time (____)	pH 4

Analysis and Conclusions

1. Did the appearance of the milk change during the process of lactic acid fermentation? If so, describe any changes you observed.

Sample answer: The appearance of the milk proteins changed during lactic acid

fermentation. At the beginning, the milk proteins looked like tiny spheres. By the end of the

process, the proteins had clumped together, forming island-like shapes.

2. Describe the bacteria you observed in the final yogurt.

Answers will vary, but may include descriptions of wormlike rods, chains of spheres, or

strings of sausages.

Expected Results
The milk proteins and fats are randomly distributed in the milk at the beginning of the fermentation. As the lactic acid accumulates, the proteins denature, coagulate, and clump.
As they observe these milk protein clumps, students will begin to notice the swarms of rods and chains of cocci of the lactic acid bacteria.
The pH will change from pH 6 to pH 4 at the end of the fermentation.

3. At the end of Part B, you estimated the number of bacteria in your field of view. Enter that number in the space below and follow the instructions to calculate the approximate number of bacteria in a spoonful of yogurt.

A = approximate number of bacteria in field of view = ____500____

On 400× power, the field of view on a microscope is a circle with a diameter of about 0.5 mm. The radius of a circle is 1/2 its diameter, or 0.25 mm. Calculate the area of the field of view in mm² and write it below. (*Hint:* The area of a circle is πr^2 [$\pi = 3.14$; r = radius].) Round to the nearest tenth.

B = area of field of view = ____0.2 mm²____

You put 0.01 mL (10 µL) of yogurt on your slide. This amount of yogurt spread out and filled the area under the cover slip. The cover slip is a square with sides approximately 20 mm long. So, the area under the cover slip would be $(20 \text{ mm})^2 = 400 \text{ mm}^2$.

C = area under cover slip = **400 mm²**

The ratio of the area under the cover slip (**C**), to the area of the field of view (**B**), is **C/B.**

Divide C by B and enter the result in the space provided.

C/B = ____2000____ = **D**

To find out the number of bacteria in the 0.01 mL sample you put on the slide (**E**), multiply the number of bacteria you observed in the field of view (**A**) by this ratio (**D**). Enter the result in the space provided.

A × D = number of bacteria in 0.01 mL sample =

____1,000,000____ = **E**

You dropped 0.01 mL of yogurt on the slide. Since a rounded teaspoon contains about 10 mL, multiply **E** by 1000 to get the approximate number of lactic acid bacteria in a rounded teaspoon of yogurt.

Number of bacteria in a rounded teaspoon of yogurt = <u>1,000,000,000</u>

4. Explain why the amount of lactic acid in the yogurt changed over time.

The amount of lactic acid in the yogurt changed over time because the lactic acid bacteria

were continually breaking down more lactose, followed by glucose, releasing energy for

life processes.

5. What can you conclude about the effects of lactic acid on milk?

Lactic acid causes changes in the milk proteins that make them form clumps, and changes

the pH of the milk.

Extension

If your instructor has samples of known lactic acid bacteria available, such as *Lactobacillus bulgaricus*, make slides and view them under the microscope at 400× magnification. Make sketches labeled with the correct names and use them to identify some of the bacteria you observed in the yogurt.

Extension
You may also have students do a report on the discovery of *Lactobacillus bulgaricus*. The history of its discovery and naming is interesting and ties in many themes of biology.

Photo Finish

Comparing Rates of Photosynthesis

Question Which will photosynthesize at a faster rate, a young ivy leaf or an older ivy leaf?

Lab Overview In this investigation, you will compare rates of photosynthesis in old and young ivy leaves by measuring the length of time it takes pieces of each leaf type to generate enough oxygen gas to float upward in a solution-filled syringe.

Introduction You may recall that chloroplasts are located in the cells of the mesophyll, the green tissue in the center of a leaf. The cells of the mesophyll have air spaces around them used for gas exchange. You will use these characteristics of leaf structure and function to measure and compare the rates of photosynthesis in different leaves.

Rates describe how measurable quantities change over time. As oxygen gas is a product of photosynthesis, the rate of photosynthesis in a leaf can be determined by measuring the amount of oxygen the leaf produces in a certain period of time. In this investigation, you will measure oxygen production indirectly. You will suspend leaf disks in a solution and apply a vacuum. The air spaces inside each leaf disk will become filled with liquid and the leaf disks will sink downward. You will then measure how quickly the leaf disks float upward. When the light reactions produce oxygen, liquid is forced out of the air spaces and the leaf disks become more buoyant. In general, the more quickly the leaf disks become buoyant enough to float, the faster they are photosynthesizing.

Prelab Activity Compare the leaf "racers" shown and read the information below. Then, answer the Prelab Questions.

Objective to measure and compare the rates of photosynthesis of young and old ivy leaves

Inquiry Skills
- predicting
- formulating testable hypotheses
- analyzing data
- evaluating and revising hypotheses

Time
- 15–20 min for Prelab Activity
- 15–20 min to make leaf disks and prepare the syringes
- 30–35 for the leaf disk race (This section of lab could go faster using an incandescent light source rather than fluorescent light.)
- 15–20 min for Analysis and Conclusions

Final Heat: 10 cc dash

| 1. | **Racer 1** Young, actively growing, light green ivy leaf | |
| 2. | **Racer 2** Older, fully grown, dark green ivy leaf | |

A Photosynthesis Race

The race will take place in two solution-filled syringes. You will suspend 10 leaf disks in each syringe, pull back on the plungers to apply a vacuum, and let the air inside the leaf disks flow out. As the air is replaced by liquid, the leaf disks will sink downwards to the "starting line," which is the bottom of the syringe. When you place both syringes near the light source to start photosynthesis, the race begins. As the leaf disks produce oxygen gas and become more buoyant, they will (unknowingly) race to their own "finish line," which is the top of the syringe.

Winning the Photosynthesis Race

When 5 of its 10 leaf disks have reached the top of the syringe, your leaf "racer" has crossed the "finish line," and you will record the time.

Prelab Questions

1. If you could design a leaf that would photosynthesize "super fast," what characteristics would it have? (*Hint:* Think about the structure of a leaf and the structure of a plant cell.) Explain your reasoning.

A leaf that could photosynthesize at a fast rate would have many mesophyll cells with many

chloroplasts, packed with grana containing large amounts of chlorophyll. There would also

be many stomata to bring in carbon dioxide.

2. Which ivy leaf do you predict will photosynthesize the fastest and win the race? Explain the reasoning behind your prediction. (This is your hypothesis.)

Some students may predict that the older leaf will photosynthesize the fastest since it has

had more time to grow and develop. Some students may predict that the younger leaf will

photosynthesize the fastest since it is actively growing and needs large amounts of energy

and materials to build new cells.

3. A rate measures how a quantity changes over time. Give an example of something you could measure the rate of. What would the units of your measurement be (for example, meters/sec)?

Answers will vary but some examples are typing (words/minute), driving (km/hour), eating

grapes (grapes/minute).

Materials

- two ivy leaves from the same plant: a dark green older leaf and a light green young leaf
- two syringes
- marker
- bicarbonate/detergent solution in a plastic cup
- single hole punch
- strong light source
- clock or watch

Alternate Materials
- Either indoor or outdoor ivy plants may be used. Instead of ivy, you could use green cabbage, Napa cabbage, or red cabbage.
- Do not use hairy leaves, lettuce leaves, or monocot leaves.
- In place of syringes, students can perform the floating disk assay in beakers. Each pair of students will need two small beakers filled with bicarbonate/detergent solution. You will need an aspirator or a 50-cc syringe to degas large numbers of leaf disks for the class. The disks will sink when they are placed in the small beakers.

Procedure

1. Obtain two ivy leaves: one younger, light green leaf (Racer 1) and one older, dark green leaf (Racer 2).

2. Using a single hole punch, punch out 10 leaf disks from the light green leaf (Racer 1).

3. Place the leaf disks you cut in a syringe barrel and immediately label the syringe.

4. Repeat steps 1–3 for the dark green leaf (Racer 2).

5. After both syringes are loaded and labeled, put in the plungers, pushing down until the plunger is touching the leaf disks. Take care not to squish them.

6. Draw up about 5 cubic centimeters (cc) of the bicarbonate/detergent solution into each syringe.

7. Invert each syringe (turn it upside down) and tap it to release air bubbles.

8. Push in the plungers to move all the air out of the tips of the syringes.

9. Place your finger over the tip of one syringe while pulling the plunger back to 10 cc as shown below. Be careful not to pull back too far or you will pull the plunger out. This creates a vacuum, allowing air to flow out of air spaces in the leaf disks.

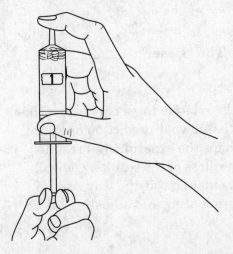

Safety and Disposal
Remind students to wear safety goggles. Tell students to take care not to spill water near light sources. Ask students to notify you immediately if a light bulb breaks and warn them not to pick up broken glass. Advise students with allergic skin conditions to wear gloves. After the lab, the solution can be poured down the drain and the leaves composted or thrown in the trash.

Advance Preparation

Two weeks or more before the lab
- Locate a source of leaves.
- Obtain 10-cc syringes without needles. Some pharmacies will donate syringes if you explain what you are using the syringes for.

One day before the lab
- Gather 15–20 dark ivy leaves and 15–20 light ivy leaves. Keep the leaves between damp paper towels.
- Prepare the bicarbonate solution by dissolving 3 g (1/2 tsp) of sodium bicarbonate (baking soda) in 400 mL of water. Add one drop of liquid detergent and stir.

10. Hold the vacuum by keeping your finger on the tip and shake the syringe several times to release the bubbles.

11. With the tip of the syringe pointing up, let go with your finger and see if the leaf disks sink. If they do, stand the syringe up in front of the light source (which is turned off). If some of the leaf disks are still floating, repeat steps 8–11 until they sink. This may take several tries. If there are one or two stubborn disks, just leave them floating.

12. After both racers are in their "starting blocks" near the light source, turn on the light and start timing. The race begins! Whenever you see a disk rise to the top, fill in the time and total number of disks that have moved up in Data Table 1.

    Race start time: _____

If you are using beakers instead of syringes, double or triple the quantity of the solution.

The day of the lab
- Set up lab stations. Syringes should be placed about 20 cm from a 100-watt bulb. Students can place their inverted syringes into test tube racks.
- If you use beakers instead of syringes, degas leaf disks for the class using an aspirator or a 50-cc syringe.

Data Table 1

Time in Minutes and Seconds	Racer 1 (light green leaf)	Racer 2 (dark green leaf)
Start time: 0 minutes	0 disks up	0 disks up
12 min, 30 sec	2	0
13 min, 30 sec	2	1
18 min, 44 sec	5	1
22 min	6	2
28 min	6	7

13. Every 2 or 3 minutes, you can rotate both syringes one turn to loosen any leaf disks that may be stuck to the sides of the syringe. When 5 of the 10 disks have floated to the top, a leaf has finished the race. Keep timing and recording data until both racers have finished.

    Race Results:

    The "Winner": ___Racer 1___ **The "Loser":** ___Racer 2___

Analysis and Conclusions

Before the race began, you predicted the relative rates of photosynthesis of the two different ivy leaves. You based your prediction on your understanding of photosynthesis. Perhaps the experimental results did not come out as you expected. Regardless of the results, you will need to consider doing further experiments. That is the way science works. Every scientist must keep experimenting and adjusting his or her hypotheses based on the data.

1. Did you predict the winner?

Student responses will vary based on their predictions.

_____

_____

2. Calculate the winner's rate of photosynthesis by completing the calculation below:

5 disks up / _____19_____ minutes = _____0.26_____ disks/min

Calculations will vary but should express rate in units of disks/minute.

3. Discuss your results with other lab groups. Are their results consistent with yours? Pool your data and fill in Data Table 2.

Data Table 2: Class Results

Lab Group	Fastest	Slowest

Expected Results
In general, disks from young, light green ivy leaves will photosynthesize more rapidly than those from older, dark green leaves.

4. How is it helpful to gather the results from several different lab groups? How is this similar to how scientific research is done?

Student responses will vary but should indicate that relying on just one group's data could

lead to incorrect conclusions. In science, repeatable results are necessary to draw

correct conclusions.

_____

5. If your results were different from the other groups, suggest a possible reason why your data might be different.

Student responses will vary based on their experiences in the lab, but a possible answer is

that the syringes were not rotated sufficiently so that the leaf disks stuck to the side of

the syringe.

_____

6. If the results were not as you predicted, suggest at least one possible reason to explain the different rates of photosynthesis you observed. Use your understanding of plants and photosynthesis in your answer.

Student responses will vary, but should suggest a logical reason for the observed data.

7. Revised Hypothesis: Based on your data, revise your hypothesis.

Student responses should take into account their observations.

8. Describe how you would set up the experiment to test your revised hypothesis.

Student responses will vary based on their revised hypothesis, but should test a new

prediction based on this hypothesis.

9. What other factors (besides rate of photosynthesis) may be involved in the ability of the leaf disks to float to the top?

Other factors (besides rate of photosynthesis) that may be involved in the ability of the leaf

disks to float to the top include damage to the disks from handling, waxiness, and

improper handling of the syringes.

Extension

Write out the procedure for the experiment you designed in Question 8 to test your revised hypothesis. Have your teacher check it over. Then, with your teacher's permission, carry out the experiment. Afterwards, share your data and conclusions with the class.

Extension
Students will think of a variety of additional questions. Review their experimental designs for safety risks, use of controlled variables, and practicality. If a student is investigating whether the number of stomata has an impact on photosynthesis, you could refer them to Investigative Lab 19A. The procedure for this lab will give the student details on how to obtain an impression of the stomata using clear nail polish and tape.

Leaf Prints

Observing the Effects of Light on Starch Production in a Leaf

Question How does light availability affect starch production in a leaf?

Lab Overview In this investigation, you will make a stencil from a piece of plastic tape and place it on the leaf of a living plant. You will then expose the plant to fluorescent light. On the second day of the investigation, you will remove the stenciled leaf from the plant and make a "leaf print" to detect which parts of the leaf contain starch.

Background During the stage of photosynthesis called the Calvin cycle, plants build molecules of a sugar called G3P from atoms of carbon, oxygen, and hydrogen. Plant cells use G3P to make glucose and other organic molecules. In plant cells, energy is stored when glucose molecules are linked together, forming *amylose,* a polysaccharide also called plant starch. When needed, plant cells can break down stored starch into glucose which fuels their life processes.

Objective to observe how plants obtain energy in the absence of light

Inquiry Skills
- asking questions
- predicting
- observing
- drawing conclusions

Time
- 20–25 min for Prelab Activity
- 20 min for Part A
- for best results, a minimum of 24 hrs between Part A and Part B, a maximum of one week
- 30 min for Part B
- 20 min for Analysis and Conclusions

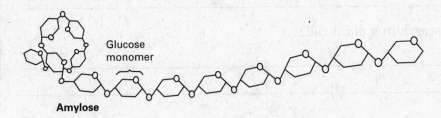

Glucose monomer

Amylose

Prelab Activity In this Prelab Activity, you will use the iodine test to detect starch in samples taken from common food plants. Iodine solution, which is normally a red-orange color, reacts with plant starch and forms a substance with an intense blue-black color.

1. Gather food cubes. Be sure to create a key for the cubes so that you do not forget what each one is.

2. With a dropper, add one drop of iodine solution to each cube. Watch for the color of the iodine solution to change. Record your observations in Data Table 1 on the next page.

Cut cubes from starchy vegetables and fruits such as potatoes, yams, carrots, turnips, and bananas. You can also use grains such as rolled oats. Examples of non-starchy samples are strawberries, apples, and grapes. Avoid very dark samples such as blueberries since the stain will not be visible. You can also demonstrate the activity for the whole class.

Data Table 1

Food Sample	Observations	Starch Present?

During periods of darkness most leaves break down their stored starch into glucose for cellular respiration. In the light, as the leaves photosynthesize, they produce more glucose that is stored as starch. Covering part of a leaf reveals that the covered part is starch-free while the uncovered area contains starch.

Prelab Questions

Answer the following questions in the spaces provided.

1. How does a plant store the sugars produced by photosynthesis?

   A plant links glucose molecules together, forming a polysaccharide called amylose or

   plant starch.

2. What is the function of starch in a plant cell?

   It is a form of stored energy.

3. What do the food samples that tested positive for starch have in common?

   Answers will vary based on the samples provided. Students may comment on the type of

   sample by stating that all the samples are seeds or roots. They may comment on similarities in

   appearance or texture.

4. If a plant is kept in darkness and cannot photosynthesize, how might the plant obtain the sugars it needs for energy?

   The plant will obtain sugars by breaking down stored starch.

Name _____ Class _____ Date_____

Materials

- colored plastic tape
- plastic cutting board
- single-edged razor blade *or an Exacto® knife*
- potted geranium plant
- fluorescent light source
- plastic foam cup
- boiling water
- clock or watch
- forceps or tongs
- beaker (250 mL)
- 70% denatured ethanol
- plastic wrap
- hot water bath or microwave oven
- clear plastic cups
- iodine solution (IKI)

Use an opaque, colored plastic tape that sticks well and can be removed easily, such as Scotch® Colored Plastic Tape 191, 1.5 in × 125 in, which is conformable and moisture-resistant.

Advance Preparation

A few days before the lab
Obtain tape, geranium plants, and other supplies.

One day before the lab
Plants should be kept in the dark for at least 12 hours before the students put tape on the leaves.

Safety and Disposal
Remind students to wear safety goggles while handling sharp instruments and ethanol. Ethanol at the concentrations used is toxic and can be absorbed through the skin. Advise students with allergic skin conditions to wear gloves while handling plant materials. Remind students to handle glassware carefully and notify you immediately of any breakage. Remind students about electrical shock hazards. Make sure all electrical cords are out of the way of foot traffic. Double-wrap leaves and plant parts before placing in trash. Iodine solution and ethanol can be flushed down the drain with large quantities of water.

Procedure

Part A: Making Your Leaf Stencil

1. Obtain a strip of plastic tape about 8 cm long. Stick the tape onto a plastic cutting board.

2. With the razor blade, make cut-outs on the plastic tape to create a stencil of your own design. **CAUTION:** *Handle the razor blade carefully to avoid injury.* You may want to outline your design with a pen first. The tape stencil needs to be small enough to fit onto one leaf of a geranium plant. Use a pen to label a corner of your tape stencil with your initials.

3. Stick the tape stencil onto the upper surface of a leaf on a potted geranium plant as directed by your teacher. Take care not to crease or detach the leaf. Make sure that the tape stencil lies flat so that no light can reach the parts of the leaf covered by tape.

Choose large flat leaves that do not have splotches, streaks, or spots.

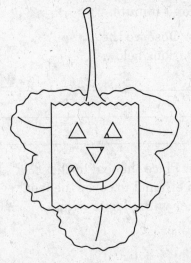

4. Place the geranium plant near a fluorescent light source. The light source should be approximately 15–25 cm from the stenciled leaf.

Keep the plants directly (15–25 cm) under a fluorescent light bank with broad-spectrum bulbs (plant lights).

5. Write your predictions in the spaces provided.

a. Which parts of the leaf will produce starch?

Sample prediction: the parts exposed to light

_____

_____

b. How will the cells in the covered parts of the leaf continue to obtain energy without light?

Sample prediction: The plant will obtain sugars by breaking down stored starch.

_____

_____

c. How do you predict your leaf will look if you stain the leaf with iodine solution after the tape has been on for several days?

Sample prediction: All the parts of the leaf that were exposed to light will contain starch

and turn black. The parts not exposed to light will not turn black because they will not

contain starch.

Part B: Developing Your "Leaf Print"

1. Remove your stenciled leaf from the geranium plant. Carefully remove the tape.

2. To make the leaf print, first whiten your leaf by removing the chlorophyll. Use a hot mitt and forceps or tongs to place your leaf in a plastic foam cup of boiling hot water provided by your teacher. **CAUTION:** *Handle hot water carefully to avoid burns.*

3. Let the leaf remain in the hot water for 1 minute.

4. Remove the leaf with forceps or tongs. Observe the leaf's appearance. Record your observations below.

Expected Results
Areas of the leaves that were covered with tape used up stored starch and could not produce more through photosynthesis. After the leaves are stained with IKI, only the uncovered areas of the leaves should turn black.

_____

_____

_____

5. Label a beaker with your group name. Place the leaf in the beaker and pour in enough denatured ethanol to cover the leaf. Immediately cover the top of the beaker with plastic wrap.

6. Carefully place the beaker containing your leaf and the denatured ethanol inside the hot water bath or microwave as directed by your teacher. Allow the ethanol to boil until the leaf is completely white. Use a hot mitt to carefully remove the beaker.

7. Use forceps or tongs to remove the leaf from the ethanol. Observe the appearance of the leaf, then place it in a plastic cup containing iodine solution.

8. Pull the leaf out occasionally with forceps to see how it is developing. Put the leaf into a plastic cup of water when the leaf print is clearly visible.

9. Draw a sketch below showing what your leaf looked like after staining with iodine solution.

Hot water bath method
Put water in a large beaker or pot. Place smaller beakers/test tubes containing the leaves and ethanol inside the larger container. Heat the water. Keep the water at a medium-low heat so that it is just hot enough to boil the ethanol gently. Watch carefully so that the ethanol does not all evaporate. When the chlorophyll is gone, take the leaves out. Once the ethanol boils, this process should just take a couple of minutes.

Microwave method
Set the microwave on 10% power level (or level 1 on some microwaves) to bring the alcohol to a boil without it boiling dry. Microwaves will vary but it should only take a couple of minutes to remove the chlorophyll. If you don't have a microwave with variable power, use a hot water bath.

Analysis and Conclusions

1. What was the leaf's appearance after boiling in water? After boiling in ethanol? Explain.

Sample answer: After boiling in hot water, the leaf was still green. After boiling in ethanol,

the leaf turned white because the chlorophyll dissolved in the hot ethanol.

2. Which parts of the leaf turned black? Explain.

The leaf parts that were exposed to light turned black because cells in those parts of the leaf

were able to photosynthesize and sugar was converted to starch.

3. If your leaf print did not appear, suggest a possible reason.

Sample answers: The leaf did not produce enough starch to show up in the iodine test. The

leaf did not contain enough starch to show up in the iodine test. The tape was puckered so

some light got in.

Extension

Repeat the procedure using a black and white negative (exposed 35 mm film) instead of tape. Tape the frame of the negative tightly against the leaf and expose it to fluorescent light for 4 to 5 days. Then, make a leaf print and compare it to the one you made from the stenciled leaf. Compare the leaf prints. Suggest possible explanations for your results.

Extension
Parts of the leaf covered by dark sections of the negative will remain white after iodine is added; parts of the leaf covered by light sections of the negative will turn black after iodine is added.

You Are a 19th-Century Cell Biologist

Observing Cell Division

Question What is the sequence of events that occurs during cell division?

Lab Overview In this investigation, you will prepare slides of onion root tips, observe cells in the process of dividing, and discover for yourself the important events of cell division.

Introduction In this lab, you will assume the role of a biologist in the mid-1890s. You are fascinated by the power of the microscope to reveal the inner workings of living cells. The invention of the compound microscope, along with new stains, make it possible for you to see cell structures that no one has ever seen before. You plan to collaborate with your colleagues to discover the events of cell division.

To start the lab, you will apply a fixative solution to the cells. The fixative solution will break the connections between cell walls so that the cells can be easily flattened into one layer on a microscope slide. The fixative solution will also quickly kill the cells, stopping them in various stages of cell division. Next, you will apply aceto-orcein stain to the cells so that you can observe what was happening to the nucleus and the chromosomes inside each cell.

Prelab Activity Before the modern compound light microscope, biologists had very limited capabilities to see the inner workings of a cell. Early simple microscopes (containing only one lens) could only magnify an image up to about $266\times$. However, with the development of the modern compound light microscope (containing an eyepiece lens and an objective lens) in the late 19th century, researchers could see images magnified up to $1000\times$. Researchers also took advantage of new dyes that became available in the 1800s to stain cells for observation under the microscope. These stains made it possible to see structures inside cells, such as the nucleus. The word *nucleus* means "a central point or mass." The nucleus got its name because it was the prominent stained object seen in the middle of each cell. The stains also enabled biologists to observe structures, now known to be chromosomes, that underwent changes during cell division.

Study the descriptions on the next page of the structures that your 19th-century "colleagues" saw inside dividing cells, using the new stains and microscopes. Then answer the questions that follow.

Objective to prepare slides of onion root tip cells and observe and sketch the events of mitosis

Inquiry Skills
- observing
- using models
- drawing conclusions
- communicating conclusions

Time
- 10 min for Prelab Activity
- 15–20 min for Part A
- 10 min for Part B
- 15–20 min for Part C
- 20 min for Analysis and Conclusions

- **Wilhelm Hofmeister** (Germany)
  Observed lumps or nuggets that appeared inside the cell and eventually separated into two masses. In German, he called these structures *Klumpen*.

- **Walther Flemming** (Germany)
  Observed cell structures he called *Knauel* that looked like tufts of yarn. He also saw these structures form a star shape.

- **Edmund Russow** (Russia)
  Observed structures in dividing cells he described as *Stabchen*, meaning "small rods." The rods were bright and highly refractive (they distorted light) when stained.

- **Edouard-Gérard Balbiani** (France)
  Observed cell structures he called *batonets etroits* (narrow, little batons) of different sizes.

- **Heinrich Waldeyer** (Germany)
  Observed colored bodies in stained dividing cells. He coined the term *chromosome* (from the Greek words *chroma* = color, *soma* = body).

Along with other colleagues, Flemming described prophase, metaphase, and anaphase. The researchers noted the continuity of chromosomal material in each new generation of daughter cells, and suggested that chromosomes were carriers of a "hereditary principle." Their work provided a basis for an understanding of the "hereditary particles" described by Gregor Mendel.

Prelab Questions

1. What were some reasons that the late 19th century was a time of many discoveries about cells?

   Scientists had new tools available. The compound microscope allowed them to view cells at a

   much higher magnification, and new stains made it possible for them to see structures inside

   the cells.

2. Write a sentence in your own words describing what you think was happening in the cells the 19th-century biologists were observing.

   Sample answer: The 19th-century scientists were observing stages of mitosis.

Name _____ Class _____ Date _____

Materials

- onion with actively growing root tips
- single-edge razor blade
- forceps
- top or bottom half of a petri dish
- test tube
- stirring rod
- transfer pipette
- warm water bath
- 2 microscope slides
- 4 plastic cover slips
- microscope
- aceto-orcein stain
- acid fixative solution

Advance Preparation

More than two weeks before the lab
Order aceto-orcein stain and ingredients for fixative solution from a biological supply company.

Five days before the lab
Obtain onions. With a washcloth, gently scrub the bottom of the bulbs. Stick toothpicks in the sides of each onion. Place them in plastic cups. Fill the plastic cup with water so that about 1 cm of the onion is submerged. It should take 2–4 days for root tips to grow to 1 cm. Change the water daily.

One day before the lab
Prepare 100 mL of fixative solution. CAUTION: Wear safety goggles while preparing the solution and make sure that the room is well ventilated.
1. Put 50 mL of water in a beaker or flask. Slowly add 40 mL of glacial acetic acid while gently stirring (always add acid to water)
2. Stir in 10 mL of 1 M HCl.
3. Pour into 4 dropper bottles or beakers with transfer pipettes. The prepared fixative can be stored in a labeled, sealed container for many months.

The day of the lab
Prepare water baths for each lab station by placing a test-tube rack in a plastic shoe box or ice chest with 50°C water. Adjust temperature with hot/cold tap water.

Procedure

Part A: Using Acid Fixative to Stop Cell Division

1. Use the razor blade to cut four root tips, each about 2 cm long, off an onion bulb. **CAUTION:** *Handle the razor blade carefully to avoid injury.*

2. Place the four root tips in the bottom of a test tube. You may need to use a stirring rod to gently push them to the bottom.

3. Add just enough fixative solution to the test tube to cover the root tips. **CAUTION:** *Put on safety goggles, aprons, and gloves before handling the fixative solution. This solution is very acidic. Avoid getting any on your skin or clothing. Use forceps to handle the "fixed" root tips at all times from now on.*

4. To help the fixative solution penetrate the cells, place your test tube in a test tube rack in a warm water bath at 50°C.

5. After 6 min, use a hot mitt to take your test tube out of the water bath. Carefully pour the fixative and the root tips into the petri dish.

6. Place two clean microscope slides side by side on a clean paper towel. Very gently pick up the root tips with forceps and place two on each slide.

7. Using the razor blade, cut off the upper part of each root so that only about 3–4 mm of the tip end is left. **CAUTION:** *Handle the razor blade carefully to avoid injury.* Using your forceps, pick up the upper part of the root tip that you have cut off and place it on the paper towel for disposal.

Part B: Staining the Cell Nuclei and Chromosomes

1. Add a drop of aceto-orcein stain to cover each root tip. Wait 2 min to let the stain soak into the root tip cells.

2. With the flat side of your forceps, squish each root tip flat, taking care to press straight down. Repeat this step with the other slide.

3. Let the stain soak into the flattened root tips for another 2 min.

4. Cover the flattened root tips with cover slips (2 per slide). Press gently down on the outside of the cover slip with the flat side of your forceps to squish the root tip completely flat (so that you will have one layer of cells). Be careful not to break the cover slip.

Part C: Making Observations of Dividing Cells

1. Look at one of your slides through the microscope. Locate and focus on the root tip cells under low power (40×) and medium power (100×), then switch to high power (400×) to see the cells and nuclei more closely. There is no need to clip down the slide. Scan both sections of the slide to make your observations.

2. Find a cell that is typical of the cells you have observed and make a detailed sketch of it on a separate piece of paper or in your notebook. Include as much detail as possible.

3. Now scan the slide for a cell that looks especially different from a typical cell. Search for those that have any differences in their nuclei. Look for any rodlike "colored bodies" like the ones that Heinrich Waldeyer observed. Draw sketches of these unusual cells on a separate piece of paper.

4. If you find a cell with something intriguing happening in the nucleus, share it with the classmates around you. Your teacher may ask you to redraw your sketch on the board.

Analysis and Conclusions

1. Your teacher will lead you in a discussion about the possible significance of what you and your classmates have observed about the cells and nuclei of dividing cells. Use the information from your observations and your classmates' observations to place the cell drawings your class has made in a logical sequence. Describe or sketch the sequence in the space below.

Student answers will vary, but the order of the sketches should follow the stages of the mitotic phase: prophase, metaphase, anaphase, telophase, and cytokinesis.

Expected Results
Most of the root tip cells students will see on their microscope slides will not be dividing. Remind students to roam around the slide looking for brightly colored rodlike figures described in the Prelab Activity. Once one student finds a dividing cell, allow that student to share his or her findings with other students. Direct students to draw detailed sketches of their observations. Some students may draw very vague sketches, or they may draw mitosis as it is depicted in a book (Xs in a neat row).

2. Answer the questions below to communicate your discoveries
about cell division.

   a. Below, make your own sketch of a cell beginning to divide.
Then, write a description of the main event or events that take
place in your sketch.

Students should
describe prophase.
Descriptions could
include chromatin
fibers are condensed
enough to see, the
nucleus disappears.

   b. Below, make your own sketch of a cell in the middle of cell
division. Then, write a description of the main event or events
that take place in your sketch.

Students should
describe metaphase
and/or anaphase.
Descriptions of
metaphase could
include that chromo-
somes are gathered
in the middle of the
cell, and the mitotic
spindle is fully
formed. Descriptions
of anaphase could
include that sister
chromatids are sepa-
rated, and micro-
tubules change
shape and pull the
daughter chromo-
somes apart.

c. Below, make your own sketch of a cell toward the end of cell division. Then, write a description of the main event or events that take place in your sketch.

Students should describe telophase and cytokinesis. Descriptions could include that the spindle disappears, chromosomes uncoil and lengthen, and the cytoplasm divides into two daughter cells.

3. Examine your sketches and descriptions. Which stage of mitosis do you think is happening in each sketch? Label your sketches appropriately.

Students should label their sketches with the corresponding stage of mitosis.

_____

_____

_____

Extension

You can examine the effects of various substances on onion root tips. Sprout more onion root tips in plain water and some in water containing acetaminophen or aspirin. After 2–4 days, compare the onion root tips. Write a hypothesis that suggests an explanation for your observation. (**NOTE:** _Check with your teacher before carrying out any experiments._)

Students may notice that the onion root tips sprouted in the aspirin or acetaminophen solutions grew more slowly than the root tips sprouted in just water. They may infer that the acetaminophen or aspirin slows or stops mitosis in onion root cells. Indeed, the solutions can cause damage to these chromosomes such as translocation or adhesiveness of sticky ends, causing the chromosomes to "glob up."

Extension
To make 500 mL of each solution:

Aspirin
Dissolve one 325 mg tablet in 1 L of water. Mix 75 mL of the solution and 425 mL of water.

Acetaminophen
Dissolve one 500 mg tablet in 1 L of water. Mix 100 mL of the solution and 400 mL of water.

Meiosis Square Dance

Modeling the Events of Meiosis

Question How can you model the events of meiosis?

Lab Overview In this lab activity you will design and perform a role-play activity in which you and your classmates use square dance movements to model the events of meiosis.

Introduction To start the lab activity, you will learn a few basic square dance movements that you and your classmates can use for your "meiosis square dance." You will work as a class to decide how to represent homologous chromosomes and develop the sequence of movements that the class will use to model the events of meiosis.

Background You and your lab partner will portray two sister chromatids that make up one chromosome in a cell undergoing meiosis. To represent a chromosome, you and your partner will wear matching kerchiefs, armbands, or stickers, stand side by side, and each hold one edge of a cardboard "centromere." Your classmates will portray other chromosomes in the same cell. Below are some square dance steps that have been adapted to help you model the events of meiosis.

- *Wheel-around:* A pair of students turns as a unit. This movement can be used to show the normal random movement of chromosomes.

- *Courtesy turn:* A pair of students, standing side by side, face another pair also standing side by side. One member of each pair walks backward, while the other member walks forward until the two pairs are back to back. You can use this sequence of movements to model how homologous chromosomes form tetrads during prophase I.

Pair 1   A–B
         ↓ ↓
         ↑ ↑
Pair 2   C–D

→

         ↑ ↑
         A–B
         C–D
         ↓ ↓

(Pair 1   (Pair 1 and
faces Pair 2)   Pair 2 face
                 away from each other)

- *Forward and back:* Two pairs of students face each other. Each pair steps forward toward the other pair, then steps backward to return to the original position.

- *Promenade:* Pairs of students form a double line and walk as a group to a different location. The movement can be adapted to model the movement and lining up of chromosomes or tetrads in metaphase I, anaphase I, metaphase II, or anaphase II.

Objective to create a role-play model of the events of meiosis

Inquiry Skills using models

Time
- 15–20 min for Prelab Activity
- 30 min for Lab
- 20 min for Analysis and Conclusions

A gym is a good place to do the meiosis dance. You could play appropriate square-dance music and use the lines on the floor as the equator of the cell and the boundaries of the daughter cells.

Prelab Activity As a class, discuss and plan the movements you will use to represent the key structures and processes of meiosis. You also need to plan how you will identify homologous chromosomes. One student will act as the "caller" to direct the movements to occur in the correct sequence. Work with your teacher to develop the "calls" that the caller will use to instruct everyone to complete each stage of meiosis. Use the table below to record your plan. Afterward, answer the Prelab Questions.

To show that they carry different alleles for the same types of genes, "homologous chromosomes" could wear the same color kerchiefs, armbands, or stickers, but of a different shade.

Choose a student with a good understanding of meiosis to be the caller, or be the caller yourself. Use your best judgment to assign partners who won't be embarrassed or feel uncomfortable with each other.

Stage of Meiosis	Movements	"Call"
Prophase I	Sister chromatids come together and hold on to a piece of cardboard. They wheel around for random movement. Pairs use a courtesy turn to form a tetrad with the homologous chromosome.	Chromatids, find your sisters. Move about randomly. Now find your homologue; pair up back to back. Form a tetrad; now form a tetrad.
Metaphase I	Tetrads promenade to the middle of the cell and line up across the spindle.	Now mosey over to the middle of the cell; stay together now.
Anaphase I	Homologous chromosomes use forward and back to show separation and migrate to opposite sides of the spindle.	Say goodbye to your homologous chromosome if there is time. Pull apart from the homologue; now pull apart. You are still in pairs; stay in pairs.
Telophase I and cytokinesis	Chromosomes promenade to the poles. The cells separate.	Two cells form as cytokinesis begins.
Prophase II	Spindle forms.	New round of cell division; stay in pairs.
Metaphase II	Chromosomes promenade to the middle of the cell.	Now mosey over to the middle of the cell; stay together now.
Anaphase II	Sister chromatids use forward and back to show separation and migrate to opposite sides of the spindle.	Pull apart from your sister now; say goodbye.
Telophase II and cytokinesis	Chromosomes arrive at the poles. The cell separates.	Four new cells form as cytokinesis begins.

Name _____ Class _____ Date_____

Prelab Questions

1. How will a chromosome be represented in the "meiosis square dance"?

Suggested answer: Two students standing side by side will represent the sister chromatids of a

chromosome. The centromere will be represented by a piece of cardboard that each student holds

with one hand.

2. How will you and your lab partner determine which "chromosome" is homologous to the one you are portraying?

Sample answer: Students portraying homologous chromosomes will wear cloth strips, yarn, or

stickers of the same color but a different shade.

3. How does your class plan to model the first cell division? The second cell division?

Answers will vary, but should indicate that the class has designated specific spaces in the

classroom for the daughter cells produced in meiosis I and meiosis II.

4. Will you and your lab partner be in the same daughter cell at the end of meiosis II? Explain.

Suggested answer: No, because sister chromatids separate during anaphase II.

Materials

- colored cloth strips, yarn, or stickers
- cardboard rectangle or file folder to represent the centromere
- instrumental square dancing music (optional)

Procedure

1. With your lab partner, put on matching cloth strips, yarn, or stickers to identify each other as sister chromatids. Position yourselves side by side, each holding the centromere (cardboard) with one hand. Look around the room to locate the student pair that is portraying your "homologous chromosome."

2. Walk around randomly with your partner until the caller directs you to locate your homologous chromosome and form a tetrad.

3. As directed by the caller, move to the middle of the cell and form a line with the other tetrads.

4. Follow the caller's directions to separate homologous chromosomes and complete anaphase I.

Sister chromatids should wear the same color. Homologous chromosomes could wear a different shade of the same color. Avoid bandanas or gang colors if this is an issue in your school. Choose colors or patterns that do not have any meaning to students.

Advance Preparation Purchase cloth from a fabric store.

5. Follow the caller's directions to move into one of two haploid daughter cells and complete telophase I.

6. Start meiosis II by walking around with your partner in the space designated for your haploid daughter cell.

7. As directed by the caller, walk with your partner to the daughter cell and line up with the other chromosomes for metaphase II.

8. As directed by the caller, drop the centromere and separate from your partner in anaphase II.

9. Follow the caller's directions to move into one of four haploid daughter cells and complete telophase II. Observe which sister chromatids (students) end up as individual chromosomes in your haploid daughter cell.

Analysis and Conclusions

1. Why did you and your partner have to find a specific pair of students at the beginning of meiosis I?

   Suggested answer: In prophase I, homologous chromosomes pair up, forming tetrads.

2. If you were to repeat the meiosis dance again, would the same sister chromatids end up as individual chromosomes in your haploid daughter cell? Explain.

   Suggested answer: The daughter cells produced the second time the class modeled meiosis II would most likely have a different combination of individual chromosomes (formerly sister chromatids).

3. What events in meiosis cause gametes to have many possible combinations of chromosomes?

   Suggested answer: Tetrads can line up differently in metaphase I with the result that in telophase I, different combinations of chromosomes can end up in the two haploid daughter cells. Also, chromosomes can line up differently in metaphase II, with the result that different combinations of chromosomes can end up in the four haploid daughter cells. Further, crossing over results in homologous chromosomes exchanging genetic material in prophase I.

Extension

Perform the dance again. This time incorporate a way to represent crossing over in your model.

Extension
One way to model crossing over would be to have students wear fabric-covered elastics or hair "scrunchies" of different colors on their wrists. During prophase they can swap the objects with a chromatid of the homologous chromosome.

Name _____ Class _____ Date_____

Family Reunion in a Dish

Determining P Phenotypes From F₁ and F₂ Phenotypes

Question How can you determine the traits of a plant from the P generation by observing the traits of the F_1 and F_2 generations?

Lab Overview In this investigation, you will germinate seeds from two consecutive crosses of Wisconsin Fast Plants®. By observing the stem color and height of the seedlings, you will determine the patterns of inheritance and the phenotypes of the P generation.

Introduction To start your investigation, you will find out more about the three types of Fast Plant seeds that your class will germinate (grow into seedlings) in the lab. Each seed type will grow into plants with the traits of one of the three generations shown in the diagram below. For example, your group may germinate seeds that grow into plants with the traits of one of the true-breeding parent plants (P generation). Another group will germinate seeds with the traits of the F_1 generation plants, and another group will germinate seeds with the traits of the F_2 generation plants. By observing the phenotypes and the patterns of inheritance of two traits, you will be able to accurately determine the phenotype of the "unknown" parent plant (P generation).

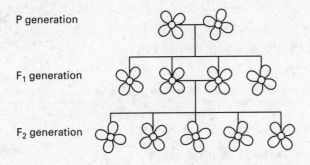

Background A *cross* occurs when sperm from one flower (contained in pollen) fertilizes eggs in a flower of a different plant. Seeds of the next generation of plants develop within the fertilized flower. Fast Plant seeds germinate in only 2 days. Within just 4 days the seedlings are large enough to easily observe many genetic traits, such as height and stem color.

Objective to observe the phenotypes of three generations of plants, determine whether certain traits are dominant or recessive, and make inferences about the phenotype of a P generation plant

Inquiry Skills
• predicting
• observing
• making inferences
• analyzing data
• drawing conclusions

Time
• 15 min for Prelab Activity
• 45 min for Part A
• 2–4 days for germination and seedling growth
• 30 min for Part B
• 20 min for Analysis and Conclusions

Fast Plants are crucifers like broccoli and cabbage. When Fast Plants first germinate, their stems are dark purple due to the pigment anthocyanin. This purple phenotype is dominant. Some plants carry a mutated gene that suppresses the production of anthocyanin; therefore, these mutant strains will have green stems.

Prelab Activity A Fast Plant can have a tall or dwarf (rosette) phenotype. The gene that determines height has two alleles, tall T and dwarf
(rosette) t. Each individual plant has either a Tt, TT, or tt genotype for
height. The T allele is dominant, and the t allele is recessive. Plants
that are heterozygous (Tt) or homozygous dominant (TT) show the tall
phenotype. However, plants that are homozygous recessive (tt) show
the dwarf (rosette) phenotype.

Study the diagram showing two consecutive crosses of Fast Plants.
Then, answer the Prelab Questions.

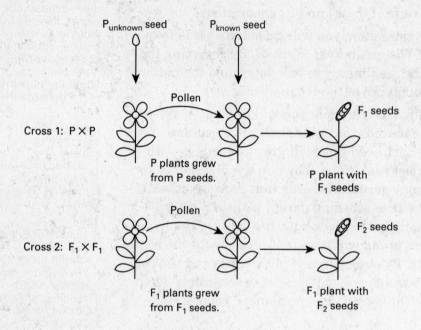

Prelab Questions

1. How many generations of Fast Plants are represented in
the above diagram? Identify them.

Suggested answer: Three generations: the P generation, F_1 generation, and F_2 generation

2. How are seeds produced to grow the next generation of
Fast Plants?

Suggested answer: The pollen (containing sperm) from one flower is used to fertilize eggs

in a flower on a different plant. Seeds then develop within the fertilized flower.

3. Which cross was performed to produce F_2 seeds?

Suggested answer: Cross 2: The F_2 seeds were produced by crossing an F_1 plant with another F_1 plant.

4. If some plants grown from the F_2 seeds had the dwarf (rosette) phenotype and others had the tall phenotype, what could you infer about the genotype and phenotype of the F_1 plants?

Suggested answer: The presence of F_2 offspring with the dwarf (rosette) phenotype implies that the F_1

generation was heterozygous (Tt). The F_1 plants would be tall.

5. Fast Plants do not normally self-pollinate. Why is this helpful to scientists performing genetic crosses with Fast Plants?

Suggested answer: Scientists can perform genetic crosses by using pollen from one Fast Plant

to pollinate the flowers of another and be certain that the resulting seeds contain genetic

material from both parent plants.

Materials

- plastic petri dish
- paper towel
- pencil
- scissors
- permanent marker
- 30 Fast Plant seeds representing P, F_1, or F_2 generation
- tape
- water reservoir (plastic margarine tub or deli container)
- fluorescent light source (optional)

Advance Preparation

A couple of weeks before the lab
Order the seeds from Carolina Biological. For 15 groups of students order 150 seeds of each type. Use the following catalog numbers: P_{known}: 15-8812; F_1: 15-8884; F_2: 15-8895 See the front of this Laboratory Manual Teacher's Edition for supplier information.
A couple of days before the lab
A sunny windowsill or fluorescent shop lights will work fine for this lab; however, a growing box will work best. For building instructions, see the literature accompanying the seeds or go to www.fastplants.org. The growing boxes are also recommended for other labs.

Procedure

Part A: Growing the Seedlings

1. Trace the outline of the petri dish with a pencil onto a paper towel. Use scissors to cut out the circle. Place the circle into the bottom of the petri dish.

2. Your group will be assigned one of the following types of seeds. Each type of seeds will grow into plants with the traits of one generation. You will collaborate with your classmates to observe the traits of the other generations.

P_{known} = true-breeding parent plant (pollen recipient)

F_1 = 1st-generation offspring plants

F_2 = 2nd-generation offspring plants

Safety and Disposal
Remind students about electrical shock hazards and tell them to take care not to spill water near the light sources. Ask students to notify you immediately if a fluorescent bulb breaks. Tell students not to pick up broken glass, and not to touch or inhale dust particles from a broken bulb. Plants and paper towels can be disposed of in the trash. Clean petri dishes with bleach for reuse.

With a permanent marker, label the back of the bottom half of the petri dish as shown below to indicate the generation of seeds assigned to your group. Note that no one in the class will have seeds representing $P_{unknown}$—the parent plant that donated pollen. Instead, you will figure out what this plant looked like by observing the traits of P_{known}, F_1, and F_2 plants.

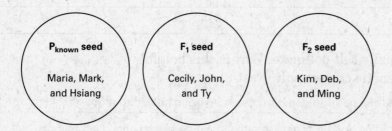

3. Add water so that the paper towel is soaking wet. Carefully pour any excess water out of the petri dish.

4. Place 30 seeds of the generation you were assigned on the paper towel as shown below. Leave the lower 3 cm without seeds.
CAUTION: *Handle seeds and plants only as directed. If you have allergies to certain plants, advise your teacher before handling any plant materials.*

Alternate Method
You may want to have students germinate the P_{known} and F_1 seeds first and then have them predict the F_2 seedling phenotype ratios. Then they can germinate the F_2 seeds to test their hypothesis and predict the phenotype of $P_{unknown}$.

Some groups may have to prepare more than one type of seed (dish) so that there will be complete sets of 3.

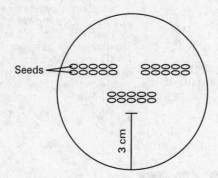

5. Put the lid on the dish. When other teams have finished placing their seeds, group together 3 plates (one of each seed type) and tape them together in a stack. Stand the plates in the water reservoir. Add water to the water reservoir so that the bottom 1 cm of the petri dishes is submerged.

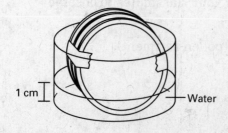

6. Place the water reservoir with your petri dish in a sunny location (windowsill) or under a fluorescent light source. **CAUTION:** *If using a fluorescent light source, move the light carefully to avoid breakage. Take care not to spill water on or near the light source, and follow all electrical safety rules.*

7. Each day, observe the emerging seedlings. By the fourth day, they should be ready to analyze.

Part B: Comparing the Phenotypes of the Seedlings

1. Observe your seedlings and the two sets of seedlings of other classmates that were grouped with yours. Study the color of the stems and leaves in all three generations. Record the two variations of this genetic trait you observe. Also record any other differences in phenotype you observe among the three generations.

P_{known} have green stems and green leaves. F_1 have purplish stems and purplish leaves.

Some of the F_2 seedlings have purple stems and some have green stems.

_____

_____

_____

2. Fill in Data Table 1 for the stem color trait of your seedlings.

Data Table 1: Group Data

Variation (phenotype)	# of P_{known}	# of F_1	# of F_2
Purple	0	30	23
Green	30	0	7

3. Pool the data from all the groups in your class for the stem color trait. Fill in Data Table 2.

Data Table 2: Class Data

Variation (phenotype)	# of P_{known}	# of F_1	# of F_2
Purple	0	150	112
Green	150	0	38

4. Study the overall height of the seedlings. What variations do you observe?

P$_{known}$ plants are about the same height as the plants in the F$_1$ generation (tall). The F$_2$ generation are

a mix of tall and short.

5. Fill in Data Table 3 for the plant height trait in your seedlings.

Data Table 3: Group Data

Variation (phenotype)	# of P$_{known}$	# of F$_1$	# of F$_2$
Dwarf (rosette)	0	0	7
Tall	30	30	23

6. Pool the data from all the groups in your class for the plant height trait. Fill in Data Table 4.

Data Table 4: Class Data

Variation (phenotype)	# of P$_{known}$	# of F$_1$	# of F$_2$
Dwarf (rosette)	0	0	38
Tall	150	150	112

7. Record the inheritance of both traits together for your group's seedlings in Data Table 5.

Data Table 5: Group Data

Combined Phenotype	# of P$_{known}$	# of F$_1$	# of F$_2$
Purple stem/ tall	0	30	18
Purple stem/ dwarf (rosette)	0	0	5
Green stem/ tall	30	0	5
Green stem/ dwarf (rosette)	0	0	2

8. Record the pooled class data inheritance of both traits together in Data Table 6.

Data Table 6: Class Data

Combined Phenotype	# of P_{known}	# of F_1	# of F_2	
Purple stem/ tall	0	150	84	*PPTT, PPTt, PpTT, PpTt
Purple stem/ dwarf (rosette)	0	0	28	*PPtt, Pptt
Green stem/ tall	150	0	28	*ppTt, ppTT
Green stem/ dwarf (rosette)	0	0	10	*pptt

*Answers to **Analysis and Conclusions**, Question 8

Analysis and Conclusions

1. From the pooled class data in Data Table 2, calculate the ratio of the phenotypes for stem color in the F_2 generation.

   The ratio should be about 3 purple : 1 green.

2. Based on your class data for the F_2 generation, is the genotype for stem color in the F_1 generation heterozygous, homozygous dominant, or homozygous recessive? Explain.

   The genotype for stem color in the F_1 generation must be heterozygous because some of the offspring

   of the F_2 generation have purple stems and some have green stems. This means the F_1 generation

   had to have alleles for both colors.

3. From the pooled class data in Data Table 4, calculate the ratio of the phenotypes for plant height in the F_2 generation.

   The ratio should be about 3 tall : 1 short.

4. Based on your data for the F_2 generation, is the genotype for height in the F_1 generation heterozygous, homozygous dominant, or homozygous recessive? Explain.

   The genotype for height in the F_1 generation must be heterozygous because some of the offspring of

   the F_2 generation have dwarf (rosette) stems and some have tall stems. This means that the F_1

   generation had to have alleles for both stem traits.

5. Based on your data, what stem height and color traits did $P_{unknown}$ have? Explain your conclusion using supporting data. Explain which variation of each character is dominant.

$P_{unknown}$ must have been rosette (dwarf) with purple stems. It must have had purple stems because

P_{known} had green stems, but all of the F_1 offspring had purple stems. This also tells us that purple is the

dominant allele. It must have been rosette (dwarf) because this trait shows up in the F_2 offspring. The

rosette (dwarf) trait is not seen in the F_1 generation because the tall allele is dominant (the F_1

generation is heterozygous).

6. Based on the class data for both traits at the same time, calculate the ratio of the phenotypes in the F_2 generation.

Phenotype	Ratio Number (reduced)
Purple stem/ tall	9
Purple stem/ dwarf (rosette)	3
Green stem/ tall	3
Green stem/ dwarf (rosette)	1

Expected Results
Students should conclude that the $P_{unknown}$ plant was dwarf and had purple stems. Students should receive results that are close to Mendel's predicted ratio of $9:3:3:1$. Variations could result, however, if not enough seeds germinated.

7. Does the data from your class approximate the $9:3:3:1$ ratio that Mendel predicted for a dihybrid cross? If not, what might explain the difference?

Answers will vary according to class data. One possible reason for a discrepancy is an insufficient

number of seedlings. Statistically, given a large number of seedlings, the ratio will be very

close to that predicted by Mendel.

8. Now that you have determined which stem color allele is dominant, decide on a letter to represent both alleles. Using T for tall and t for dwarf (rosette) and the letters you decided on for the color alleles, go back to Data Table 6 and fill in the possible genotypes for each phenotype next to the table.

Extension

Design a new cross between two specific genotypes of the F_2 generation and predict the genotypes and phenotypes of the next generation.

Extension
Students should choose two possible genotypes from the F_2 generation and use a Punnett square to predict the phenotype and genotype of the next generation.

Albino Seeds

Observing Effects of Environmental Factors on Phenotype

Question How can environmental factors affect the phenotype of seedlings?

Lab Overview In this investigation you will germinate seeds obtained from a genetic cross between two heterozygous plants with a normal green phenotype. Each parent plant carried the dominant allele for the green phenotype (*G*) and the recessive allele for an albino (colorless) phenotype (*g*). You will place one petri dish containing the seeds from this cross in a brightly lit environment and a second petri dish in a dark environment. You will observe the seedlings' phenotypes after 7 to 10 days of growth. Then you will switch the seedlings' environments and observe the phenotypes a second time.

Background The parent plants of the seeds you will use in the lab were heterozygous for a gene involved in chlorophyll production. Chlorophyll is a green pigment molecule that absorbs light energy during photosynthesis. Each parent plant carried one allele for normal chlorophyll production (*G*) and one allele associated with impaired chlorophyll production (*g*). As the normal allele is dominant, both parent plants produced chlorophyll and were green. Seeds that receive two recessive *g* alleles will develop into seedlings that cannot produce chlorophyll. These seedlings, which are white instead of green, are called "albino" plants. The possible combination of alleles is shown below.

Genotype	Predicted Phenotype
GG	green plant
Gg	green plant
gg	albino (white) plant

In this lab, you will study whether a change in environmental conditions can alter the predicted phenotype.

Prelab Activity Like the plants you will study in this lab, humans also have certain phenotypes that can be altered by environmental factors. For example, a person may inherit genes for tallness but never reach his or her possible adult height due to poor nutrition. Scientists have conducted a number of studies to determine the effects of heredity and environment on height. Compare the results of the two height studies described on the next page. Then, answer the Prelab Questions.

Objective to observe how environment can affect phenotype

Inquiry Skills
- predicting
- calculating
- observing
- making inferences
- drawing conclusions

Time
- 15 min for Prelab Activity
- 20–25 min to setup Part A. Seeds germinate for 6–10 days.
- 25 min for Part B. Seedlings should be left in new environment for 3 more days.
- 20 min for Analysis and Conclusions

Note that in the lab we refer to the seeds generically; however, you should be aware that the seeds used are tobacco seeds.

Even without chlorophyll, an albino tobacco seedling can grow for a limited time because it derives nutrients from its seed. Once the food is used up, however, the seedling will not be able to photosynthesize and will die before it produces seeds. This keeps the albino gene rare in the tobacco plant population. Heterozygotes pass the gene on when they cross-fertilize or self-pollinate.

Height Study A: Height measurements were collected for pairs of genetically identical twins who had been separated at birth and raised in different homes. The data showed that the height measurements for each pair of twins were very close to the same.

Height Study B: The average height of adults living in Britain today was calculated and compared to the average height of adults who lived in Britain 200 years ago. The results of this study showed that people living in Britain today are quite a bit taller than their ancestors were 200 years ago.

Prelab Questions

1. Based on the results of Study A, which would you conclude has a greater effect on height: heredity or environment? Explain your reasoning.

   Sample answer: The results of Study A support the conclusion that heredity has a greater effect on height than environment. Twins that were genetically identical grew to the same height, even though they were raised in different homes.

2. Based on the results of Study B, what would you conclude about the roles of heredity and environment in determining adult height? Explain your reasoning.

   Sample answer: The results of Study B support the conclusion that environment plays a role in determining adult height. The people living in Britain 200 years ago probably could have reached a taller adult height, but did not due to environmental factors such as limited food.

3. If you were one of the researchers in Study A and Study B, what are some questions you would ask about your results?

   Sample answer: If I were a researcher in Study A, I would ask about the similarities and differences of the homes each twin grew up in. What was the diet of each twin like? If I were a researcher in Study B, I would ask about the overall health of adults living in Britain now compared to 200 years ago. I would ask how the typical diet of a British child now compares to the diet of a British child 200 years ago.

Name _____ Class _____ Date _____

Materials

- 2 petri dishes (plastic)
- marker
- white paper towel
- scissors
- water in plastic cup
- dropper
- 50 seeds
- aluminum foil

Procedure

Part A: Setting Up and Germinating Seeds, Days 1–6

1. With a marker, label the bottom of one petri dish "A." Label the bottom of the other petri dish "B." Write your initials on both.

2. Using the bottom of one petri dish as a guide, use a pencil to draw two circles on a white paper towel. Cut out the circles and place one circle in the bottom of each petri dish.

3. Use a dropper to add a small amount of water to each petri dish. Add just enough water to completely moisten the paper towels.

4. Place 25 seeds in each petri dish and place the lids on the dishes. **CAUTION:** *Handle seeds and plants only as directed. If you have allergies to certain plants, advise your teacher before handling any plant materials.*

5. Wrap Dish A with aluminum foil. Cover the dish completely so that no light can get in. Put the wrapped petri dish in the area designated by your teacher.

6. Place Dish B in the brightly lit area designated by your teacher. **CAUTION:** *If you are using a fluorescent light source, move carefully to avoid breakage. Take care not to spill water on or near the light source, and follow all electrical safety rules.*

7. Use information in the Background to calculate the phenotype ratios of the seedlings that will grow in the dishes. Record the ratios in the spaces provided below.

Predicted ratio in Dish A (in the dark) _____

Predicted ratio in Dish B (in the light) _____

8. Check the petri dishes over the next few days (days 2–6). If you open a dish in a lighted area, be sure to cover it as soon as you are done with your observations. If the paper towels start to dry out, use a dropper to add some water. Add enough water to moisten the paper towels, but be careful not to drown the seeds.

Part B: Observing the Effects of Environment on Phenotypes, Days 7–10

1. Depending on the temperature in the room, your seedlings will appear sometime between Day 7 and Day 10. Observe the seedlings in each of your petri dishes and record your findings in Data Table 1.

Data Table 1

Day _____			
Environment of Petri Dish	Total Number of Seedlings in Dish	Number of Albino Seedlings in Dish	Number of Green Seedlings in Dish
Dish A (dark)	25	25	0
Dish B (light)	25	5	20

(actual results may vary)

Expected Results
Dish B seedlings, first grown in light, should show about a 3 green : 1 albino phenotype ratio. All seedlings in Dish A, first grown in the dark, will be albino, regardless of genotype. Tobacco plant genes for chlorophyll production require exposure to light to be expressed.

2. After recording your data, completely remove the aluminum foil from Dish A. Add water as needed to both dishes. Use the foil you removed from Dish A to wrap Dish B. Cover the dish completely so that no light can get in. Put the wrapped petri dish in the area designated by your teacher for three days.

3. Place Dish A (now unwrapped) in the brightly lit area designated by your teacher for three days.

4. What do you think will happen to the phenotypes of the seedlings in the two dishes over the next three days? Write your predictions in the spaces below.

a. Phenotypes of seedlings grown in a dark environment and moved to a brightly lit environment:

_____

_____

b. Phenotypes of seedlings grown in a brightly lit environment and moved into a dark environment:

_____

_____

5. After three days, observe the seedlings again and record your results in Data Table 2.

Data Table 2

Day _____			
Environment of Petri Dish	Total Number of Seedlings in Dish	Number of Albino Seedlings in Dish	Number of Green Seedlings in Dish
Dish A (dark to light)	25	6	19
Dish B (light to dark)	25	22	3

Analysis and Conclusions

1. Calculate the ratio of green plants to albino plants in Dish B using the data you collected in Part B, Step 1.

__4__ green : __1__ albino

(Student answers will vary.)

2. Pool the data collected by your class in Part B, Step 1. Record the class data in Data Table 3.

Data Table 3

Day _____			
Environment of Petri Dish	Class Total Number of Seedlings	Class Total Albino Seedlings	Class Total Green Seedlings
Dish A (dark)	200	200	0
Dish B (light)	200	49	151

3. Use the class data to calculate the ratio of green plants to albino plants for the seedlings exposed to light first. Do the class data differ from your data? Explain.

__3__ green : __1__ albino

Student answers will vary according to results. In general, the larger the number of seedlings in

the sample, the closer the ratios will be to the ratios predicted by Mendel.

4. What are the genotypes of any albino seedlings found in Dish B during Part B, Step 1?

Suggested answer: The albino seedlings found in Dish B during Part B, Step 1 are homozygous

recessive, *gg*.

5. What are the possible genotypes of any green seedlings found in Dish B?

The green seedlings found in Dish B could be either heterozygous (*Gg*) or homozygous

dominant (*GG*).

6. Did changing the environments of your petri dishes cause any changes in the phenotypes of the green seedlings? Explain.

Suggested answer: Yes, most of the green seedlings in Dish B turned white (albino phenotype) when

left in a dark environment for three days.

7. Did changing the environments of your petri dishes change the phenotypes of any white seedlings in Dish A or Dish B? Explain.

Suggested answer: Dish A: Yes, some of the white seedlings became green when exposed to

light. These seedlings must have *Gg* or *GG* genotypes, and therefore, carry the gene for normal

chlorophyll production. Dish B: No, because the white seedlings were genetically albino or

genotype *gg*. These seedlings do not carry a copy of the gene for normal chlorophyll production

and cannot produce chlorophyll under any environmental conditions.

8. Hypothesize why seeds with genotypes that should lead to normal chlorophyll production (*GG* or *Gg*) might display the albino phenotype when grown in the dark.

Sample answer: Plants need light to produce chlorophyll.

9. In nature, genetically albino plants (genotype *gg*) do not survive long enough to produce seeds. Why do you think some plants still carry the mutant *g* allele?

Suggested answer: Plants that are heterozygous (*Gg*) can produce chlorophyll and have the

normal green phenotype. These plants can survive long enough to produce seeds and pass on the

mutant *g* allele.

Extension

Design an experiment to answer the following questions: How long will the albino seedlings survive without chlorophyll? Is there a way to alter the environment to extend the seedlings' lives? **CAUTION:** *Do not carry out any investigations without permission from your teacher.*

Extension
Check student experimental designs for proper use of controls and variables and for safety considerations.

Berry Full of DNA

Exploring Properties of Strawberry DNA

Question What properties of DNA can be observed in a test tube?

Lab Overview In this investigation you will break open strawberry cells, prepare a filtered extract containing strawberry DNA, and separate out molecules of DNA in a test tube.

Background Every cell in a strawberry contains eight copies of each of its chromosomes. As a result, strawberries contain large amounts of DNA. After this lab, you will never eat a strawberry again without thinking of how much DNA is in it! Strawberry DNA is easy to extract because strawberries are easy to mash, and ripe strawberries produce enzymes that contribute to the breakdown of cell walls. To extract the DNA, you will first break strawberry cells apart mechanically, by crushing them. Next, you will add detergents to dissolve the cell's plasma membranes. A filtering step then removes cell organelles, broken cell walls, membrane fragments, and other cell debris. The result will be a red-colored solution containing DNA and other small dissolved molecules such as sugars and proteins. When cold ethanol is layered on top of this solution, molecules of ethanol repel the DNA molecules, and the DNA clumps together. A ropelike clump of many DNA molecules forms that is large enough to see with the unaided eye.

Prelab Activity Observe this sketch of a plant cell. Notice that the DNA is located inside the nucleus. Afterward, answer the Prelab Questions on the next page.

Objective to extract DNA from strawberries and observe its properties

Inquiry Skills
- observing
- making inferences
- drawing conclusions

Time
- 15–20 min for Prelab Activity
- 30–40 min for the Lab Activity
- 15–20 min for the Analysis and Conclusions

The salt in the detergent solution keeps the proteins in the extract layer so that they do not precipitate with the DNA.

Make a model of a strawberry cell to describe the lab steps. Use a light-colored latex helium-quality balloon to represent the plasma membrane. Place hard candies inside the balloon to represent organelles. Use smaller candies to represent proteins. For the nucleus, use a round plastic container from a candy machine and fill it with thread. You will need to cut off part of the stem of the balloon to get the container inside. Blow up the balloon. To represent the cell wall, place the filled balloon inside a green plastic strawberry basket. Ask students what the different parts of the model represent. Discuss the lab procedure, demonstrating the effects on the model. Add more thread to represent DNA from other cells.

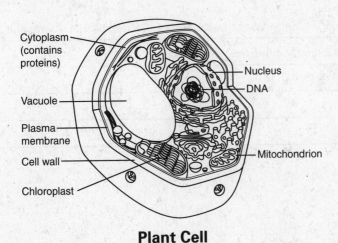

Cytoplasm (contains proteins)

Nucleus

DNA

Vacuole

Plasma membrane

Cell wall

Mitochondrion

Chloroplast

Plant Cell

Prelab Questions

1. To isolate strawberry DNA, you must separate it from other cell materials. Some of the lab steps you will use are listed in the left column below. Match the letter of each lab step with its effects on strawberry cells and enter your answers in the spaces provided.

Lab Steps	Effects on Strawberry Cells
a. Mash the fruit to a slush.	__a__ breaks open the cells
b. Filter the strawberry extract.	__c__ dissolves plasma membranes
c. Add detergent solution.	__d__ clumps DNA together
d. Layer cold ethanol over filtered extract.	__b__ separates organelles and cell debris, such as fragments of cell walls and membranes, from DNA and small dissolved molecules such as proteins and sugars

2. If a molecule of DNA is invisible even under a microscope, how will you be able to see the strawberry DNA you extract?

Many molecules of DNA will clump together, forming a much thicker strand of DNA that can be seen with the unaided eye.

3. Why do you think the clump of DNA molecules has a ropelike shape?

The clump of DNA molecules has a ropelike shape because each DNA molecule is long and threadlike. When many threads wrap together, they make a rope.

Materials

- self-sealing plastic freezer bag
- strawberry
- 10 mL detergent solution
- filtration apparatus: cheesecloth, funnel, and test tube
- ice-cold ethanol
- test tube (clear plastic or glass)
- stirring rod or inoculating loop
- test tube rack (optional)
- microcentrifuge tube (optional)

Procedure

1. Place one strawberry in a self-sealing plastic freezer bag. Press the air out of the bag, and seal it carefully. Mash the bagged strawberry with your fist for 2 min.

2. Add the detergent solution to the bag. Press the air out carefully and seal the bag.

3. Mash the bagged strawberry for 1 min.

4. Set up your filtration apparatus as shown below. If a test tube rack is available, place the test tube securely in the rack.
   CAUTION: *Handle glassware carefully to avoid breakage.*

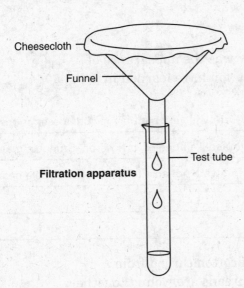

Cheesecloth

Funnel

Test tube

Filtration apparatus

5. Pour the liquid extract into the filtration apparatus, and let it drip directly into the test tube, as shown above.

6. When the test tube is about 1/8 full, remove the funnel. Discard any extra mashed strawberry pulp with the cheesecloth.

7. Slowly drizzle cold ethanol along the side of the test tube, until the test tube is about half full of liquid. The ethanol should form a separate layer on top of the filtered extract.

Safety and Disposal
Remind students to wear safety goggles when handling the DNA extraction buffer and observing the precipitation of DNA. Ethanol at the concentrations used is toxic and can be absorbed through the skin. Tell students to wash their hands well after doing the extraction. Flush test tube contents down the drain and wash test tubes for reuse.

Advance Preparation

One or two days before the lab
- Obtain plastic self-sealing storage bags, fresh or frozen strawberries, and cheesecloth. Freezer storage bags work best because they are thick and less likely to break. If you are using frozen strawberries, thaw them before the lab.
- Prepare the detergent solution (DNA extraction buffer). For 100 lab groups, combine in a large beaker:
  – 100 mL (3/8 cup) of shampoo (without conditioner), or 50 mL of liquid dishwashing detergent
  – 15 g NaCl (2 tsps)
  – 900 mL water
- Cut cheesecloth squares (two layers thick) large enough to hang over the edge of the funnel.

The day of the lab
The 90% ethanol must be kept cold. For easy dispensing, place ethanol in several small dropper bottles and keep them on ice in a convenient location.

8. Dip the loop or rod into the tube to where the ethanol and extract layers meet, as shown below. Gently twirl the loop or rod. Keep the tube at eye level so that you can see what is happening. Observe the characteristics of the DNA as it precipitates (clumps together). If a microcentrifuge tube is available, place some of the DNA you prepared into the tube. Be sure to cap the tube tightly. This will give you an opportunity to examine the DNA closely.

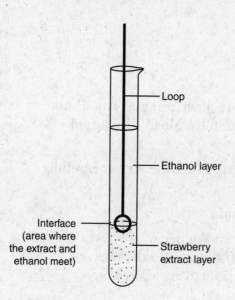

Loop

Ethanol layer

Interface
(area where
the extract and
ethanol meet)

Strawberry
extract layer

Expected Results
When students layer the ethanol on their strawberry extract, they will see fine white strands of DNA form at the interface. When they stir the DNA into the ethanol layer, the DNA will form fibers that will spool onto the stirring rod or loop like cotton candy.

Analysis and Conclusions

1. Describe the DNA you extracted. How was the appearance of the DNA similar or dissimilar to what you have learned in Concept 11.2 about DNA structure?

Student descriptions of extracted strawberry DNA will vary but may include descriptions of long,

thin fibers, threads that look like spider silk, threadlike noodles, and so on. Students may answer

that they could see "strings of nucleotides," but were not able to discern the double helix.

2. A person cannot see a single strand of cotton thread from 30 meters away, but if thousands of threads are wound together into a rope, the rope can be seen at some distance. How is this statement an analogy to the DNA extraction you did?

Sample answer: Individual DNA molecules are far too narrow to see with the unaided eye, but if there

are many thousands of strands clumped together, they form a mass thick enough to be visible.

3. DNA dissolves in water, but not in ethanol. Explain what happened when the ethanol came in contact with the strawberry extract during the DNA extraction.

Sample answer: The DNA dissolved in the detergent solution so we could not see it. When it got

stirred into the ethanol, it clumped together and formed thicker and thicker strands large enough to see.

_____

_____

4. In order to study human genes, scientists must first extract the DNA from human tissues. Would you expect the method of DNA extraction for human DNA to be the same as the method you used to extract DNA from strawberries? Why or why not?

Sample answer: Yes, similar in that cells would need to be broken apart. But because animal cells

do not have cell walls, they would be easier to break apart, and there would not be any cell wall

debris to filter out.

_____

5. List two possible scientific questions that could be explored by studying strawberry DNA.

Sample questions: How is the DNA of wild strawberries different from the DNA of strawberries

sold in most stores? How does the DNA from a parasite resistant strawberry compare with

other strawberries?

_____

Extension

Strawberry cells are octoploid (each cell contains eight sets of chromosomes), whereas banana cells are triploid (each cell contains three sets of chromosomes). Which do you predict will yield a greater quantity of DNA—5 g of strawberry tissue or 5 g of banana tissue? With permission from your teacher, do the following experiment to test your prediction.

With a laboratory balance, measure 5 g of strawberry tissue and 5 g of banana tissue. Place each sample in a separate, self-sealing plastic bag. Repeat the DNA extraction procedure to compare the relative amounts of DNA in each sample.

Extension
Students will find that they can extract substantially more DNA from the strawberry sample than from the banana sample. However, keep in mind that there are several variables that could affect their results, such as the amount of sugar and carbohydrate in each, and the size and fragility of each cell.

Radical Radishes

Quantifying the Effects of Radiation on Radish Seedlings

Question How does radiation affect the germination of radish seeds and the characteristics of the seedlings?

Lab Overview In this investigation your class will germinate (grow into seedlings) radish seeds that have been exposed to varying amounts of radiation in a process called *irradiation*. You will calculate the percentage of the seeds that germinate and study the characteristics of the resulting seedlings. Afterward, you will use your data to draw conclusions about how genetic mutations may have affected the radish plants' traits and ability to survive.

Background Like all seeds, each radish seed contains a plant embryo. Each seed also contains starch, fats, and proteins that provide energy and building materials for the growing seedling. When a seed first absorbs water, cells in the plant embryo start to divide (by mitosis) and the embryo begins to grow. The young stem and leaves grow upward, and the roots grow downward.

The radish seeds you will use in this investigation have been exposed to cobalt-60, a radioactive isotope of the element cobalt. Cobalt-60 gives off gamma rays, a short-wavelength form of electromagnetic energy with more energy than x-rays. Exposure to gamma rays does not make the seeds themselves radioactive, but many molecules in the seeds can be affected. Gamma rays can break covalent bonds in molecules such as DNA. As a result, the DNA in cells exposed to gamma rays may have many nicks and breaks. Extensive DNA damage can kill a cell. But, living organisms have "repair enzymes" that fix DNA damage.

Genetic mutations can occur if DNA is not repaired correctly. For example, deletions and insertions can occur if a small part of the DNA sequence is lost or misplaced when broken ends are rejoined. When the mutated genes are transcribed and translated, they may produce proteins that do not work properly. When the cell divides, these mutant genes can be passed on to the new cells. Because the seeds used in this lab were exposed to gamma rays, mutations may have occurred that will be passed on as the embryo cells divide in the growing seedlings. You may observe some visible effects of proteins that do not work properly.

Objective to quantify the effects of radiation and observe the effects of the resulting damage to an organism's DNA

Inquiry Skills
- predicting
- observing
- making measurements
- calculating
- collecting data
- controlling variables
- organizing data
- drawing conclusions
- communicating conclusions

Time
- 15 min for Prelab Activity
- 20–30 min for Part A
- 15–20 min for Part B, 2–3 days later
- 15–20 min for Analysis and Conclusions

If students seem concerned about working with irradiated seeds, remind them that the seeds themselves are not radioactive.

Prelab Activity Complete the Prelab Activity below. See pages 236–237 in your textbook to review these steps.

1. For each base in the DNA sequence in Diagram A, write in the appropriate mRNA base. Then use the genetic code chart to fill in the correct amino acid in the polypeptide for each mRNA codon.

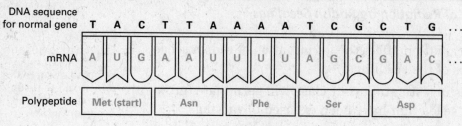

DNA sequence for normal gene: T A C T T A A A A T C G C T G ...

mRNA: A U G A A U U U U A G C G A C ...

Polypeptide: Met (start) | Asn | Phe | Ser | Asp

Diagram A

Second base in codon

	U	C	A	G	
U	UUU ⎫ Phe UUC ⎭ UUA ⎫ Leu UUG ⎭	UCU ⎫ UCC ⎪ Ser UCA ⎪ UCG ⎭	UAU ⎫ Tyr UAC ⎭ UAA Stop UAG Stop	UGU ⎫ Cys UGC ⎭ UGA Stop UGG Trp	U C A G
C	CUU ⎫ CUC ⎪ Leu CUA ⎪ CUG ⎭	CCU ⎫ CCC ⎪ Pro CCA ⎪ CCG ⎭	CAU ⎫ His CAC ⎭ CAA ⎫ Gln CAG ⎭	CGU ⎫ CGC ⎪ Arg CGA ⎪ CGG ⎭	U C A G
A	AUU ⎫ AUC ⎪ Ile AUA ⎪ AUG Met or start	ACU ⎫ ACC ⎪ Thr ACA ⎪ ACG ⎭	AAU ⎫ Asn AAC ⎭ AAA ⎫ Lys AAG ⎭	AGU ⎫ Ser AGC ⎭ AGA ⎫ Arg AGG ⎭	U C A G
G	GUU ⎫ GUC ⎪ Val GUA ⎪ GUG ⎭	GCU ⎫ GCC ⎪ Ala GCA ⎪ GCG ⎭	GAU ⎫ Asp GAC ⎭ GAA ⎫ Glu GAG ⎭	GGU ⎫ GGC ⎪ Gly GGA ⎪ GGG ⎭	U C A G

First base in codon | Third base in codon

2. When the cell containing this DNA was irradiated, damage occurred to the DNA that resulted in changes to its sequence. Fill in Diagram B and compare your results to Diagram A. Then answer the Prelab Questions on the next page.

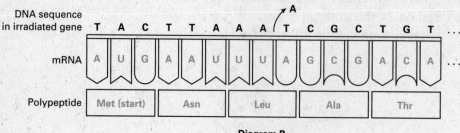

DNA sequence in irradiated gene: T A C T T A A A A↑A T C G C T G T ...

mRNA: A U G A A U U U U A G C G A C A ...

Polypeptide: Met (start) | Asn | Leu | Ala | Thr

Diagram B

Prelab Questions

1. What type of mutation occurred in this strand of DNA? Explain how this may have happened.

Suggested answer: Deletion. Possibly the DNA broke apart as a result of the radiation. Enzymes did

not repair it correctly, and a base was lost.

2. Is it likely that these mutated genes could produce a working protein?

Suggested answer: The genes will most likely not produce a working protein. The polypeptide

sequence is different from the sequence produced by the normal DNA in Diagram A.

3. If this protein is involved in a radish seed's response to the absorption of water, how might the mutation affect germination?

Sample answer: The seed may not germinate without the protein.

Materials

- small growing container
- labeling tape
- marker
- potting soil
- water
- bucket or other drainage container
- 10 radish seeds exposed to cobalt-60
- metric ruler
- calculator (optional)

Use seed starting mix or a mixture of 1 part peat moss to 1 part vermiculite. This mix holds water much better than regular potting soil.

Procedure

Part A: Planting Seeds

1. In the space provided above Data Table 1 on the next page, record the amount of radiation exposure your seeds received. Note that radiation exposure is measured in KR (kilorads).

2. Label a growing container with your and your lab partners' initials, class section, date, and the amount of radiation exposure your seeds received.

3. Fill the growing container with potting soil to about 1 cm below the rim. Water the soil well and let the excess water drain into a bucket or other drainage container.

4. Evenly space your 10 seeds on the soil surface. Cover the seeds with a 0.5-cm layer of soil.

Advance Preparation

A few weeks before the lab
- Order irradiated radish seeds from a biological supply company.
- Place growing containers on a cafeteria tray to make watering easier.
- Collect 4-inch nursery pots. You can also use film canisters as growing containers.

A couple of days before the lab
A sunny windowsill or fluorescent shop lights will work fine for this lab; however, you could also use a growing box such as the type recommended for Investigative Lab 10 and several other labs. See the front of this Laboratory Manual Teacher's Edition for construction instructions.

5. Make predictions about your radish seedlings based on the amount of radiation exposure the seeds received.

Predictions:

Student predictions will vary. Students working with seeds that received the highest levels of radiation

may predict that their seeds will not germinate. Those that are working with seeds that

received the lowest levels of radiation may predict there will be no effect.

Part B: Making Observations and Collecting Data

1. After your seedlings sprout (48–72 hours), observe their general appearance and measure the height of each seedling. Record your data in Data Table 1. (**NOTE:** *If fewer than 10 seedlings sprouted, draw a line though each unused row.*)

Data Table 1: Group Data

Radiation exposure: _____ KR

Seedling	Height of Seedling (cm)	General Appearance, Color, and Leaf Shape
1		
2		
3		
4		
5		
6		
7		
8		
9		
10		

Safety and Disposal
Remind students about electrical shock hazards and tell them to take care not to spill water near the light sources. Ask students to notify you immediately if a fluorescent bulb breaks. Tell students not to pick up broken glass and not to touch or inhale dust particles from a broken bulb. Students should wash their hands after handling the seedlings and soil. Seedlings and soil can be disposed of in the trash. Growing containers can be cleaned with bleach and saved for reuse.

2. Calculate the average height of your seedlings that sprouted. (*Hint:* To calculate the average height, add the height measurements together and divide by the number of seedlings.)

Average height of seedlings: _____ cm

3. Share your data with your classmates. To compare differences between seedlings with different radiation exposures, organize the class data in Data Table 2. To calculate the percentage of seeds germinated for each radiation exposure, use the sample formula below.

$$\frac{\text{number of 0 KR seedlings}}{\text{number of 0 KR seeds planted}} \times 100\% = \% \text{ of 0 KR seeds germinated}$$

Data Table 2: Class Data

Radiation Exposure	% of Seeds Germinated	Average Height of Seedlings (cm)	General Observations
0 KR (control)	100%	3 cm	Look healthy
50 KR	96%	3 cm	Some plants have redder stems than the control.
150 KR	78%	1.5 cm	Some leaves have a yellowish color.
500 KR	20%	0.5 cm	Leaves are wrinkled.
4000 KR	0	—	—

Analysis and Conclusions

1. Create a bar graph that shows the percentage of germinated seeds versus level of radiation. (*Hint:* The level of radiation should be on the *x*-axis of your graph.)

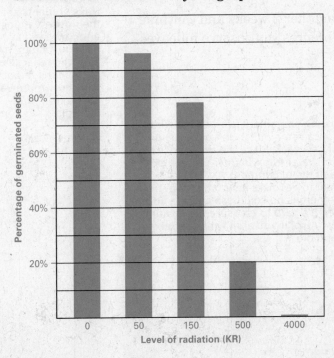

2. How did radiation affect the ability of the seeds to sprout? Support your answer with data from the experiment.

Sample answer: The more radiation, the fewer seeds sprouted. From the data, I estimate that 50% of

the seeds would be killed at approximately 200 KR. 4000 KR destroys 100% of the seeds.

3. What effect did radiation have on the height of the seedlings?

Sample answer: Radiation slowed growth, which led to dwarfed seedlings.

4. What effect did radiation have on the general appearance of the seedlings?

Sample answer: Higher levels of radiation led to color changes in the plants' stems and leaves.

Radiation also led to changes in the appearance of the leaves. At higher levels, the leaves looked

wrinkled.

5. Explain on a cellular level how radiation may have led to the effects you observed.

Sample answer: Radiation caused damage to the DNA within the cells of the embryo. As germination

occurred, the embryo's cells divided and passed on the damaged DNA. This led to the production of

nonworking proteins and the seedlings' abnormal growth and appearance.

Extension

Allow the radish seedlings to grow for another 3 weeks and continue making observations. Describe any differences you observe in leaves and flowers.

Extension
Have students share their observations after 3 weeks. In general, plants exposed to larger amounts of radiation will show more variations from the controls.

Alternate Methods
You can collect free film canisters to use as growing containers from a local film developer. Pierce a small hole in the bottom of a canister with a drill or an ice pick. Feed a small strip of felt through the hole to act as a wick. Place the canisters on a cafeteria tray. To water them, pour a thin layer of water into the tray. You will probably only need to water them once in the course of the experiment.

You can also germinate the seeds on wet paper towel disks inserted into petri dishes. The advantages of this method are that there is no soil mess and the germination process can be better observed. However, it's hard to measure the seedling height because they twist and turn as they grow. Also, if you aren't careful to keep the paper towels moist, the seedlings dry out and die.

You Are A Cytogeneticist

Observing Human Chromosomes

Question What can you learn about chromosome structure and number from observing cultured human cells using cytogenetic (syt oh juh NET ik) techniques?

Lab Overview You will take on the role of a cytogeneticist as you prepare and analyze a chromosome spread from cultured human cells. You will observe human chromosomes and study their different shapes. It is possible that you will observe chromosomal mutations as well.

Background Cytogenetics is the study of the structure and function of chromosomes. A cytogeneticist in a laboratory grows (cultures) cells from human tissues, prepares chromosomes for analysis, and examines the chromosomes for abnormalities. Chromosomes can be prepared from any cells that contain nuclei. To study the chromosomes, the cytogeneticist usually views cells through the microscope and prepares karyotypes. With these techniques, it is possible to discover abnormalities in chromosome structure, such as deletions, translocations, and inversions, as well as errors in chromosome number, such as trisomy 21.

Cytogenetic techniques can also be used to study chromosomal abnormalities in cancer cells. For example, some cancer cells have extra chromosomes, missing chromosomes, or chromosomes with missing pieces. Unlike normal human cells, which stop dividing in the laboratory after a limited number of cell divisions, many types of cancer cells divide as long as nutrients are provided. The cells you will use in this investigation are from a line of human cancer cells that has been grown in laboratories for more than 50 years. These cells are descended from a sample of cancer cells taken from a woman named Henrietta Lacks, who died in 1951. The cells are called "HeLa" cells after her.

Prelab Activity A cytogeneticist in a lab is preparing human cells for a chromosome spread. Read the list of steps on the next page explaining how to prepare the cells. Then study the drawings showing what the cells look like at each step. Afterward, answer the Prelab Questions.

Objective to prepare human chromosome spreads from a human cancer cell culture and use a microscope to observe the different shapes and lengths of chromosomes

Inquiry Skills
- observing
- classifying
- making inferences

Time
- 10–15 min for Prelab Activity
- 15 min for Part A
- 20–30 min for Part B
- 20 min for Analysis and Conclusions

If some students seem concerned about working with cancer cells, remind them it is not possible to "catch" cancer from the cells.

HeLa cells were instrumental in developing the polio vaccine. They have been a useful tool for researchers studying protein synthesis, viral growth, cancer treatments, and the effects of radiation. The cells have been studied in labs on every continent and even in space. HeLa cells bring up many difficult questions regarding the use of human tissues for research. Numerous articles and books on HeLa cells are available that could help you manage a class bioethics discussion.

Table 1: Making a Chromosome Spread

Step	View of Cells	What Is Happening
1. Colchicine (a chemical that stops dividing cells in meta-phase) is added.		Chromosomes are fully condensed in metaphase. Colchicine prevents the chromatids from separating.
2. Cells are placed in a hypotonic solution to make the cells swell.	Movement of water	Water enters the cells. The cells swell as their volume increases.
3. Cells are flattened by dropping them onto a microscope slide. Then the chromosomes are stained. You will perform this step in the lab activity.		Flattening the cells causes the chromosomes to spread out across the slide. Staining the chromosomes makes them easier to see.

Most of the cells the students view will not be in metaphase. Remind students to be patient as they search.

After the cells are placed in the hypo-tonic medium, the cells are fixed in a methanol/acetic acid preservative solution.

Prelab Questions

1. List the steps to make a chromosome spread. Describe the pur-pose of each step.

Colchicine is added to the cells to stop mitosis at metaphase when the chromosomes are fully

condensed and easiest to observe. Then, the cells are placed in a hypotonic medium. This

increases the volume of the cells and makes them swell. Next, the cells are dropped on a slide.

This flattens the cells so that the chromosomes spread out. Finally, the chromosomes are stained

to make them easier to see.

2. What kinds of chromosomal abnormalities can be found using cytogenetic techniques?

Using cytogenetic techniques, it is possible to discover abnormalities in chromosome structure,

such as deletions, translocations, and inversions, as well as errors in chromosome number,

such as trisomy 21.

3. What types of chromosomal abnormalities might be seen in can-cer cells, such as the HeLa cells you will observe in the lab?

HeLa cells and other cancer cells may have extra chromosomes, missing chromosomes, or

chromosomes with missing pieces.

Name _____ Class _____ Date _____

Materials

Each CellServ Kit #4 contains 15 tubes of HeLa metaphase blocked cells, stains, and permount (optional—for preserving the slides after viewing)

- microscope slide
- marker
- paper towel
- cotton ball or wood block
- microcentrifuge tube of prepared HeLa cells
- 3 transfer pipettes
- stain 1 and stain 2
- petri dish
- microscope
- immersion oil (optional)
- clock or watch with a second hand (optional)

1000× magnification will give best results, but 400× will work. Lenses should be clean for best results. Chromosomes cannot be seen with a mirrored microscope.

Procedure

Part A: Preparing a Chromosome Spread

1. Mark the microscope slide with your initials in one corner and place it on a paper towel with your initials facing up. Prop the slide at a 45-degree angle with the cotton ball so that your initials are positioned at the upper end of the slide. **CAUTION:** *Handle the slide carefully to avoid breakage.*

2. Carefully open the tube of prepared HeLa cells. Mix up the cells by using a transfer pipette to gently draw them up and replace them several times. **CAUTION:** *The solution in the tube contains an acetic acid fixative that is toxic. Handle the solution with care.*

3. Carefully hold the pipette about 1 meter above the slide. Aiming at the upper third of the slide, slowly drop the cells onto the slide one drop at a time. Upon impact, the cells will slide downward. Try to drop each drop from a slightly different height. Afterward, close the tube tightly and put it aside.

4. Blow gently on the slide to further spread the chromosomes. **CAUTION:** *Be careful not to inhale directly over the slide to avoid breathing in fumes.*

5. Allow the slide to air dry. When the slide is completely dry, place it in a petri dish. Pour Stain 1 into the petri dish until the slide is covered. Leave the slide in the stain for 10 seconds. Pour the stain back into its container. Use a transfer pipette to remove any excess stain from the petri dish. **CAUTION:** *Take care to avoid spilling or touching the stains.*

6. Repeat Step 5 with Stain 2.

7. Rinse the slide by filling the petri dish with water. Repeat until the water is clear. Pick up the slide by the edges and gently shake off excess water. Dry the underside only of the slide.

Advance Preparation

3–4 weeks before the lab
Order CellServ Kit #4 and specify when you plan to do the lab. The cells can be stored for 2 weeks at 0°C. See the front of this Laboratory Manual Teacher's Edition for ordering information.
Day before the lab (optional)
Results may be slightly better if the slides are chilled. Put one slide for each lab group in a beaker and fill it with 95% ethanol. Place the beaker in the freezer overnight (or at least an hour before the lab). Take out the slides just before the lab.

Safety and Disposal
The classroom should have adequate ventilation. Students should wear plastic gloves, safety goggles, and lab aprons while preparing slides. Have students wash their hands thoroughly afterward. If any of the methanol/acetic acid solution gets into a student's eye, flush the eye with water for 15 min and seek medical attention. Remind students not to inhale fumes from the HeLa solution. Used slides can be discarded. Save stains for reuse, or dispose of these substances according to federal, state, and local requirements.

Part B: Observing and Analyzing the Chromosomes

1. Place the slide on the microscope stage. Under low power, focus on the flattened cells. These are easily seen as cells stained pink. Use the diaphragm to adjust the light coming into the microscope. Too much light will make it difficult to see the cells.

2. Switch to medium power and search the field of view for dark purple specks. Gently move the slide on the stage to scan the entire slide. Adjust the light as needed.

3. After you locate some dark purple specks, center them in the field of view and switch to 400× power. Adjust the light as needed and use the fine-focus knob to bring the specks into focus.

4. You will be able to see the chromosomes under 400× power. If your microscope does not have a 100× objective lens, skip Step 5 and record your observations as directed below.

5. If your microscope has 4 objective lenses on it, you probably have a 100× objective lens. It is the longest lens on your microscope. If your microscope has a 100× objective lens, follow the procedure below.
   a. Once you have the chromosomes focused under 400×, center the chromosomes in the field of view.
   b. Swing the 40× objective lens out of the way and add 1 drop of oil onto the slide where the light is shining through.
   c. Swing the 100× objective lens in place. The tip of the lens will be immersed in the oil.
   d. Focus only with fine focus knob. Adjust lighting if necessary.

Observations

Count the chromosomes you see under the microscope and sketch them in the space below. Note the location of any centromeres that you can see. Also, pay particular attention to the overall length of each chromosome compared with others that you can see.

Sketch

Student illustrations will vary.

Name _____ Class _____ Date_____

Analysis and Conclusions

1. Examine your sketch of the chromosome spread. Consider the abnormalities that cytogeneticists can detect in cancer cells using a light microscope. Do you detect any of these abnormalities?

Student answers may vary, but the most apparent abnormality in most HeLa chromosome

spreads is the presence of far more than 46 chromosomes.

2. Why do you think making a chromosome spread is an important step in identifying chromosomal mutations?

The more spread out the chromosomes are, the less likely that some chromosomes are stacked

behind others. Also, you need to see the length of the chromosome to determine if a piece

is missing.

3. As a cytogeneticist, your next step to further analyze these cells would be to photograph the spread and make a karyotype. How is the photograph used to make a karyotype? What types of abnormalities could you notice using a karyotype?

The cytogeneticist would study the photograph of the chromosome spread to look for the

homologous chromosomes. When the chromosomes are paired in a karyotype, the

cytogeneticist could discover abnormalities such as deletions, translocations, and inversions,

as well as errors in chromosome number, such as trisomy 21.

Extension

If you were unable to find a chromosome spread on your slide to examine, think about possible reasons why the procedure did not work. What part of the procedure was most likely to blame? Propose a way to do that part of the procedure differently and try out your method to see if you get better results. (**NOTE:** *Always check with your teacher before conducting any experiments.*)

Extension
Students may wish to try different objects to prop the slide, try to prop the slide at different angles, or drop the cells from different heights. Review all revised procedure plans for safety.

Genetic Profile

Studying the Inheritance of Earlobe Phenotype

Question How can you determine the inheritance pattern for earlobe phenotypes in three generations of a family?

Lab Overview In this investigation you will construct a pedigree chart showing the inheritance pattern of earlobe phenotypes. To construct the pedigree, you will collect data on earlobe phenotypes from three generations of one family.

Introduction To start your investigation, you will learn how to recognize the free earlobe phenotype and the attached earlobe phenotype. You will gather class data and determine the approximate percentages of people with each phenotype in your class. In addition, you will study a pedigree chart showing genetic relationships in three generations of one family and practice preparing a pedigree chart for a different family.

Background The inheritance of earlobe phenotype in humans generally follows Mendel's principles. The allele for the "free" earlobe phenotype (F) is generally dominant, and the allele for the "attached" earlobe phenotype (f) is generally recessive. Like many other human traits, however, earlobe phenotype can be influenced by more than one gene. Environmental factors such as frequent wearing of heavy earrings can also affect earlobe appearance.

Objective to collect information about a family's history, organize the information into a family tree, and apply Mendel's concepts of dominant and recessive alleles and his principle of segregation

Inquiry Skills
- observing
- making measurements
- collecting data
- making inferences

Time
- 15 min for Prelab Activity
- approximately 1 week for Part A
- 20–30 min for Part B
- 20 min for Analysis and Conclusions

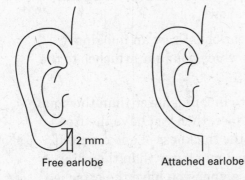

2 mm

Free earlobe   Attached earlobe

Neither earlobe phenotype has any known biological advantage. As a result, the frequencies in which these phenotypes occur tend to remain the same from generation to generation in populations made up of diverse, unrelated individuals (such as your class). However, there may be differences in the frequencies of each phenotype in groups of related individuals. Within a family, the frequency for the two phenotypes may differ significantly from the general population.

Many students tend to equate frequency with dominance. This is a good opportunity to address that commonly held idea and remind students that some dominant traits can occur rarely in a population.

Below is a pedigree showing the inheritance of earlobe phenotype in one family. Siblings, parents, aunts and uncles, cousins, and grandparents (both sides) were observed. The families of great-aunts and great-uncles are not included. Study the pedigree to see how different family relationships are represented.

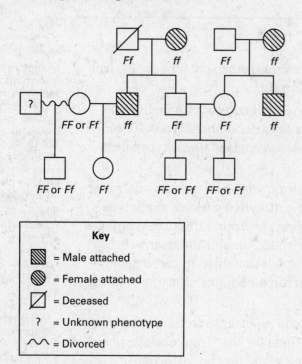

Key

▨	= Male attached
◉	= Female attached
▱	= Deceased
?	= Unknown phenotype
∿	= Divorced

Prelab Activity Follow the steps below to determine your earlobe phenotype and the phenotype of your lab partner. Then, answer the Prelab Questions.

1. Use a mirror to look at one side of your face. If necessary, push your hair back so that one earlobe shows.

2. Determine the lowest point of the earlobe. Draw an imaginary line from that point to the point at which your ear attaches to the side of your face.

3. If the imaginary line passes more than 2 mm lower than the point at which your ear attaches to your face, then you have the free earlobe phenotype (1 mm is about the thickness of one dime). If the imaginary line passes less than 2 mm lower than the point at which your ear attaches to your face, then you have the attached earlobe phenotype. (See the diagrams on the previous page.)

Prelab Questions

1. Which earlobe phenotypes do you and your lab partner have?

Answers will vary according to student observations.

Name _____ Class _____ Date _____

2. Record class data in Data Table 1.

Data Table 1

Total Number of Students	Students With Attached Earlobes	Students With Free Earlobes	Percentage With Attached Earlobes	Percentage With Free Earlobes
32	10	22	31%	69%

3. Draw a family pedigree based on the following information:

Mabel and Henry had two sons, Greg and Doug, and one daughter, Joan. Both sons are married but have no children. Joan married Frank and had three sons, Mark, Kevin, and Ryan. Each of these sons married and had two daughters. Joan and Frank divorced. Joan later married Tom, who had a daughter, Ann, from his previous marriage to Kathy.

Pedigree:

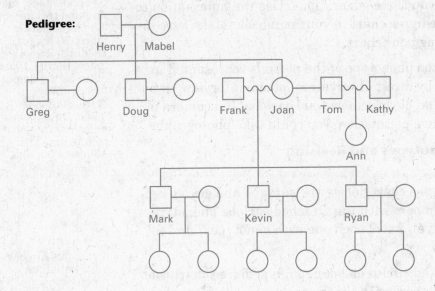

Materials

- notebook
- pencil
- camera (optional)

Procedure

Part A: Collecting Data From a Family

1. Select a family to work with to obtain earlobe phenotype data for your pedigree chart. A good choice would be a family that you can visit to make observations or to look at photos of three generations. You may choose to work with your own family, or the family of a friend or neighbor. If there is no family that you can observe in person you can interview some family members over the phone. Let your teacher know if you are having a hard time finding an appropriate family.

2. Talk to the family and gather basic information on the family members that make up three generations. Use the information to construct a rough pedigree chart in your notebook. Make sure to draw a key explaining your chart.

3. Determine the earlobe phenotype of the persons represented in your pedigree chart by direct observation, phone interview, or by looking at a photo that clearly shows one earlobe. If a camera is available and you have permission, you could take photographs.

Part B: Identifying Genotypes and Revising Pedigree Chart

1. On your rough pedigree chart, locate the squares and circles representing family members with the attached earlobe phenotype (homozygous recessive). Label each one with genotype *ff* and fill in the squares or circles.

2. Locate the squares and circles on your rough pedigree chart that represent family members with the free earlobe phenotype. As the allele for this phenotype is dominant, you may or may not be able to determine whether these family members are heterozygous (*Ff*) or homozygous dominant (*FF*). Label each square or circle appropriately.

3. Redraw the final version of your pedigree chart on the next page. Make sure to include a key explaining your chart, your name, and the date.

Name _____ Class _____ Date_____

Final Pedigree:

Analysis and Conclusions

1. How did you identify the genotypes of the family members shown in your pedigree chart?

Sample answer: As the allele for the free earlobe phenotype is dominant (*F*), all family

members with the attached earlobe phenotype must have two recessive alleles (genotype *ff*).

If a family member with the free earlobe phenotype has a parent with attached earlobes

(genotype *ff*), then that person must be heterozygous (genotype *Ff*). These family members

have one copy of the dominant *F* allele that gives them the free earlobe phenotype,

and they also have one copy of the recessive *f* allele that they received from the parent with

attached earlobes.

2. What is the frequency of each earlobe phenotype in the family that you studied? Divide the number of family members with the same phenotype by the total number of family members for whom you have phenotype data. Then multiply by 100% to get the percentage.

Answers will vary according to student data. In data collected from one family, the frequencies were calculated as follows:

number with free earlobe phenotype/total number of individuals = 25/34 = 73%
number with attached earlobe phenotype/total number of individuals = 9/34 = 27%

3. Compare the frequencies of both earlobe phenotypes you calculated in Question 2 with the frequencies you calculated for your class (see Prelab Questions). Why might the frequencies differ?

Student data will vary. A possible explanation for an observed difference is that the students in

the class are a diverse group of unrelated individuals, while a family is a group with many

related individuals.

4. If the inheritance pattern of the attached earlobe phenotype in your pedigree chart represented a genetic disorder that led to death during childhood, how would this disorder have affected the family you studied?

Answers will vary according to student data. In the example given, the family would not exist as

shown because one grandparent on each side of the family had the attached earlobe phenotype.

If the attached earlobe phenotype had been a genetic disorder that led to death during childhood,

both of these grandparents would have died before they were old enough to marry or

have children.

Extension

Trace the inheritance pattern of another phenotype through the same family. Your teacher will give you examples of other human traits that are usually inherited according to Mendel's principles. Make a separate pedigree chart for this trait and share your findings with the class.

Extension
Students could trace the inheritance pattern of widow's peaks (dominant) vs. straight hairlines, hitchhiker's (curved) thumb vs. straight thumb (dominant), or the ability to roll one's tongue (dominant).

A Glowing Transformation

Inserting Useful Genes Into Bacteria

Question How can bacterial cells be genetically transformed with plasmid DNA containing a jellyfish gene?

Lab Overview In this investigation you will mix plasmid DNA containing the gene for green fluorescent protein (GFP) with *E. coli* bacteria. You will culture the bacteria and then check for "glowing" bacteria that have the GFP gene and produce the GFP protein.

Introduction As you may recall from earlier chapters, bacteria are prokaryotes. Although prokaryotes do not undergo meiosis, they can undergo other processes that result in genetic mixing. For example, in transformation, bacteria pick up plasmids containing different genes from the environment. To start your investigation, you will explore what happens in a bacterial cell when it is genetically transformed. You will learn about the pGLO plasmid that you will use in the laboratory, which contains recombinant DNA. Using materials from the pGLO™ Bacterial Transformation Kit developed by Bio-Rad Laboratories, you will discover how this plasmid can be used to move jellyfish genes into bacterial cells, and find out how to select for transformed bacteria that express these jellyfish genes.

Background Small circular DNA molecules called plasmids occur naturally in many bacteria. Although plasmids come in different sizes, they are much smaller than the bacterial chromosome, and generally contain only a few genes. Plasmid DNA is replicated and expressed inside bacterial cells. Copies of a plasmid can also move from one bacterial cell to another.

Using restriction enzymes, biologists can "cut and paste" desired genes into a plasmid. The recombinant plasmid you will use, called pGLO, has been engineered with several different genes, including one from a bioluminescent (glowing) jellyfish. This gene codes for green fluorescent protein (GFP), a protein that glows a brilliant green color when exposed to ultraviolet (UV) light. The GFP gene is "switched on" in the presence of the sugar arabinose. When grown on agar containing arabinose, transformed bacteria that contain the pGLO plasmid make the GFP and appear bright green in UV light. When no arabinose is present, these bacteria appear white under UV light because GFP is not produced. The pGLO plasmid also carries a gene for producing beta-lactamase (*bla*), a protein that provides resistance to the antibiotic ampicillin. Bacterial cells that contain the pGLO plasmid produce beta-lactamase and can grow into colonies on agar plates containing ampicillin, whereas other bacterial cells would die.

Objective to transform bacteria with plasmid DNA, select for the cells that have incorporated the plasmid, and observe the result of gene expression

Inquiry Skills
• observing
• making measurements
• asking questions
• analyzing data
• drawing conclusions

Time
• 15–20 min for Prelab Activity
• 40–45 min for Part A
• 15 min for Part B (a day or two after Part A)
• 15–20 min for Analysis and Conclusions

Bio-Rad includes an extensive instructor's guide with the pGLO™ Bacterial Transformation Kit. The instructor's guide provides more detailed background and advance preparation information.

You will move copies of the pGLO plasmid into bacterial cells through the process of genetic transformation. To begin, you will mix plasmid DNA with bacterial cells in a solution of calcium chloride ($CaCl_2$). You will then "shock" the bacteria by exposing them to heat. This treatment makes the cell walls of some of the bacteria permeable enough for the plasmid to enter the cells. After these steps, you will culture (grow) the bacteria on agar plates containing ampicillin and arabinose to select for transformed bacteria that contain the pGLO plasmid.

Prelab Activity Study the drawing that shows what happens in a bacterial cell during transformation. Afterward, answer the Prelab Questions.

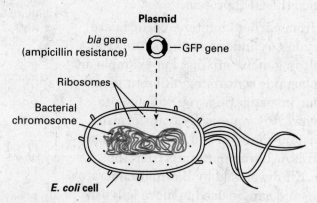

Once the plasmid is within the bacterium, protein synthesis begins. Beta-lactamase is produced and provides resistance to ampicillin. If arabinose is present, then GFP is also produced.

Prelab Questions

1. Many different structures play a role in the bacterial transformation technique that you will carry out. Order the following items from smallest to largest: bacterial chromosome, plasmid, ribosome, bacterial colony, bacterial cell.

   Suggested answer: ribosome, plasmid, bacterial chromosome, bacterial cell, bacterial colony
   _____

   _____

2. The GFP gene comes from the jellyfish *Aequorea victoria*. Why do you think an *E. coli* bacterial cell can produce a protein from genetic information in jellyfish DNA?

   Suggested answer: The DNA of all organisms has the same basic chemical composition. The basic
   _____

   process for transcribing and translating DNA and RNA is similar in all organisms.
   _____

   _____

3. What is the significance of the *bla* gene? How does it allow you to select for transformed bacterial cells containing the pGLO plasmid?

Suggested answer: The *bla* gene causes bacteria to produce beta-lactamase, which provides resistance

to the antibiotic ampicillin. Bacterial cells that have taken in the pGLO plasmid have a copy of the

bla gene and are resistant to ampicillin. If you try to grow the bacteria on agar plates containing

ampicillin, only the cells carrying the plasmid will survive and grow into colonies.

4. Will the colonies that grow on agar plates containing ampicillin also glow in the presence of arabinose? Explain your prediction.

Sample answer: Yes, they will glow. Both the *bla* gene and the GFP gene are on every copy of

the pGLO plasmid.

Materials

- hand-held UV lamp (one per class)
- two microcentrifuge tubes*
- foam tube rack*
- marker
- calcium chloride (CaCl$_2$) solution*
- 5 sterile transfer pipettes
- plastic cup for biohazard waste containing 10% bleach solution
- crushed ice
- 2 foam cups
- starter agar plate with colonies of *E. coli**
- 6 sterile inoculating loops*
- pGLO plasmid DNA*   *These materials are provided
- hot and cold tap water   in the Bio-Rad kit.
- thermometer
- LB nutrient broth*
- 3 agar plates (2 with ampicillin, 1 with ampicillin and arabinose)*
- clock or watch with second hand

IMPORTANT: You will be working with a non-disease-causing laboratory strain of bacteria called *E. coli* K-12. When working with these bacteria, however, it is important to use sterile techniques to avoid contaminating your culture with other bacteria. In general, anything that will come into direct contact with the *E. coli* bacteria, such as the tips of the inoculating loops and the transfer pipettes, should not touch any laboratory surfaces or your skin. Carefully follow all instructions regarding proper handling and disposal of materials.

Advance Preparation
This is a brief summary. See kit handbook for a complete preparation guide.
A few weeks before the lab
Order pGLO™ Bacterial Transformation Kit(s) from Bio-Rad Laboratories. See the front of this Laboratory Manual Teacher's Edition for supplier information.
3–7 days before the lab
Prepare agar plates. Add water to ampicillin and arabinose. Pour plates. Wait until the agar bottle is cool enough to hold in your hand before adding the ampicillin. To make the agar, you need a microwave, 1-L flask, 500-mL graduated cylinder, and distilled water.
24–36 hours before the lab
Streak out *E. coli* culture. Instructions can be found in your kit handbook.
The day of the lab
- Set up student work stations.
- Turn on incubator and adjust it to 37°C or set out heating pad.

NOTE: There is one key difference between this lab and the procedure outlined in the kit handbook. The handbook calls for each group to receive a fifth nutrient agar plate without ampicillin or arabinose to which they will add *E. coli* without plasmid. When incubated, this plate will produce the same results as the *E. coli* starter plate.

Procedure ⬡ ✋ ☣ ⬙ 🗑 ⬙

Part A: Transforming *E. coli* Cells With Plasmid DNA

1. Before starting the transformation procedure, observe the starter plate (*do not remove the petri dish lid*) with colonies of *E. coli*. Each bacterial colony appears as a small rounded growth on the agar surface. Shine the UV lamp on the colonies and observe them. **CAUTION:** *Avoid looking directly into the UV lamp or at reflected UV light for an extended time.* Then, shine the UV lamp on the tube of pGLO plasmid DNA to determine whether the DNA glows. Record your observations below.

   Bacteria: ___Colonies are visible, but not glowing._____

   pGLO plasmid DNA: ___pGLO plasmids do not glow._____

2. Label one of the closed microcentrifuge tubes with a plus (+) sign (for "with plasmid") and the other with a minus (−) sign (for "without plasmid"). Place both tubes in the foam tube rack.

3. Open the microcentrifuge tubes. Using a sterile transfer pipette, add two drops of calcium chloride ($CaCl_2$) solution to each tube.

4. Fill one foam cup with crushed ice. Then, place the rack with both tubes on ice.

5. Remove the lid from the *E. coli* starter plate. Using a new inoculating loop, gently scoop up one colony of bacteria and place it into the microcentrifuge tube labeled "+." Swirl the loop gently so that all the bacteria become suspended in the solution. Discard the loop in the plastic cup for biohazard waste. Using a new loop, scoop up a different bacterial colony and swirl it into the microcentrifuge tube labeled "−." Discard the second loop in the biohazard waste cup.

6. Use a new inoculating loop to obtain a small amount of pGLO plasmid DNA from its tube. To do this, dip the loop in the plasmid solution so that the loop fills with a thin film. Check to make sure that liquid is present inside the loop. Place the loop with the plasmid solution into the microcentrifuge tube labeled "+" and carefully mix the loopful of DNA into the suspension of *E. coli* cells. Do not add anything to the tube labeled with the minus sign (−). Close both tubes tightly. Place the used loop into the biohazard waste cup.

7. Keep the rack with both tubes on ice for 10 min.

8. Prepare a warm water bath for the heat shock step. Mix hot and cold tap water in the second foam cup until the water temperature is 42°C.

Safety and Disposal Ask students to notify you of allergies to ampicillin. Do not allow students to handle the ampicillin. Tell students to handle glassware carefully and not to look directly at the UV light. Remind them to wash their hands after handling *E. coli* cultures. Waste materials containing bacteria should be sterilized before disposal. See kit handbook for instructions.

When the plasmid is captured in the loop, it will look like the thin soap film that forms inside the plastic ring children use to blow soap bubbles.

9. After the tubes have been on ice for 10 min, move the rack with both tubes into the 42°C water bath for 50 sec. Make sure the tubes are pushed all the way down into the rack so that they come in contact with the water. After 50 sec, put the rack and tubes back on the ice for 2 min.

10. Remove the rack from the ice. Using a new sterile transfer pipette, add three drops of LB nutrient broth to each tube. Then, allow the tubes to sit at room temperature for 10 min.

11. You will receive three agar plates labeled as in the figure below. Write the date and your initials on each plate. The label "LB" means that the agar was mixed with LB nutrient broth. The label "amp" means that the agar was mixed with ampicillin. The label "ara" means the agar was also mixed with arabinose. The "+" and "−" labels indicate which type of bacteria you will add to the plates—the bacteria with plasmids or the bacteria without plasmids.

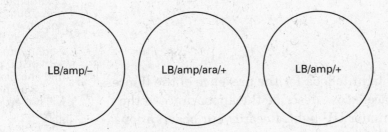

LB/amp/−   LB/amp/ara/+   LB/amp/+

Demonstrate to students the proper technique of spreading bacteria onto agar. You'll find instructions on page 14 in the kit handbook.

12. Open the plate labeled "LB/amp/−." With a new transfer pipette, place two drops from the tube of untransformed cells (labeled "−") on the agar surface. Use a new loop to spread the liquid on the agar surface. (**NOTE:** *Do not dig the loop into the agar.*) Quickly cover the plate with its lid. Place the used pipette and loop into the biohazard waste cup.

13. Open the plate labeled "LB/amp/ara/+." With a new transfer pipette, place two drops from the tube containing transformed cells (labeled "+") on the agar surface. Use a new inoculating loop to spread the liquid, then cover the plate. Place the used pipette and loop into the biohazard waste cup.

14. Open the plate labeled "LB/amp/+." With a new transfer pipette, place two drops from the tube of transformed cells (labeled "+") on the agar surface. Use a new inoculating loop to spread the liquid, then cover the plate. Place the used pipette and loop into the biohazard waste cup.

15. Incubate the plates upside down over the weekend at room temperature, or overnight at 37°C, as directed by your teacher. The *E. coli* starter plate should be left out at room temperature.

Students can stack their agar plates and tape them together. Be sure that students turn their agar plates upside down for incubation, or condensation will fall onto the agar. Be sure that the incubator does not get warmer than 40°C or the agar will dry out and the bacteria will die. Heating pads should be set on low. At room temperature, colonies will be apparent after 48–96 hours.

Part B: Observing Colonies of Transformed and Untransformed *E. Coli* Cells

1. Observe the colonies of *E. coli* cells on the three plates you prepared in steps 12–14 of Part A and those on your *E. coli* starter plate. In the space below, draw a sketch of each plate. Label each plate, and add notes describing what you observe.

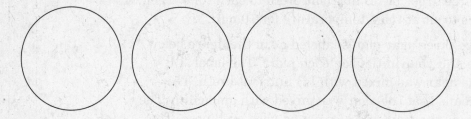

Expected Results
• The *E. coli* that were mixed with pGLO plasmid and placed on LB/amp/ara plates will grow and glow under UV light.
• The *E. coli* that were mixed with pGLO plasmids and placed on LB/amp plates will grow, but they will not glow.
• The *E. coli* that were not mixed with pGLO plasmid and placed on the LB/amp plate will not grow or glow.
• The *E. coli* on the starter plate will grow to cover the LB plate.

2. Use the hand-held UV light to look for the presence of the fluorescent protein. In the space below, describe the appearance of the colonies on each plate under UV light. Record your observations in Data Table 1.

Data Table 1

Plate	Appearance Under UV Light

Analysis and Conclusions

1. What did you see when you observed *E. coli* bacteria under UV light in Step 1 of Part A? Was it what you expected? Explain.

   The *E. coli* bacteria observed in Step 1 did not glow under UV light. This outcome was expected, because these cells did not yet contain the gene for GFP.

2. What did you see when you observed pGLO plasmid DNA under UV light in Step 1 of Part A? Was it what you expected? Explain.

The plasmid DNA did not glow under UV light. This was as expected because the plasmid

is just DNA. The GFP molecule is a protein that is produced by a cell through transcription

and translation.

3. Did bacteria that were not mixed with pGLO plasmid DNA grow on the agar plate containing ampicillin? Explain.

The bacteria that were not mixed with pGLO plasmid DNA did not grow on the plate containing

ampicillin. The bacteria were killed because they did not carry the gene for the enzyme that

breaks down ampicillin.

4. Did bacteria that were mixed with pGLO plasmid DNA grow on the plates containing ampicillin? Explain.

Yes, some of the bacteria that were mixed with pGLO plasmid DNA grew on the plates containing

ampicillin. These bacteria were able to survive and grow because they received the pGLO plasmid

containing a gene for an enzyme that breaks down ampicillin.

5. Do the colonies on both the + plasmid plates glow under UV light? Are the results what you expected? Why or why not?

Only the + plasmid plate with arabinose glows under UV light. This outcome was expected because the

bacteria can produce GFP only in the presence of arabinose.

Extension

Take on the role of a biotechnologist who wants to find commercial uses for green fluorescent protein. What useful applications might there be for a protein that glows? Think about ways that GFP might be used in industry, medicine, research, or in consumer goods. Then create a chart listing your ideas for possible uses and potential products.

Extension
Review student charts for creativity and practicality.

Name _____ Class _____ Date _____

Tell-Tale Pattern

Solving a Crime with DNA Fingerprinting

Question How can a DNA fingerprint be used to identify DNA from a crime scene?

Lab Overview In this investigation you will use gel electrophoresis to make DNA fingerprints from three simulated DNA samples. Two of the samples represent DNA evidence found at a crime scene. The other sample represents DNA from a person suspected of committing the crime. By comparing the banding patterns formed by the DNA fragments in each sample, you will determine whether or not the suspect's DNA matches the crime scene evidence.

Introduction To start your investigation, you will find out how polymerase chain reaction (PCR) and gel electrophoresis techniques are used to make a DNA fingerprint from DNA evidence collected at a crime scene. You will also compare banding patterns made by DNA fragments as they separate by size during gel electrophoresis.

Background Each person's DNA contains particular sections called genetic markers that are highly variable from individual to individual. Through the processes of PCR and gel electrophoresis, genetic markers from a DNA sample can be separated into a banding pattern, known as a DNA fingerprint. The probability of two people having the same DNA fingerprint is somewhere between one in 100,000 to one in 1,000,000,000.

Making a DNA fingerprint requires a combination of several laboratory techniques. First, a sample of DNA must be obtained (in this case, from a crime scene). Then, scientists produce many copies of DNA segments using PCR. To start PCR, technicians add primers for many different genetic markers to the DNA sample. DNA polymerase and nucleotides are also added. Through alternating rounds of heating and cooling, the DNA polymerase makes many copies of the sections of DNA carrying genetic markers that match the primers. The resulting DNA is then loaded on a gel. The gel is placed under an electric current (gel electrophoresis). The shortest DNA fragments move through the gel the fastest, while longer fragments move more slowly. Staining the DNA reveals a banding pattern. Each band represents a set of fragments that are all of a particular length. DNA samples from different people form distinctive banding patterns, because of their particular combinations of genetic markers.

Objective to observe how gel electrophoresis can be used to separate DNA fragments and make a DNA fingerprint

Inquiry Skills
• making inferences
• asking questions
• analyzing data
• drawing conclusions

Time
• 10–15 min for Prelab Activity
• 50 min for Part A
• 30 min for Part B (the class after Part A)
• 15–20 min for Analysis and Conclusions

The crime scenario for this lab is not described in detail so that you can choose an intriguing scenario appropriate for your students. You can make up a case or give them a real-life example. Before students start the lab, describe the scenario, such as a robbery or breaking and entering. Give each group three DNA samples. Mix and match the samples as you wish to make the suspect appear guilty or innocent.

Anytime a criminal comes in contact with something at the scene of a crime, some DNA may be left behind. Because the PCR technique can make copies of even tiny amounts of DNA, enough DNA evidence can be obtained from skin cells, hair, saliva, or blood left at a crime scene to make a DNA fingerprint. DNA evidence can be obtained from cells left on a weapon, a doorknob, or even a coffee cup.

Criminals may leave their cells behind on smoked cigarettes, inside discarded latex gloves (ironically worn to avoid leaving fingerprints!), or in saliva used to seal an envelope.

Prelab Activity Study the diagram showing banding patterns from several different DNA samples. Then, answer the Prelab Questions.

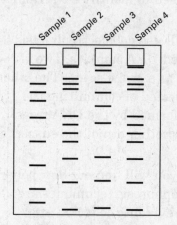

Results of gel electrophoresis

Prelab Questions

1. What causes the DNA fragments to form bands on the gel?

Suggested answer: During gel electrophoresis, DNA fragments separate according to size.

2. How can the banding pattern be used to identify a person?

Suggested answer: DNA samples from different people form different banding patterns because of

their particular combinations of genetic markers.

3. Compare the banding patterns on the gel shown in the diagram above. What can you conclude about the original DNA samples?

Suggested answer: Two of the patterns match (Samples 2 and 4). This evidence supports the

conclusion that these two DNA samples came from the same individual.

Name _____ Class _____ Date _____

Materials

- gel electrophoresis chamber
- agarose gel
- gel electrophoresis buffer
- three samples of PCR-generated DNA fragments
- micropipette and 3 tips   (**NOTE:** *Many gel electrophoresis labs call for the use of ethidium bromide stain, rather than methylene blue. Avoid using ethidium bromide in any lab because it is a known mutagen.*)
- power supply
- methylene blue stain
- staining tray
- spatula (optional)
- bottled water
- large plastic container
- ruler

Procedure

Part A: Running a Gel 🧫 🖐 🧪 👤 🧼

1. Remove any tape or shield that may be covering the ends of the gel. Place the gel in the electrophoresis chamber so that the wells are closest to the negative electrode (−). The negative electrode is usually black. Check how the lid will fit and where the negative electrode will attach. Since DNA is negatively charged, it will move toward the positive electrode (+) on the far side of the chamber during electrophoresis.

2. Pour in enough buffer to submerge the gel.

3. Label the diagram below to record which sample you will load in each well.

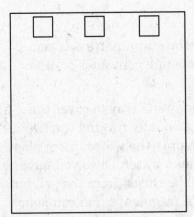

4. Use a micropipette to take up 20 μL of Sample 1. Make sure the sample fills the end of the pipette tip (no air at the smallest end).

Advance Preparation

A few weeks before the lab
Determine materials you need to order, or decide on which kit to order. Be sure to order a kit with pre-cut plasmid or lambda phage DNA.

Two kits that provide many of the needed materials for this lab are *DNA Fingerprinting I* from Edvotek and *PCR Forensics Simulation Kit* from Carolina Biological. See the front of this Laboratory Manual Teacher's Edition for contact information.

The day of the lab
Prepare the agarose gel according to kit directions. Cast the gel and allow it to set for 20 min. Remove the combs from the gels. Set up lab stations.

Safety and Disposal
To avoid risk of electric shock, do not use electrophoresis chambers without safety lids. Verify that students have turned off power supplies before removing the lids. Methylene blue will stain almost anything it comes in contact with. Student should wear gloves, aprons, and goggles at all times. Have students wash their hands after the lab. The buffer and used stain can be flushed down the drain with excess water. All other materials can be disposed of in the trash. See your kit instructions for specific disposal information.

5. Place the micropipette tip below the surface of the buffer, directly above the well. Do not put the tip all the way into the well, but about 2 mm above it.

6. If your hand is shaky, steady it with your other hand or rest your wrist on the side of the gel chamber. Slowly press down the plunger and let the sample drip into the well.

7. Change tips. Repeat steps 4–6 to load the other two samples in separate wells.

You may want to have students practice loading gels using just sample buffer for one or two wells before loading the DNA samples.

8. Place the lid securely on the electrophoresis chamber. Do not move or jiggle the chamber. Connect the lid to the power supply. Make sure that the red connector goes in the red (+) plug and the black connector goes in the black (−) plug. **CAUTION:** *To avoid any risk of injury due to electric shock, always follow your teacher's instructions regarding proper use of the chamber and the power supply.*

9. As directed by your teacher, turn on the power supply to 100 volts. Let the gel run for the time period indicated by your teacher.

Run the gel until the blue dye in the loading buffer is 1 cm from the positive end of the gel. If you are using a chamber that is set up to run two rows of gel at the same time, the gel should run for about 20–30 min. For most other chambers, the gel should run for 30–40 min.

10. After running the gel and turning off the power supply, you will need to apply methylene blue stain to make the DNA fragments visible. To begin, open the chamber and move the gel to the staining tray with a spatula or with gloved hands. Be careful not to drop or bend the gel, as it may break.

11. Add enough methylene blue stain to cover the gel. **CAUTION:** *Handle methylene blue with care. It will stain almost anything it comes in contact with.* Follow your teacher's instructions regarding how long the gel should remain in the stain.

Staining time varies depending on the stain used. See kit instructions.

Part B: Destaining the Gel and Observing Banding Patterns

No special storage is required if a day or two separate Part A and Part B.

1. Wearing gloves, gently hold the gel in the staining tray as you pour excess stain back into the original stain container or other container designated by your teacher.

2. Add just enough bottled water to the staining tray to cover the gel. Let the gel destain for 30 min, occasionally rocking the tray gently back and forth. Every 10 min, empty the water into a plastic container and refill the tray with clean water. Once you have finished this step, the excess stain will be rinsed from the gel, but the stain will still be bound to the DNA fragments. You can pour all of the used wash water down the sink.

Students will have down time while they are destaining the gel. You may want to assign an activity, worksheet, or some other work to complete while they wait. If needed, the gel can be left to destain in water overnight.

3. Observe the banding patterns made by the DNA samples. In the diagram on the next page, add the labels for your samples and use a ruler to draw the bands as they appear on your gel.

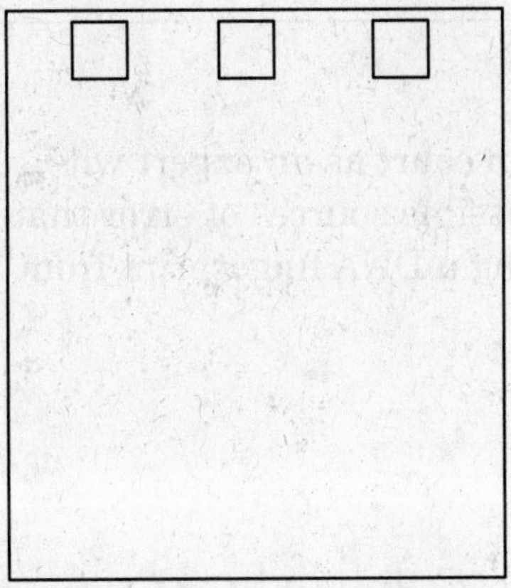

Analysis and Conclusions

1. Summarize the DNA fingerprinting process.

Sample answer: A sample of DNA is collected. Copies of certain sections of the DNA are made using

the PCR technique. The resulting DNA fragments are run on a gel through the process of gel

electrophoresis. The DNA fragments separate according to length, forming a banding pattern.

The banding pattern is known as a DNA fingerprint.

2. Explain why you loaded the wells closest to the negative electrode in the electrophoresis chamber.

Suggested answer: Since DNA is negatively charged, it moves toward the positive electrode.

3. What is the role of methylene blue in this lab?

Suggested answer: Methylene blue stains the DNA fragments so that you can see the banding patterns.

4. Compare the DNA fingerprints of the individuals represented by the three samples.

Answers will vary based on the samples students tested.

5. If these DNA fingerprints were made to assist law enforcement in a criminal investigation, describe the effect your results could have on the investigation.

Answers will vary based on the scenario the students were given and the samples students tested.

Extension

Prepare written testimony you would give in court as an expert witness in this case. In your report, identify possible sources of error that could occur throughout the process of making a DNA fingerprint from crime-scene evidence.

Extension
Particular student reports will vary depending on the scenario presented to the students and their results. Possible sources of error are mislabeled or switched samples or contamination of the DNA.

Birds on an Island

A Simulation of Natural Selection

Question Can natural selection change the frequency of traits in a population in only a few generations?

Lab Overview In this investigation you and your classmates will use a simulation exercise to explore how the frequencies of three beak phenotypes change over several generations in a population of birds on an island.

Introduction To start your investigation you will learn about a population of birds called medium ground finches on Daphne Major, one of the Galápagos Islands. Then you and your classmates will simulate the fitness of birds of a fictional species called *Saccharae utensilus*. This bird species has three possible variations in beak phenotype. Each "bird's" ability to acquire food will determine whether it dies, or whether it survives and reproduces. The number of offspring produced depends on the amount of food each bird acquires, which can vary greatly under changing environmental conditions. After simulating changes in the bird population for six generations, you will analyze data to discover how the frequency of each beak phenotype in the population changed over the generations.

Background Medium ground finches typically feed on small, soft fruit and seeds. The birds prefer soft seeds because they are easier to crack. However, during periods of drought, food becomes scarce. The birds are forced to eat more hard seeds that are difficult to break open. Scientists Peter and Rosemary Grant and their team studied the island's population of medium ground finches and discovered that there are significant variations in the beak depths of individual birds. Birds with deeper beaks are better able to crack open hard seeds than birds with shallower beaks. These variations in beak depth made it possible for some of the medium ground finches to get enough food to survive and reproduce during long droughts.

Objective to discover how variations in beak phenotypes lead to differential success in a bird population

Inquiry Skills
- predicting
- calculating
- analyzing data
- observing
- graphing
- drawing conclusions

Time
- 15 min for the Prelab Activity
- 30–40 min for the Procedure
- 15–20 min for Analysis and Conclusions

This simulation is based on the research of Peter and Rosemary Grant, who studied finches on the Galápagos Island Daphne Major over a period of several decades. During the drought of 1977, all the easy-to-eat seeds and juicy fruits were either not produced or were soon devoured. The most common seed available toward the end of the drought was the seedpod of the caltrop plant (a vine). This seedpod is spiked and dry and very hard to open. In fact, the spikes are so sharp that they can puncture a tire. However, some medium ground finches were successful in cracking them open. The Grant research team took many types of measurements of the birds. The research team concluded that during the drought, the gene pool of the medium ground finches changed. There was a larger percentage of finches with deeper beaks than before. During the heavy rains of El Niño in 1983, food was plentiful and the finches produced many offspring. The island experienced an overpopulation of finches. Smaller finches that required less food for survival reproduced, while many larger birds could not obtain enough food to survive.

Prelab Activity To find out more about the variations in beak depth found in the medium ground finch population of Daphne Major, follow the steps below. Afterward, answer the Prelab Questions.

1. With a metric ruler, measure the beak depths of the two medium ground finches pictured below. Record your measurements in the spaces provided.

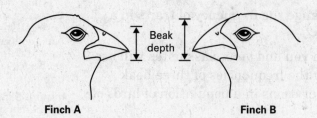

Finch A   Finch B

Medium ground finches

Finch A Beak Depth: ___9___ mm

Finch B Beak Depth: ___11___ mm

2. Study the graph below showing the average beak depth found in the medium ground finch population over a period of 8 years.

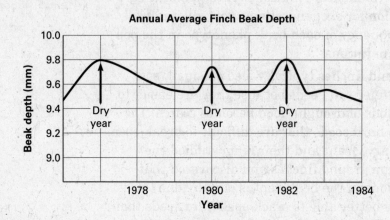

Annual Average Finch Beak Depth

Prelab Questions

1. In which years did the medium ground finch population have the largest average beak depth? Were these wet years or dry years?

Suggested answer: 1977, 1980, 1982. All three years were dry years.

Name _____ Class _____ Date_____

2. Which of the two finches you measured in the Prelab Activity do you think would be more likely to survive and reproduce in a drought year? Explain.

Suggested answer: Finch B. Birds with the deepest beaks are more apt to survive in dry years

because they are better able to crack open and eat harder seeds.

Materials

- plastic spoon, knife, or fork
- self-sealing plastic sandwich bag
- food pieces (candies, unshelled nuts, beans, etc.)
- plastic container for nest (optional)

Rules of the Island

a. You may not use your hands except to hold the plastic utensil (your "beak") and open the plastic bag (the "nest").

b. You may not push other "birds," deliberately knock the food out of the other "birds' beaks," or steal food from the other "birds' nests."

c. You must put your nest in the same general area as the other birds' nests.

d. When your teacher says that time is up, stop where you are. If you have food held securely in your beak, you may bring it to your nest.

e. Do not eat any of the food.   Stabbing food with the utensils is allowed.

Procedure 🔖

(**NOTE:** *Not every student will participate in the simulation for each round. If you are not participating in the simulation for a round, your responsibility is to collect the data and share it with those who did participate.*)

1. Holding your "beak" in your hand, gather food and return to your nest to deposit it. Go to the food source to get more food as many times as possible until time is up.

2. When your teacher tells you the round is over, follow Table 1 on the next page to determine if you collected enough food to survive to the next round and reproduce.

Safety and Disposal
Tell students to take care not to injure themselves or others while moving around or using their utensil "beaks." Ask students with allergies to nuts or other foods to notify you before starting the activity. Remind students never to taste or eat anything in the laboratory. Any food that comes into direct contact with a lab bench should be discarded. No special disposal is required. If possible, it is best to conduct this activity in a non-laboratory setting. Foods should be placed on a sheet or tablecloth if they will be consumed after the activity.

Advance Preparation

A week before the lab
- Do a practice run with a few students to see how much time to allow for each round. If you do not allow enough time, then none of the "birds" will survive to the next round. If you allow too much time, you may not have enough students to represent all of the offspring.
- If possible, you may want to do this lab outside or in a gymnasium where there is plenty of open space.
- Obtain plastic utensils and two types of finch food such as marshmallows or other soft candy for the wet season, and jelly beans or other hard candy or nuts for the dry season. To ensure students don't eat the food, use dried beans, lentils, or hard nuts in shells such as almonds or Brazil nuts. See the annotation on page 160 for instructions to set up Round 1 and Round 2.

Table 1

Food Pieces Collected	Outcome
Fewer than 6	Does not survive
6–11	Survives but does not reproduce
12–17	Survives and produces 1 offspring
18–23	Survives and produces 2 offspring
24–29	Survives and produces 3 offspring

Start Round 1 with one student per beak type. Round 2 should include the students who "survived" Round 1, plus additional students to represent their offspring. For example, assume the student with the plastic knife collects 12 pieces of candy, the one with the spoon collects 18 pieces, and the one with the fork collects 6 pieces. In Round 2 there would be three students with knives, four students with spoons, and one student with a fork. Students who are not participating in the current round can keep records of survival and reproduction.

3. In Data Table 1 below, record the initial population size for each beak variation in Round 1 as well as the total population size. (You will need to collect data from your classmates to record these numbers.) Next, use the following formula to calculate the frequency of each variation as a percentage. Enter your results in Data Table 1.

$$\frac{\text{variation population size}}{\text{total population size}} \times 100\% = \text{frequency of variation in total bird population}$$

4. After rounds 2 and 3 are complete, fill in the rest of Data Table 1.

Data Table 1   (Answers will vary based on student data.)

Beak Variation	Round 1 Pop. Size	Round 1 % Frequency	Round 2 Pop. Size	Round 2 % Frequency	Round 3 Pop. size	Round 3 % Frequency
Spoon						
Fork						
Knife						
Total		/////		/////		/////

5. Fill in Data Table 2 to calculate the change in frequency of each beak variation over rounds 1–3.

Data Table 2   (Answers will vary based on student data.)

Beak Variation	% Frequency in Round 3 (A)	% Frequency in Round 1 (B)	Change in % Frequency (A − B)
Spoon			
Fork			
Knife			

6. Now suppose that your island is experiencing a drought. The type of food available for the island's birds to eat has changed. Perform rounds 4–6 in the same way you performed rounds 1–3. Record the results in Data Table 3.

Before students begin Round 4, switch the food supply. Replace the soft wet season foods with hard dry season foods.

Data Table 3   (Answers will vary based on student data.)

Beak Variation	Round 4			Round 5			Round 6		
	Pop. Size	% Frequency		Pop. Size	% Frequency		Pop. size	% Frequency	
Spoon									
Fork									
Knife									
Total		////////			////////			////////	

7. Fill in Data Table 4 to calculate the change in frequency of each beak variation over rounds 4–6.

Data Table 4   (Answers will vary based on student data.)

Beak Variation	% Frequency in Round 6 (A)	% Frequency in Round 4 (B)	Change in % Frequency (A – B)
Spoon			
Fork			
Knife			

Expected Results In the wet season when softer foods are used, the students using forks and knives will "survive." However, in the dry season, when they cannot stab the foods, they do not fare as well.

Analysis and Conclusions

1. Was there one beak phenotype that was more successful than another in rounds 1–3? If so, which one?

Students' answers will vary depending on the type of candy used. However, they will most likely

answer that the knife or fork variations were the most successful since they were able to use these

"beaks" to stab several soft candies during each trip to the food source.

_____

_____

2. On the same *x*- and *y*-axes, plot three line graphs representing the success of each beak variation throughout the six rounds. Plot rounds 1–6 on the *x*-axis. Plot the percent frequency of each variation on the *y*-axis. Be sure to title your graph and label the axes and the three graph lines.

Student graphs will vary based on their data.

3. Describe the pattern of change for each beak type as displayed in your graph. Identify the most successful beak type or types and suggest reasons for the success.

Students' answers will vary but should discuss how the beak shapes enabled them to efficiently

capture the different types of food.

4. Did the frequency of the different beak variations change when the food supply changed? Relate this to what you learned about the finches on Daphne Major.

Sample answer: Yes, when the food supply changed, the knife variation was especially affected. While

the forks and spoons could scoop up the food, the knives could barely carry back one piece at a time.

On Daphne Major during dry years, many of the finches with small beaks did not survive because they

were unable to crack open harder seeds and expand their food supply.

5. How do you think the results of the Grants' research might have been different if the beak-depth variations were not genetically-based traits (were not passed on from generation to generation)?

Suggested answer: If beak depth were not a genetic trait, then the percent frequencies of the variations

in depth would not change after a dry year.

6. Competition and variation are two factors that play key roles in natural selection. Describe how these two factors resulted in natural selection in the population of ground finches on Daphne Major during drought years.

Suggested answer: There are variations in the depth of beaks among medium ground finches. During

drought years, finches with deeper beaks have more access to food. These finches are more apt to

survive and reproduce than finches with less deep beaks.

Extension

Work with a classmate to make a list of ways that the model in this activity simulated natural conditions and ways that the model differed from natural conditions. Suggest one change to the model that could control for an additional variable or more closely simulate the natural world.

Extension
Students may respond that the activity differed from natural conditions since factors such as predation, competition, and disease were not accounted for. Other factors such as individual students' coordination and problem-solving ability also played a role in the simulation.

Additional Resources
Weiner, J. *The Beak of the Finch.* Vintage Books, 1995.
Grant, P. R. and J. Weiner. *Ecology and Evolution of Darwin's Finches.* Princeton University Press, 1999.

Protein Print

Muscle Proteins and Evolutionary Relationships

Question How can muscle protein fingerprints be used to study evolutionary relationships among organisms?

Lab Overview In this investigation you will isolate muscle proteins from tiny samples of muscle tissue taken from different types of animals. You will use gel electrophoresis to separate the proteins and compare their protein fingerprints.

Introduction Modern classification compares anatomical features, stages of embryonic development, and molecular evidence from DNA and protein sequences to suggest how different organisms might be related. Scientists hypothesize that the more recently two species branched from a common ancestor, the more similar their DNA will be. Because DNA codes for amino acid sequences, which make up specific proteins, species that produce similar proteins are likely to be more closely related than species that do not produce similar proteins.

Molecular biologists use a tool called protein fingerprinting to compare the proteins found in different species. To make a protein fingerprint from muscle tissue, lab technicians first separate proteins from muscle tissue by immersing the muscle tissue in a buffer solution. Some proteins dissolve in the buffer. The buffer and proteins are then loaded on a gel, and the gel is placed under an electric current (gel electrophoresis). (To review gel electrophoresis, see Concept 13.4 in your textbook.) The shortest proteins move through the gel the fastest, while longer ones move more slowly. Staining the gel reveals a banding pattern. Each band represents proteins of a particular length. Muscle protein samples from different animal species form distinctive banding patterns because of their specific proteins. Scientists hypothesize that animals that are closely related produce more of the same proteins than animals that are less closely related. Therefore the banding patterns of closely related animals should be more similar to each other than those of animals that are not closely related.

If a group of animals all produce a certain protein, the scientist may compare the amino acid sequences that make up that protein in each animal. Scientists also hypothesize that animals that are closely related and produce a protein that has the same function will have similar amino acid sequences for that protein. Try this method of analysis yourself by comparing the amino acid sequences of three different animals in the Prelab Activity. Then answer the Prelab Questions.

Objective to infer how species might be related by comparing protein fingerprints through electrophoresis

Inquiry Skills
- observing
- classifying
- analyzing data
- making inferences
- using equipment and technology

Time
- 20 min for Prelab Activity
- 15 min for Part A
- 60–90 min for Part B (You could cut this time in half, but the resolution will not be as good.)
- 45 min for Part C (Before they are stained, gels that have been run can be wrapped in plastic wrap and stored in a refrigerator overnight. Or, you may choose to stain and destain the gel for students.)
- 20 min for Part D (If the gel sits in destain solution for more than one day, the dye may fade and the proteins will be difficult to distinguish.)
- 15 min for Analysis and Conclusions

Prelab Activity The table below contains the amino acid sequences for a protein produced by three different animals. (While the exact amino acids that make up a protein may differ from species to species, the proteins are considered to be the same protein if they perform the same biological function.) Although amino acids usually are represented by three letters, for simplicity the table represents each amino acid with a single letter. For example, the letter "Q" represents the amino acid glutamine.

Sample	Amino Acid Sequence														
	1	2	3	4	5	6	7	8	9	10	11	12	13	14	15
Animal 1	G	L	S	D	G	E	W	Q	L	V	L	N	V	W	G
Animal 2	V	L	S	E	G	E	W	Q	L	V	L	H	V	W	A
Animal 3	V	L	S	H	G	E	N	C	L	C	L	H	V	W	G
continued . . .	16	17	18	19	20	21	22	23	24	25	26	27	28	29	30
Animal 1	K	V	E	A	D	I	P	G	H	G	Q	E	V	L	I
Animal 2	K	V	E	A	D	V	A	G	H	G	Q	D	I	L	I
Animal 3	K	V	H	A	D	V	A	C	H	G	K	H	I	L	I
continued . . .	31	32	33	34	35	36	37	38	39	40	41	42	43	44	45
Animal 1	R	L	F	K	G	H	P	E	T	L	E	K	F	D	K
Animal 2	R	L	F	K	S	H	P	E	T	L	E	K	F	D	R
Animal 3	F	L	H	K	G	H	P	E	H	K	G	K	F	D	R

Compare the sequences in the three animals. Circle the amino acids that differ among the three animals. For example, amino acid 1 is G in Animal 1, but V in Animals 2 and 3. Then record the assigned amino acid numbers that differ between the animals on the lines provided. The first two differences for each amino acid sequence comparison have been recorded for you as examples.

Differences in amino acid sequence between Animal 1 and Animal 2:

1, 4, 12, 15, 21, 22, 27, 28, 35, 45

Total number of differences: 10

Differences in amino acid sequence between Animal 1 and Animal 3:

1, 4, 7, 8, 10, 12, 18, 21, 22, 23, 26, 27, 28, 31, 33, 39, 40, 41, 45

Total number of differences: 19

Differences in amino acid sequence between Animal 2 and Animal 3:

4, 7, 8, 10, 15, 18, 23, 26, 27, 31, 33, 35, 39, 40, 41

Total number of differences: 15

Name _____ Class _____ Date_____

Prelab Questions

1. Which of these three animals would you hypothesize are likely to be the most closely related to each other? Explain.

Suggested answer: The data suggest that Animal 1 and Animal 2 are more closely

related to each other than either animal is to Animal 3.

2. Which of the three animals would you hypothesize are least closely related to each other? Explain.

Suggested answer: The data suggest that Animal 1 and Animal 3 are the least

closely related to each other.

3. Explain why amino acid sequencing is thought to be a useful tool for inferring evolutionary relatedness.

Suggested answer: The amino acid sequence of proteins is coded for by DNA. Comparing the similarity

of amino acid sequences reveals the similarities of DNA. Scientists hypothesize organisms that are

closely related will have DNA that is more similar than organisms that are not closely related.

Materials

- 8 microcentrifuge tubes
- labels
- 1000 µL of extraction buffer
- micropipette and 5 tips
- 4 muscle tissue samples
- knife or scissors
- foam tube rack
- hot water bath
- gel electrophoresis chamber
- agarose gel
- running buffer (Tris-Glycine-SDS)
- power supply
- Coomassie blue stain
- staining tray
- spatula (optional)
- destain solution or bottled water
- large plastic container
- white paper towel or tissue
- light box

For muscle tissue samples, you can use chicken, pork, beef, fish, shrimp, or crab.

Procedure

Part A: Preparing Protein Samples

1. Obtain 8 microcentrifuge tubes, 4 containing extraction buffer solution and 4 without buffer solution. Assign a letter to each muscle tissue sample. Fill in the key on the next page. Then, for each sample, label two tubes (one containing the buffer and an empty tube) with the appropriate letter.

Key

Muscle Tissue Sample	Letter on Tubes
Make sure students can tell the difference between muscle and fat.	

Advance Preparation

A couple of weeks before the lab
Order supplies from Bio-Rad Laboratories or Carolina Biological. You can order the materials individually, or Carolina offers a protein gel electrophoresis kit (it is more economical to buy the materials separately if you plan to do this lab for several years). See the front of this Laboratory Manual Teacher's Edition for contact information. For agarose, order Bio-Rad's high-strength analytical grade agarose or Carolina's biological agarose for protein gels. For extraction buffer, order Bio-Rad's Laemmli Sample Buffer or Carolina's Protein Extraction Buffer. Both companies also offer standards so that students can identify actin and myosin (proteins found in all vertebrate muscle tissue). Note that both Carolina Biological and Bio-Rad sell fish protein electrophoresis kits. These kits use acrylamide gels, which require a vertical chamber.

The day before the lab
Use bottled or distilled water to dilute the concentrated running buffer. Add the running buffer to the agarose, and then melt the agarose. **CAUTION:** *The detergent in the buffer can make the agarose boil over.* For 100 mL of gel (about 3 gels), heat for 2.5 min on 30% power. Take out the container and swirl it. Heat for 10 sec at a time until the agarose is clear-colored and melted. Or, boil 3 cm of water in a pot. Place a beaker of agarose solution in the water. Swirl occasionally. Remove it when the agarose is melted. When the gel is cast, cover it with a layer of buffer and allow it to sit overnight.

The day of the lab
• Remove the combs from the gels. Place 250 µL of extraction buffer into each tube that will receive a piece of muscle tissue.
• Boil water for the hot water bath during the lab. Pour the water into foam cups, just as the students are ready to use it.

2. Cut a tiny piece of muscle (about half the size of a pencil eraser) with a knife or scissors and place the sample in the appropriately labeled microcentrifuge tube containing the buffer. **CAUTION:** *Handle sharp instruments with care to avoid injury.* Use soap to clean the knife or scissors afterward.

3. Hold the first tube between the thumb and index finger of one hand, while flicking the tube with your other index finger 15 times. This action will help dissolve the proteins in the buffer. Repeat for the other three tubes containing tissue samples. Afterward, allow the tissue samples to sit in the foam tube rack for 5 min.

4. Pour only the liquid from each tube containing the tissue and buffer to the appropriately labeled empty tube.

5. Place the tubes now containing the liquid into the foam tube rack. Make sure the tubes are pushed all the way down into the rack. Place the foam tube rack in the 95°C hot water bath for 5 min. **CAUTION:** *Handle the foam cup with care, as the water is hot enough to cause burns.* The heat will denature the proteins, causing them to unravel and lose their unique shapes. The buffer contains negatively charged ions. All of the protein molecules in the buffer will become negatively charged, regardless of their initial charge. This will later cause the proteins to travel towards the positive end of the gel electrophoresis chamber. After 5 min, remove the tube rack from the hot water bath and place it to the side.

Part B: Running the Gel

1. Remove any tape or shield covering the ends of the gel. Place the gel in the electrophoresis chamber so that the wells are closest to the negative (−) electrode (usually black). Check how the lid will fit and where the negative electrode will attach. The dissolved proteins and buffer solution are negatively charged and will move toward the positive (+) electrode.

2. Cover the gel with about 0.5 cm of the running buffer solution.

3. Label the diagram below with the letter of the sample you will load in each well.

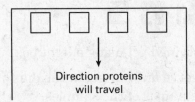

Direction proteins
will travel

4. Use a micropipette to take up 30 microliters (μL) of the first protein sample. Make sure the sample fills the end of the pipette tip.

5. Place the micropipette tip below the surface of the buffer above the well. If your hand is shaky, steady it with your other hand or rest your wrist on the side of the gel chamber. Slowly press down the plunger and let the sample flow into the well. Stop when the well begins to overflow.

6. Change tips. Repeat steps 4–6 to load the other samples in separate wells.

7. Place the lid securely on the electrophoresis chamber. Be careful not to move or jiggle the chamber. Connect the lid to the power supply. The red connector goes in the red (+) plug and the black connector goes in the black (−) plug. **CAUTION:** *To avoid any risk of injury due to electric shock, follow your teacher's instructions regarding proper use of the chamber and the power supply.*

8. Turn on the power to 100 volts. Let the gel run for the time indicated by your teacher. After running the gel and turning off the power supply, take off the lid.

Part C: Staining and Destaining the Gel

1. Remove the gel from the chamber with a spatula or gloved hands and transfer it to the empty staining tray. Be careful not to drop or bend the gel, as it will break.

2. Pour in just enough Coomassie blue stain to cover the gel. **CAUTION:** *Handle Coomassie blue with care to avoid staining your clothing or skin.* Follow your teacher's instructions regarding how long the gel should remain in the stain.

3. Wearing gloves, gently hold the gel in the staining tray as you pour the excess stain back into the original stain container, or another container designated by your teacher.

4. Pour some destain solution into the tray. Gently swirl it around. Secure the gel with your hand, as you pour the discolored destain solution down the drain.

5. Fill the tray with destain again. Place a white paper towel or some tissue in with the gel to absorb excess stain. Let the gel destain overnight.

You could have students wrap their destained gels in plastic wrap. If you then photocopy the gels, the banding pattern will be preserved on paper.

Part D: Analyzing the Gel

1. During your next class, view the destained gel using a light box.

2. Sketch the banding patterns you observe on your gel in the diagram below. Label the wells with the names of the samples.

Analysis and Conclusions

1. Based on your protein fingerprinting results, which of the animals would you hypothesize are the most closely related? Explain.

Students' responses will vary based on the samples tested.

2. Which of the animals would you hypothesize are the least closely related? Explain.

Students' responses will vary based on the samples tested.

3. Discuss errors that could have occurred during the experiment that may have affected the quality of your results.

Students' responses will vary.

Extension

Research the animals whose muscle tissues you tested in this lab. Compare similarities and differences among the animals. Draw a hypothetical phylogenetic tree to demonstrate their possible evolutionary relationships. Describe the phylogenetic tree in words.

Extension
Phylogenetic trees are hypothetical. There is no right or wrong answer. Base your critique on the student's explanation of the shape of the tree.

Additional Resource
University of Arizona Biotechnology Project
http://biotech.biology.arizona.edu/

Eat Your Greens

Exploring Classification

Questions How can humans distinguish between crucifers and edible plants of other families? Can white cabbage butterflies recognize crucifers?

Lab Overview In this investigation you will learn how to use a tool called a dichotomous key to classify species. Then you will use your senses to distinguish between crucifer plant leaves and other edible plant leaves. Finally, you will perform an experiment to find out if white cabbage butterfly larvae can distinguish the leaves of crucifers from the leaves of other plants.

Introduction Crucifers (KROO suh furs) are a family of plants that include broccoli, mustard, cabbage, and several other familiar edible plants. Plants in the crucifer family produce chemicals called glucosinolates (gloo KOH sin oh layts). These plants also produce an enzyme that breaks down glucosinolates into two compounds. One of these two compounds is toxic to many insects. This keeps many insects from feeding on crucifers. However, some insects, such as the larvae of white cabbage butterflies, can tolerate the compound and in fact prefer crucifer leaves to any other type of leaf. This ability to tolerate the glucosinolate product provides an evolutionary advantage to the white cabbage butterfly larvae, since they do not have much competition for this food source.

Although larvae can kill a crucifer plant if they consume too many of the plant's leaves, the interaction between the adult butterfly and the crucifer is beneficial to both insect and plant. Adult butterflies feed on the nectar from the crucifer plant's flowers. As they travel from flower to flower, they pollinate the plants, enabling the crucifer to produce offspring.

In the Prelab Activity, you'll practice classifying crucifers. Then in the investigation you will test your own and the white cabbage butterfly larvae's abilities to distinguish crucifers from other leafy plants.

Prelab Activity Observe the flowers or flower photos provided by your teacher. Use the dichotomous key on the next page to identify the crucifers. You may also be able to tell which plants are most closely related to each other. After you are finished, find out the correct identifications from your teacher. Then answer the Prelab Questions.

Objective to classify plants in the crucifer family and explore the ability of white cabbage butterfly larvae to distinguish crucifers

Inquiry Skills
- observing
- classifying
- collecting data
- predicting
- making inferences
- drawing conclusions

Time
- 20 min for Prelab Activity
- 20 min for Part A
- 20 min for Part B
- 10 min for Part C
- 20 min for Analysis and Conclusions

The white cabbage butterfly *(Pieris rapae)* lays its eggs primarily on plants in the crucifer family, such as broccoli, cabbage, radish, turnip, and mustard. Sensory organs located on the feet of white cabbage butterflies detect the glucosinolate products in crucifer leaves. White cabbage butterflies then lay eggs on the crucifer leaves.

The larvae feed voraciously on the crucifer leaves. The larvae prefer crucifer leaves to any other type of food, and may starve to death rather than feeding on other types of leaves.

A Dichotomous Key for Identifying Crucifers

1. Number of petals
   1a. Four petals .... go to Step 2
   1b. Other number of petals .... cannot be a crucifer

2. Shape of flower petals
   2a. Shaped like a cross .... go to Step 3
   2b. Not shaped like a cross .... cannot be a crucifer

3. Location where petals attach
   3a. On top of the ovary .... cannot be a crucifer
   3b. Below the ovary .... crucifer, go to Step 4

4. Shape of crucifer seed pod
   4a. Long and narrow .... some common examples are: turnip, cabbage, cauliflower, radish, wallflower, mustard, jewel flower
   4b. Oval .... some common examples are: peppergrass, bladder pod, alyssum, watercress

Good flowers to use for non-crucifers are pansies, poppies, fuchsia, evening primroses, and geraniums. Do not use daisies.

If it is not possible for you to collect these flowers, you can print pictures from the Lab 15 Online Companion.

Prelab Questions

1. Which, if any, of the flowers did you classify as crucifers? Explain your reasoning.

   Students' answers will vary based on the samples they were given.

   _____

   _____

   _____

2. Based on the dichotomous key, what flower characteristics do *all* crucifers have in common?

   Suggested answer: All have four petals; all flowers are shaped like a cross; all the flowers

   are attached below the ovary.

   _____

3. Describe any difficulties you had in classifying the flowers.

   Students' answers will vary.

   _____

   _____

   _____

4. A researcher placed male and female adult white cabbage butter-flies in a container with the three plants listed in the table below. Compare the numbers of eggs the females laid on the different types of leaves. Use the information from the Background and dichotomous key to help you develop one or more hypotheses that might explain the data.

Type of Plant	Total Number of Eggs
Radish	158
Alyssum	45
Primrose	0

Suggested answer: Radish plants and alyssum are crucifers, while primrose is not. Radish plants

produce a higher level of glucosinolate products.

Materials

- numbered paper plates
- leaves from selected greens
- petri dish
- paper towel
- pencil
- scissors
- water
- white cabbage butterfly larvae
- paintbrush or feather

Procedure

Part A: Using Senses to Classify Greens

1. Your teacher will provide you with numbered samples of washed leafy greens from a supermarket. These are all edible plants that are in the crucifer family or in the lettuce family. Smell each numbered sample. Describe the smell of each sample in Data Table 1 on the next page.

2. As directed by your teacher, taste a tiny piece of each leaf type. **CAUTION:** *Only taste the leaves your teacher directs you to taste. Do not taste other plant leaves, as many plants are toxic. This part of the procedure should only be performed in a non-laboratory classroom using no laboratory equipment.* In Data Table 1 on the next page, write a short description of the flavors you detect in each leaf.

Advance Preparation

Two weeks before the lab

Order white cabbage butterfly eggs from Carolina Biological. See the front of this Laboratory Manual Teacher's Edition for contact information. Five days before the eggs arrive, sow radish seeds or purchase cabbage or broccoli plant six-packs from a nursery so that you will have food for the larvae. The eggs will arrive with specific care instructions. They should hatch in 48 h. Allow the larvae to feed and grow for 7 days.

One day before the lab

Obtain two types of leaves from the lettuce family (any variety of lettuce, spinach, beet tops, or chard) and two types of crucifer leaves (mustard, green or purple cabbage, turnip, radish, collard, broccoli, or cauliflower).

Day of the lab

Designate an ID number for each type of leaf (for example, lettuce = #1, cabbage = #2, etc.). Label paper plates with these numbers and place several washed leaves of that type of plant on the plate.

Safety and Disposal

Before the lab, ask students to notify you of any food allergies. Remind students never to taste or eat anything in the laboratory. Have students do the Part A tasting step in a non-laboratory setting, or assign it for homework. Warn students not to taste leaves from unknown plants as they may be poisonous. Review guidelines for handling live animals.

Remind students to handle sharp instruments with care. After completing the lab, have students wash their hands thoroughly with soap. Freeze insect larvae overnight in a plastic bag before disposal.

Data Table 1

Plant ID#	Description of Smell	Description of Taste
		The glucosinolate products give crucifers a pungent, sweet, mustard taste. Some students may not be able to distinguish the crucifer leaves from other leaves.

3. Use your observations to develop a hypothesis classifying the plants into two groups: crucifers and non-crucifers. Explain the reasoning behind your proposed classification.

_____

_____

_____

4. After you are finished classifying the edible leaves, your teacher will reveal which leaves are from plants in the crucifer family and which are from plants in the lettuce family. Record the correct identifications in the spaces provided.

   ID numbers and names of the plants in the crucifer family:

   _____

   _____

   ID numbers and names of plants in the lettuce family:

   _____

   _____

Part B: Preparing a Test of the Ability of White Cabbage Butterfly Larvae to Recognize Crucifers

1. Use a pencil to trace the outline of the bottom of a petri dish onto a piece of paper towel. Cut out the circle. With a pencil, draw two lines to divide the circle into four equal sections as shown. Close to where the two lines intersect, label the sections 1, 2, 3, and 4.

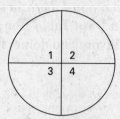

Paper towel circle with sections labeled

2. Place the paper towel circle inside the bottom of the petri dish. Add just enough water to dampen the paper towel.

3. Obtain more samples of the four different types of leafy greens you tested in Part A. Cut about a 2-cm by 2-cm piece from each type of leaf. Place one leaf square in each section of the petri dish. Be sure to make a key so that you know what type of green is in each section. For example:

Section 1 = spinach   Section 2 = mustard greens

Section 3 = lettuce   Section 4 = cabbage

4. With a paintbrush or feather, gently transfer three white cabbage butterfly larvae to the petri dish. Be careful not to injure the larvae during the transfer.

5. Place the lid on the petri dish. Label the lid with your lab group's initials and class. As directed by your teacher, place the closed petri dish in a safe place overnight.

Larvae can survive more than one day in the petri dish. If they run out of food, they may pupate.

6. What do you predict will happen to the leaf squares after one day with the white cabbage butterfly larvae? Choose one of the following predictions, or make your own. Explain the reasoning behind your prediction.

a. The larvae will prefer the leaves of the crucifers, but will eat small amounts of the other leaves as well.

b. The larvae will only eat the crucifer leaves and the others will be left untouched.

c. The larvae will not be able to distinguish between the different types of leaves and will eat them equally.

d. other (Write your own prediction.)

_____

_____

_____

Part C: Observing the Feeding Patterns of the White Cabbage Butterfly Larvae

During your next class, carefully examine all four leaf squares in the petri dish. Look for tiny circles or semicircles chewed out of the leaves. Also look for droppings left by the larvae. Record your observations in Data Table 2 on the next page.

Data Table 2

Plant Sample # and Name	Crucifer? (yes/no)	Observations
1		
2		
3		
4		

Analysis and Conclusions

1. Based on the leaves you tasted in Part A, what flavor(s) would you say that crucifer leaves have in common? Were you able to correctly classify the leaves that were in the crucifer family by tasting them?

Suggested answer: Crucifer leaves have a distinctive aftertaste with pungent, spicy mustard, and

cabbage flavors. Student classifications will vary.

2. Based on your findings in Part C, does it appear that white cabbage butterfly larvae can recognize crucifers? Explain.

Suggested answer: Yes, it does appear that larvae can distinguish crucifers. The crucifer samples

in the dish had small bites taken out of them, while the non-crucifer samples were not touched.

(Occasionally, a couple of bites will be taken out of the other leaves, but this is rare.)

3. If a scientist wanted to determine whether a certain edible plant was more closely related to cabbage than to lettuce, what are at least three possible ways to find out?

Suggested answer: A scientist could use a dichotomous key to study the flowers, use white cabbage

butterfly larvae to see if they will eat the leaves, or test for the presence of glucosinolate products.

4. Why might it be an advantage for white cabbage butterfly larvae to be able to recognize plants in the crucifer family?

Suggested answer: Many other insects cannot eat crucifers because the glucosinolate products

are toxic to them. The white cabbage butterfly larvae feed on the crucifer leaves without much

competition from other insect species.

_____

Extension

Humans can distinguish crucifers from other leafy plants due to a chemical in crucifers that causes humans to detect a certain taste. Do white cabbage butterfly larvae detect crucifers in the same way, by recognizing a chemical? Write a hypothesis and a prediction. With your teacher's permission, perform an experiment to find out if your prediction is correct. Grind cabbage leaves with a little water in a blender. Then use cheesecloth to filter out the juice. Soak a lettuce leaf for a few minutes in the cabbage juice. Place the treated lettuce leaf, an untreated lettuce leaf, and a lettuce leaf that was rubbed against another lettuce leaf in a petri dish with white cabbage butterfly larvae. Record your observations. Discuss whether or not your results support your hypothesis and prediction.

Extension
If the Extension will be performed in the classroom or laboratory, assist students with use of the blender. Remind students again about guidelines for handling live animals and about not tasting foods in a laboratory setting.

You Are a Paleontologist

Observing and Comparing Fossilized Bones

Question How can fossilized bones suggest information about the evolutionary history of species?

Lab Overview In this investigation you will take on the role of a paleontologist researching the history of birds, as you examine and piece together part of a skeleton from duplicate fossilized bones. Then you will compare the partial skeleton to skeletons of a modern-day alligator and bird.

Introduction Paleontologists observe skeletal features and make inferences about an animal's behavior, such as how it moved and how it obtained food. As you may recall from Chapter 14, paleontologists also compare similar skeletal structures of organisms to hypothesize the evolutionary relationships of species. In this lab, you will examine a partial skeleton of a dinosaur that shows several bird-like characteristics.

Background In 1964 scientist John Ostrom discovered the fossil skeleton that you will study in an area called the Cloverly Formation in Bridger, Montana. The area that Ostrom and his team prospected that field season had not yielded as many fossils as they had hoped. However, on the last day of the season, Ostrom discovered some bones he could not identify. The next year he returned to search for more of the skeleton. Eventually this newly discovered, extinct animal was named *Deinonychus.*

Deinonychus lived during the early Cretaceous period, approximately 100 million years ago. It belonged to a group of dinosaur species called *theropods,* relatively small meat-eating dinosaurs that walked on two legs. The animal received its name, which means "terrible claw," because the second toe on each of its hind feet had a large, sharp claw that probably was used to tear the flesh from prey. The claws were held up off the ground as the animal moved about, possibly preventing the claws from wearing down.

As you will observe, *Deinonychus's* skeleton shares many features of the skeletons of both modern alligators and birds. Many researchers hypothesize that the ancestor of birds was a feathered theropod. However, other researchers hypothesize that theropods and birds share common features because they had a common ancestor from which both lineages evolved separately. Much further research is needed to evaluate these two hypotheses. In this lab, you will model the work performed by paleontologists as you examine *Deinonychus* and identify the reptilian characteristics its skeleton retains as well as the bird-like features it displays.

Objective to piece together a partial paper dinosaur skeleton and compare its skeletal features to those of a modern alligator and bird

Inquiry Skills
• observing
• classifying
• making inferences
• using models
• predicting

Time
• 15 min for Prelab Activity
• 20 min for Part A
• 15 min for Part B
• 15 min for Analysis and Conclusions

A fossil of *Archaeopteryx* was first discovered in 1861. Over the years, there has been much debate concerning whether the creature was the first bird or a dinosaur with bird-like characteristics. In recent years, many newly discovered fossils continue to fuel the debate. In the 1990s several dinosaur fossils with "proto"-feathers were found in China. Raptors with wish-bones and bird-like folding legs were also discovered. In 1995, paleontologists found a fossil of a bird with a body similar to *Archaeopteryx* and a head similar to modern-day birds. These fossils point to the possibility that the raptors and birds living during the Cretaceous period had a common ancestor that lived in the Jurassic period.

In the Prelab Activity, read about how fossils are removed from the ground and how they are transported. Then answer the Prelab Questions that follow.

Some scientists think that the evidence of the first birds may have disappeared because bird bones do not fossilize as well as other types of animal bones.

Prelab Activity Removing fossils from rock is a long process that requires skill and a lot of patience. First, the rock surrounding the top and bottom of the fossils is removed with large earth-moving equipment. Scientists use smaller equipment such as shovels, picks, and brushes when working close to a fossil. Before removing a fossil from the ground, workers must encase it in a plaster "jacket" to prevent it from crumbling during transport to the laboratory. After treating a fossil with glue to harden it, paleontologists cover the top of the fossil with tissue paper or foil to protect it from the plaster. The plaster is allowed to harden on the top and sides of the fossil. Then the paleontologist climbs under the fossil and frees it from the ground. The fossil is removed from the rock and flipped over so that plaster can be applied to the bottom side.

In the lab, a person called a "preparator" begins the long process of removing the plaster jacket and the small bits of rock still surrounding the fossil. The preparator may use a microscope and tools as fine as needles to clean the fossils literally one grain of sand at a time. Once the bones are free from the rock, paleontologists may make casts (plastic duplicates) of the bones to send to other paleontologists so they can collaborate in studying them.

Prelab Questions

1. Describe the process by which paleontologists and their team remove fossils from rock.

    Suggested answer: Large earth-moving equipment is used to move rock. Then smaller hand equipment

    is used to remove bits of rock and dirt from the fossils. The fossils are covered in plastic wrap

    or foil to protect them. Then they are covered with plaster. A paleontologist works under the fossils to

    remove them from the rock. The fossil block is then removed from the earth, tipped over, and plaster is

    applied to the bottom side. The fossils are now ready to transport to a laboratory for study.

2. Fossil skeletons are rarely complete. How do you think casts and collaboration help paleontologists create more complex skeletal models?

    Suggested answer: If a scientist at one lab or museum is missing a key piece of a skeleton, the

    scientist can request a cast of the missing bone from a colleague.

Name _____ Class _____ Date _____

3. What role do you think inferences play in the work of a paleontologist?

Students' responses will vary, but one response could be that if certain bones are not available for

observation, the paleontologist will have to infer what the bone may have looked like based on other

bones in the sample and the homologous bone in a similar species.

Materials

- replica fossilized bone "casts" (see the end of the lab)
- scissors
- paper
- tape or glue

Safety and Disposal
Remind students to use scissors with care to avoid injury. No special disposal required.

Alternate Methods
To make this lab more realistic and more challenging, you could cut out the bone pieces and place them in envelopes. Randomly remove one bone from each envelope and place it in a different envelope. Lab groups will then have to collaborate to get all the pieces that they need.

Procedure

Part A: Piecing Together *Deinonychus*

1. Cut out the "casts" and spread them out on a flat surface. **CAUTION:** *Handle scissors with care to avoid injury.* Note that this is only a partial skeleton. Very seldom does a fossil dig produce a complete skeleton. In this fossil dig, for example, paleontologists were only able to obtain the limbs from the left side of the animal's body. Try to fit the bones together. First, locate recognizable bones such as the skull and backbone.

2. Use the reference skeletons in Part B below to guide you in the placement of the other bones. Collaborate with other groups if you cannot decide where to place a bone.

3. Once you have decided how the bones should be connected, tape or glue them in place on a piece of paper. See solution on page 183.

Part B: Comparing *Deinonychus* to a Modern-Day Alligator and Bird

Look closely at the scapula, sternum, tail, and feet of all three skeletons. Note that both *Deinonychus* and the bird have an extra toe that points backward. Fill in the data table on the next page by checking off which features you observe in each skeleton.

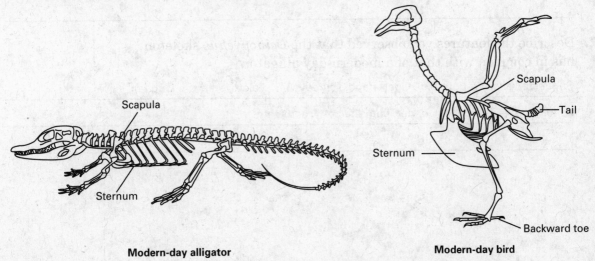

Modern-day alligator

Modern-day bird

Data Table

Characteristic	Alligator	Bird	*Deinonychus*
Narrow scapula (shoulder blade)		✓	✓
Wide scapula (shoulder blade)	✓		
Prominent sternum (breastbone)		✓	✓
Three primary toes on hind feet		✓	✓
Four primary toes on hind feet	✓		
Extra toe that points backward		✓	✓
Hind legs underneath the body rather than to the sides	✓	✓	✓
Long tail	✓		✓
Short tail		✓	
Claws on front feet	✓		✓
Claws only on hind feet		✓	
Bipedal (walks on 2 legs)		✓	✓
Quadrupedal (walks on 4 legs)	✓		
Teeth	✓		✓

(**NOTE:** *This data table includes only a small subset of the characteristics paleontologists examine when comparing dinosaur skeletons to those of modern-day animals.*)

Analysis and Conclusions

1. Which part of the *Deinonychus* skeleton did you find the most difficult to identify and put in place? Explain.

   Students' responses will vary.
   _____
   _____
   _____

2. Describe the features you observed that the *Deinonychus* skeleton has in common with that of a modern-day alligator.

   Suggested answer: Both the alligator and *Deinonychus* skeletons have a long tail, claws on the
   hands/front feet, hind legs underneath the body, and teeth.
   _____
   _____

3. Describe the features you observed that the *Deinonychus* skeleton has in common with that of a modern-day bird.

Suggested answer: Both the bird and *Deinonychus* skeletons have a narrow scapula, prominent ster-

num, three primary toes, a toe that points backward, and hind legs underneath the body. From the

skeletons it appears that *Deinonychus* was bipedal, as are modern-day birds.

4. Scientists ask the following two questions when inferring whether some dinosaurs may have been the link between ancestral reptiles and modern-day birds:

- Are there any fossil birds that retain more reptilian features than birds that are now living?

- Are there any fossil reptiles that show more bird-like features than any reptiles now living?

Does *Deinonychus* provide an answer to either of these questions? Explain.

Sample answer: *Deinonychus* was a reptile that appears to have displayed many bird-like features.

The alligator, a modern-day reptile, does not show as many bird-like features as *Deinonychus*.

Extension

On a separate sheet of paper, sketch an example of what you think the earliest bird may have looked like. Write a paragraph explaining the features of the bird in your sketch.

Extension
Provide students with colored pencils to enhance their creativity.

Additional Resources
Dingus, L. and T. Rowe. *The Mistaken Extinction: Dinosaur Evolution and the Origin of Birds.* W.H. Freeman, 1997.

Holmes, T. and L. Holmes. *Feathered Dinosaurs: The Origin of Birds.* Enslow Publishers, 2002.

Sloan, C. *Feathered Dinosaurs.* National Geographic Society, 2000.

Expected results of piecing together *Deinonychus* bones

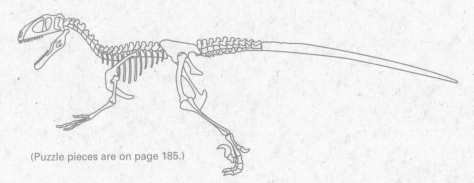

(Puzzle pieces are on page 185.)

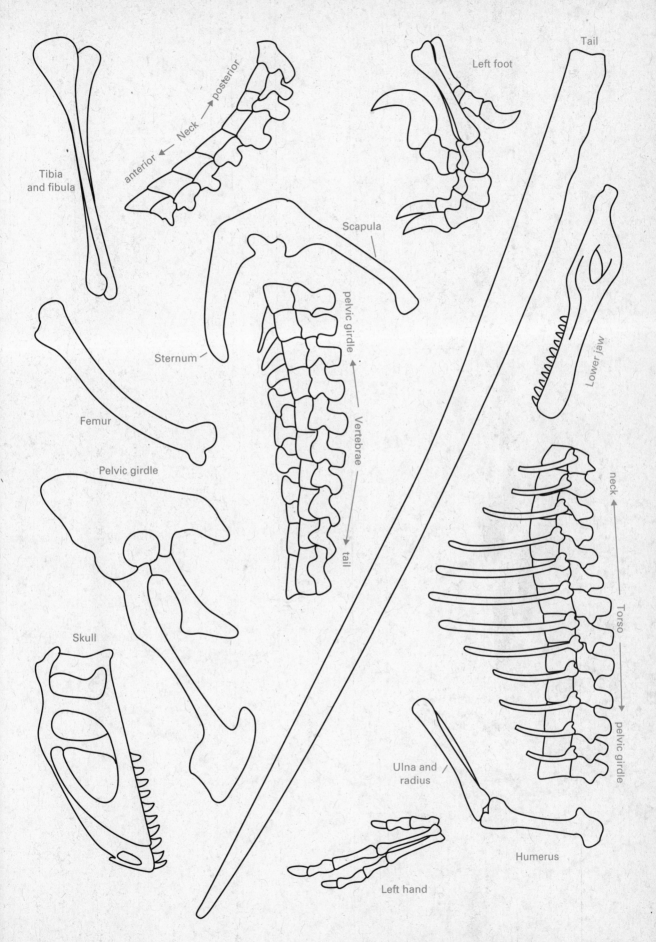

Tibia and fibula

Neck

anterior ← Neck → posterior

Left foot

Tail

Scapula

Femur

Sternum

pelvic girdle

Vertebrae

tail

Lower jaw

neck

Pelvic girdle

Skull

Torso

pelvic girdle

Ulna and radius

Humerus

Left hand

Name _____ Class _____ Date _____

Sari Solution

Discovering Methods to Prevent Cholera Epidemics

Inquiry Challenge How can the bacteria that cause cholera (*Vibrio cholerae*) be removed from river water without the use of chemicals or expensive equipment?

Lab Overview In this inquiry investigation, you will learn how *Vibrio cholerae* can live in and on the bodies of copepods, tiny animals that live in fresh and salt water. Using simulated river water, you will develop an inexpensive filtering method to remove copepods.

Introduction To start your investigation, you will read about how *Vibrio cholerae* causes disease and the relationship between the bacteria and copepods. Then, you will decide which abundant and cheap materials can be used to make a practical tool to filter the copepods.

Background *Vibrio cholerae* is a rod-shaped, motile bacterium with one flagellum. When consumed by humans, *Vibrio cholerae* attaches to the small intestine. The bacteria then produce a toxin that causes the small intestine to secrete massive amounts of water and salts. Without proper medical care, more than 50 percent of those with severe cholera infections die from dehydration and loss of salts.

The most common source of cholera infection is drinking water containing *Vibrio cholerae*. In the United States and other developed nations, water is filtered and treated to remove and kill microorganisms. While filtration and chlorination have decreased cholera in developed nations, people in many developing nations continue to suffer from cholera. For example, in developing nations such as Bangladesh, many people live in poverty in crowded areas without water treatment facilities.

If a person consumes about 1,000,000 *Vibrio cholerae* bacteria, the person will most likely develop cholera. Almost all the *Vibrio cholerae* bacteria are associated with tiny crustaceans called copepods. Up to 10,000 *Vibrio cholerae* bacteria can attach themselves to and inside one copepod, which is about the size of an uncooked grain of rice. If the copepods are removed from water before the water is consumed, then the *Vibrio cholerae* will also be removed.

Objective
to test if sari cloth can be used effectively to eliminate *Vibrio cholerae* from water by filtering out copepods

Inquiry Skills
• predicting
• observing
• designing experiments
• drawing conclusions

Time
• 15–20 min for Prelab Activity
• 20 min for Part A
• 15 min for Part B
• 15 min for Analysis and Conclusions

There is a specific chain of events that usually occurs before a cholera outbreak. First, a warming trend encourages marine phytoplankton growth. Zooplankton, such as copepods, feed on the abundant phytoplankton and reproduce rapidly. As the zooplankton increase in number, so do the numbers of *Vibrio cholerae,* and a cholera epidemic may then follow.

Copepod

Vibrio cholerae

Prelab Activity Scientist Dr. Rita Colwell and her colleagues looked for a simple method to remove *Vibrio cholerae* from drinking water using household materials. Suppose you are one of the researchers working with Dr. Colwell. You have collected 1 L river water containing copepods. Your task is to determine the best method of filtering the water to reduce the occurrence of cholera. Study the list below of household items commonly found in Bangladeshi homes. Think about how these items might be used to filter the copepods, and thus *Vibrio cholerae*, from the water. When you are finished, answer the Prelab Questions.

You may wish to assign the reading of "A Cholera Lesson" and "Spying Diseases From the Sky" for homework after students have completed the Prelab, but before they do the main lab activity. (See the end of this lab for the complete references.)

Common Household Items

- clay jar or pot
- bangle bracelets
- spices
- cloth for saris (garments)
- bamboo matting

Prelab Questions

1. Discuss the relationship between copepods and cholera.

Suggested answer: Copepods in fresh water may carry the bacteria that cause cholera infections.

If a person drinks water containing enough copepods carrying *Vibrio cholerae,* the person may

develop cholera.

2. Which common household items from the list above do you think would work best for filtering out the copepods? Explain your reasoning.

Student responses may vary, but they are likely to suggest clay jars and cloth.

3. Devise a method for using these materials to filter the water.

Suggested answer: Place cloth over a clay jar. Pour the water through the cloth and into

the jar. (Note that this is the filtering method devised by Dr. Colwell and her colleagues.)

Materials

- simulated Bangladeshi water (copepod culture)
- plastic droppers
- well slides
- microscope
- transparent metric ruler
- new sari cloth (or other cotton cloth)
- worn sari cloth (or other cotton cloth)
- graduated cylinder
- clear plastic cups

Procedure

Part A: Observing and Measuring Copepods

1. Place a drop of copepod culture on a well slide. View the slide through the microscope using low power and focus on the copepods. (**NOTE:** *The copepods in the culture* do not *carry* Vibrio cholerae.)

2. Determine the approximate size of a copepod by estimating how much of the field of view it takes up under low power. (You can measure the diameter of the field of view under low power by placing a transparent metric ruler across the stage.)

Part B: Designing and Carrying Out Your Experiment

1. Before designing your filtration technique, follow the steps below to determine the size of the holes in the weaves of the new and worn cloth.

   a. Place the transparent metric ruler on the microscope stage. Under low power, measure the diameter of the field of view in millimeters. Calculate the field of view of the medium- and high-power objectives using these formulas:

$$\frac{(\text{diameter of low-power field of view}) \times (\text{power of low-power objective})}{(\text{power of medium-power objective})}$$

= diameter of medium-power field of view

Diameter of medium-power field of view = _____

$$\frac{(\text{diameter of medium-power field of view}) \times (\text{power of medium-power objective})}{(\text{power of high-power objective})}$$

= diameter of high-power field of view

Diameter of high-power field of view = _____

   b. Examine the cloth through the microscope. Estimate the size of one hole in the weaves of the new and old cloth based on how much of the diameter of the field of view one hole takes up.

Advance Preparation
Two weeks before the lab
- Order copepods from a biological supply company to use as a seed culture. The copepods should arrive with complete culture instructions.
- Purchase sari cloth from an Indian or Middle Eastern clothing retailer or cotton fabric from any fabric store. You can search online for retailers of cotton sari material.

Safety and Disposal
Students should wear goggles when working with the copepods; however, they may remove them to look through the microscope. Tell students to handle glassware carefully to avoid breakage. Remind students to wash their hands after handling the simulated Bangladeshi water (copepod culture). Water containing copepods can be flushed down the drain. Used cloths can be washed or discarded in the trash. To clean glassware for reuse, soak in a 10% bleach solution for 20 min, rinse with water, and air-dry.

2. Predict whether new or old cloth will be more effective at filtering out copepods. Explain your prediction.

_____

_____

_____

3. Design an experiment to answer the following questions.
 a. Is new cloth or old cloth the most effective filter?
 b. Once you have decided whether new or old cloth is more effective, how many layers of cloth are necessary to completely filter out the copepods?

Write the experimental procedure you plan to use below.

Student procedures will vary.

4. Have your teacher review your procedure, then revise it as necessary based on your teacher's suggestions.

Name _____ Class _____ Date_____

5. Carry out your experiment. Record your data in the space below.

Analysis and Conclusions

1. What problems did you face when you performed your experiments? If you performed the experiments again, explain what you would do differently.

Sample answer: The cloth was hard to keep over the jar with one hand while pouring with the other.

Using two people would be better. Alternatively, the cloth could be wrapped or tied in place over

the jar.

2. Which type of cloth, new or old, did you find was the most effective? Explain.

Student answers will vary based on their findings. Generally, the older fabric is more effective than

the new fabric. When the cloth is worn, the holes are not as rigid and defined as in new cloth,

causing the holes to be smaller.

3. How does the size of a copepod compare to the size of the holes in the cloth?

Student answers will vary. Typically, fully-grown copepods are about twice the size of the holes in

the cloth.

4. Suppose a science writer visits your class while you are doing this lab and is writing a feature article about your work. The writer challenges the notion that sari cloth can be an effective filter for bacteria and tells you that cholera bacteria are far too small to be filtered with cloth. Write an explanation that supports the effectiveness of sari filters.

Suggested answer: The bacteria themselves can't be filtered out with the cloth. However, since most

of the bacteria are inside or stuck to the outside of a larger organism, the copepod, they will be

indirectly filtered out with the copepods. My results show that the copepods are significantly

larger than the hole size of either worn or new cloth.

Extension

You have observed how sari cloth can be used to remove copepods from a water supply. Design an experiment that would enable scientists to determine if the amount of *Vibrio cholerae* bacteria in a contaminated water sample would change after filtering with this method. Recall that in the lab you only modeled the system for bacteria removal. The copepods did not carry *Vibrio cholerae*.

Extension
Review students' experimental designs. Experiments could involve viewing water samples under a microscope to look for bacteria.
  An alternative to the provided **Extension** is to have students research the scientific process involved in discovering the link between copepods and *Vibrio cholerae* using the references listed.

References
Dold, Catherine, "The Cholera Lesson." *Discover* vol. 20, no. 2. (February 1999): 71-75.
Plummer, C.M. "Deadly Cholera." *ChemMatters* (February 1995): 12-13.
Travis, J. "Spying Diseases From the Sky: Satellite data may predict where infectious microbes will strike." *Science News* vol. 152 (August 2, 1997): 72-73.

The Right Prescription for Bacteria

Determining Antibiotic Sensitivity

Question How can the effectiveness of an antibiotic against particular bacteria be tested?

Lab Overview In this investigation you will perform a sensitivity test to examine the effectiveness of two antibiotics on two types of bacteria. You will place paper disks containing the antibiotics on bacterial cultures and then observe whether the growth of the bacteria is slowed (inhibited). Sensitivity tests may be used by health professionals to determine which antibiotic to prescribe for a particular infection.

Introduction Antibiotics are produced naturally by fungi or bacteria, or synthetically in a lab. Antibiotics work by killing bacteria outright or by preventing the bacteria from undergoing binary fission (reproducing). Not every type of antibiotic works against every type of bacteria. Differences in bacterial cells sometimes protect the cells from certain antibiotics. For example, sometimes a bacterium contains a gene for an enzyme that can destroy the antibiotic. These enzymes may be passed from one bacterium to another. Some bacteria have "collected" several of these antibiotic-resistance genes and therefore are not affected by many antibiotics.

The cell walls of some bacteria, called Gram-negative bacteria, have an outer membrane that the cell walls of Gram-positive bacteria do not. This outer membrane prevents some antibiotics from entering a Gram-negative bacterial cell. Gram-negative bacteria also have thinner cell walls than Gram-positive bacteria. You will test both a Gram-negative bacterial culture and a Gram-positive bacterial culture in this investigation.

Once you add the paper disks to the agar plates, the antibiotics will diffuse from the paper disks into the agar. The concentration of the antibiotics will be highest in the area right around each disk. If the bacteria continue to grow right to the edge of a disk, then the bacteria are not very sensitive to that antibiotic. However, a clear area around a disk indicates that the bacteria are unable to grow. The diameter of the area where there is no bacterial growth is a measure of the sensitivity of the bacteria to the antibiotic.

In the Prelab Activity, you will examine the case of a patient who cannot seem to "get over" a throat infection. Study the results on the next page of the sensitivity test from her throat culture (a culture of bacteria collected from her throat). Then, answer the Prelab Questions that follow.

Objective to explore one method for testing the sensitivity of bacteria to certain antibiotics

Inquiry Skills
- observing
- making measurements
- drawing conclusions
- communicating conclusions

Time
- 15 min for Prelab Activity
- 15 min for Part A
- 10 min for Part B
- 15 min for Part C (1–3 days after Part B)
- 10–15 min for Analysis and Conclusions

Penicillin and tetracycline are the recommended antibiotics for this lab. Penicillin, which acts by inhibiting an enzyme that allows the cell wall to increase in size during binary fission, will most likely only affect the Gram-positive sample. Tetracycline, which acts by inhibiting ribosomal activity and thereby preventing protein synthesis, will likely affect both samples.

(**NOTE:** *Only use non-pathogenic bacteria in this lab.*)

Recommended non-pathogenic Gram-positive bacteria are *Bacillus subtilis* and *Staphylococcus epidermidis*. Recommended Gram-negative bacteria are non-pathogenic strains of *E. coli*.

Prelab Activity Valencia has a painful throat infection. Even after taking an antibiotic for ten days, she still has a sore throat. Her doctor used a long cotton swab to collect a sample of bacteria from her throat. In the lab, technicians streaked the swab across an agar plate to produce a culture called a *bacterial lawn*. Disease-causing *Streptococcus* bacteria thrived on the agar plates. Since the first antibiotic treatment was not successful, the lab technician did a sensitivity test to determine which antibiotic would be most effective in curing Valencia's infection. The lab technician tested three different antibiotics. Study the results of the test below to determine the effectiveness of the antibiotics labeled "A," "B," and "C" against the *Streptococcus* bacteria.

Some diseases caused by Gram-negative bacteria with which students may be familiar are salmonella (*Salmonella enteritidis*), cholera (*Vibrio cholerae*), and black plague (*Yersinia pestis*). Some diseases caused by Gram-positive bacteria with which students may be familiar are anthrax (*Bacillus anthracis*), tetanus (*Clostridium tetani*), and botulism (*Clostridium botulinum*).

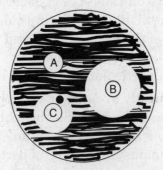

Antibiotic sensitivity test on bacterial lawn produced from Valencia's throat culture

Prelab Questions

1. Which antibiotic (A, B, or C) do you think would be most effective in treating Valencia's throat infection? Explain.

Suggested answer: Antibiotic B would be the most effective. While bacteria continue to live and

grow right up to Antibiotic A, and close to Antibiotic C, no bacteria survive near Antibiotic B.

2. Notice the small cluster of bacteria near Antibiotic C. Explain a reason why these bacteria grow where other bacteria do not.

Suggested answer: The small cluster of bacteria growing near Antibiotic C most likely consists of

bacteria with a gene that makes them resistant to this antibiotic.

Materials

- 2 agar plates
- labels or masking tape
- marker
- 2 cultures of bacteria
- 2 plastic inoculating loops
- plastic cup for biohazard waste containing 10% bleach solution
- antibiotic disks
- forceps or toothpicks
- metric ruler

Alternate Materials
- If you use small petri dishes you will not need as much agar.

- You can use a heating pad on its lowest setting instead of a bacterial incubator. Place subculture plates upside down to prevent condensation. However, once the antibiotic disks are placed on the agar you cannot keep the plates upside down. Instead, prevent condensation by placing the plates under the heating pad. Once you have used a heating pad as a bacterial incubator, do not use it at home.

IMPORTANT: *Although you will be working with nonpathogenic (non-disease-causing) bacterial cultures, it is always important to use sterile techniques when working with any bacteria to avoid contaminating your culture with other bacteria commonly found in the environment. In general, anything that will come into direct contact with the bacteria, such as the tips of the inoculating loops, should not touch any laboratory surfaces or your skin. Carefully follow all instructions regarding proper handling and disposal of materials used in this investigation.*

Procedure

Part A: Making the Bacterial Lawn

1. Label each agar plate with the name of one of the bacteria you will be testing.

2. Gently use the loop to gather the bacteria from the surface of the first culture. Do not dig the inoculating loop into the agar. Gather enough bacteria on the loop so that you can see a clump.

3. Streak the bacteria over the entire surface of the appropriately labeled sterile agar plate. Do not dig the loop into the agar. Be sure to spread the bacteria in all directions across the entire surface of the agar.

4. Place this loop in the plastic cup for biohazard waste.

5. Repeat steps 2–4 for the second bacterial culture.

Part B: Placing the Antibiotic Disks on the Bacterial Lawn

1. You will place one of each type of antibiotic disk on the agar plates. **CAUTION:** *Do not touch the antibiotic disks with your hands.* The disks should not touch each other, nor should they touch the sides of the agar plate. Once the disks are placed on the agar, they cannot be moved. Use forceps to place the first disk directly on the agar. If the disk is contained in a dispenser, dispense the disk onto the inside lid of the petri dish first, then grasp it with forceps and place it on the agar. Cover the petri dish with its lid.

2. Repeat Step 1 with the other streaked bacterial culture.

3. According to your teacher's instructions, incubate the cultures overnight at 37°C or at room temperature for 2–3 days.

Part C: Observing the Agar Plates

1. Observe the milky film of bacteria on the surface of the plates and the area along the edge of the antibiotic disks.

Advance Preparation
For instructions to prepare agar plates and cultures see the end of this lab.

Safety and Disposal
Ask students to notify you of allergies to penicillin or tetracycline. Warn students not to touch the antibiotic disks with their hands. Remind them to wash their hands with soap after handling the bacterial cultures. Forceps can be stored for reuse and loops can be thrown away after being sterilized in the 10% bleach solution or in a 70% alcohol solution. To kill the bacteria before disposal, flood the plates with a 10% bleach solution for 1 hour or place the plates in a biohazard bag and autoclave for 30 min. Dispose of the plastic dishes with the bacterial cultures.

2. Measure the diameter in mm of any clear zones around the antibiotic disks. Record your data in the table below.

Data Table

Name of Bacteria	Type of Antibiotic	Diameter of Clear Zone (mm)

Analysis and Conclusions

1. Why was it important to place the disks on the agar plates so that they did not touch each other?

Suggested answer: If the disks were placed so close together that they touched, it would be difficult

to tell which antibiotic was effective against the bacteria.

2. Which bacteria were sensitive to which antibiotics? Explain.

Students' responses will vary based on the antibiotics and bacteria used in the lab.

3. From your results, can you determine which bacteria are Gram-positive and which are Gram-negative? Explain.

Students' responses will vary based on the antibiotics and bacteria used in the lab. However, for

most there will be a clear zone around the penicillin disk on the agar plate containing the Gram-positive

bacteria, but there will not be a clear zone (or there will be a much smaller clear zone) on the plate con-

taining the Gram-negative bacteria.

4. Is there any evidence of antibiotic-resistant bacteria on your agar plates? Explain.

Students' responses will vary based on their results. On some agar plates, there may be small clusters

of bacteria growing in otherwise clear zones. In this case, students should reply that these bacteria

must be resistant to the antibiotic.

Name _____ Class _____ Date _____

Extension

To observe the two types of bacteria under a microscope, make a wet mount by streaking a small amount of bacteria on a slide with an inoculating loop, adding a drop of water, and placing a cover slip over the sample. Place a fine thread under the cover slip to help you focus. You won't see the bacteria at all on low power, so focus on the thread, then switch to medium power. Be sure to adjust the lighting on the microscope in order to see the bacteria. Follow the instructions in a Gram stain kit to do a Gram stain of the two different types of bacterial cultures. (See pages 362–363 in your textbook for an explanation of the Gram staining technique.) Sketch the two types of bacteria using colored pencils.

Advance Preparation

2–3 days before the lab
Prepare two agar plates for each lab group, plus several extra for subcultures for each class.

The easiest way to prepare agar is to obtain sterile, bottled Luria or nutrient agar. Remove the lid and melt the agar in a boiling water bath or in a microwave on low power. Watch the agar to make sure it does not boil over. Once it boils, allow it to cool so that you can comfortably hold the bottle in your hand. If you pour the agar when it is too hot, air will be drawn in and the samples could be contaminated.

You can purchase irradiated, sterile powdered agar from companies such as Bio-Rad. Then add bottled water and melt the agar. Or, prepare sterile agar yourself with a pressure cooker. Mix the agar according to the directions. Fill beakers half-full with agar. Cover with foil. Place beakers in a pressure cooker and add water (about 1.5 cm deep). Secure the lid and heat on high until the pressure valve jiggles. Lower the heat, but allow the valve cover to jiggle for about 15 min. Turn off the heat and allow the cooker to cool. Do not cool it off with cold water or release the pressure.

Store the agar plates upside down at room temperature. Do not store them in the refrigerator.

The day before the lab
Streak actively growing bacteria onto several agar plates for each class.

Extension
Gram staining is used to distinguish bacteria based on the structure of their cell wall. Gram-negative bacteria have a thin peptidoglycan cell wall and an additional lipopolysaccharide layer. Gram-positive bacteria have only a thicker peptidoglycan cell wall. When treated with crystal violet stain and iodine, both types of bacteria turn purple as the peptidoglycan layers are stained. However, because the peptidoglycan layer is so thin in Gram-negative bacteria, the stain can be washed away. When a dark pink stain is then applied, it binds to the Gram-negative bacteria. In the end, Gram-positive bacteria remain purple, while Gram-negative bacteria become pink.

Protists Feast on Yeast

Observing Feeding in Paramecia

Question How do protists such as *Paramecium* eat?

Lab Overview In this investigation you will add dyed yeast to a culture of paramecia, then observe how the paramecia eat the yeast.

Introduction To begin the investigation you will read information about how *Paramecium* consume and digest their food. Then you will use this information and a few simple objects to build a model demonstrating how *Paramecium* feed.

Background Paramecia are unicellular organisms covered with cilia, which function in feeding and locomotion (moving from one place to another). An indentation along one side of the cell, the oral groove, is lined with cilia that sweep food into the cell. The end of the groove is sometimes called a gullet. The cell's plasma membrane bulges inward and pinches off a sac containing food, called a food vacuole. Food vacuoles merge with lysosomes (sacs containing digestive enzymes) and circulate throughout the cell. As the food is digested, nutrients diffuse from the vacuole into the cell. Later, undigested contents are released from the paramecium through a hole called the anal pore.

Objective to observe feeding in *Paramecium*, specifically the formation of food vacuoles and the action of cilia

Time
• 20 min for the Prelab Activity
• 15–20 min for Part A
• 20 min for Part B
• 20 min for Analysis and Conclusions

Inquiry Skills
• observing
• predicting
• asking questions
• drawing conclusions

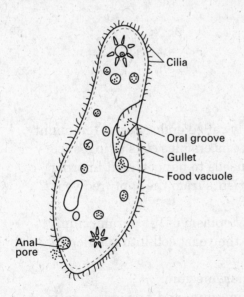

Paramecium

In this lab you will watch paramecia feed on yeast (a unicellular fungus). The yeast cells are dyed red so that you can see them enter the paramecia. As the yeast cells are digested in the vacuoles, the acidic environment of the vacuole will cause the red dye to turn blue.

Prelab Activity Do the following mini-activity, and then answer the Prelab Questions.

Membrane Model

Design a model showing how paramecia ingest food using the following materials.
- plastic grocery bag (paramecium)
- 4 small objects (yeast cells)
- rubber band

While designing your model keep the following rules in mind:
- The objects cannot enter through the opening of the bag.
- You can insert your hands into the opening of the bag to manipulate the "paramecium."
- The inside of the bag cannot come in contact with the outside environment.
- The objects should enter the bag at the same time.

Sketch or describe your model in the space below.

Objects you can use to represent the yeast cells are beads, macaroni, or wrapped candy. With a hand inside of the bag, a student should grab the small objects outside of the bag and pull them inward. As they do so, an open-ended "vacuole" will form. Students should use the rubber band to close off the vacuole inside the bag. Now the "yeast" is within the "paramecium," but not in direct contact with the interior of the protist cell.

Prelab Questions

1. The method you modeled is actually called endocytosis. You might recall from Chapter 6 that endocytosis enables cells to ingest certain particles. What do you think needs to happen next in order for the paramecium to get the nutrients from the captured yeast? Explain your choice.
   a. The yeast is released into the cytoplasm of the paramecium.
   b. Digestive enzymes break apart the yeast cell into smaller molecules the paramecium can use.
   c. The yeast is pushed out of the paramecium.
   d. The yeast grows inside the paramecium and provides it with nutrients.

   Suggested answer: b. Lysosomes merge with food vacuoles and expose the yeast to enzymes that
   digest the yeast cells into smaller particles that the paramecium can use.

2. When the food vacuoles turn blue, what does this indicate?

Suggested answer: Lysosomes have released acids that have caused the red dye to turn blue.

_____

_____

Materials

- *Paramecium* culture
- transfer pipette
- well slide with cover slip
- toothpick
- yeast paste (dyed with Congo red)
- microscope
- colored pencils

Small cotton fibers can be placed on the slides to help slow down the paramecia.

Procedure

Part A: Observing Ingestion of Yeast

1. Use a transfer pipette to draw up a small amount of the *Paramecium* culture. Be sure to draw up some of the sediment at the bottom of the dish, where most of the paramecia are found.

2. Place 2 drops of the *Paramecium* culture in the indentation of the well slide.

3. Use the point of a toothpick to pick up a tiny speck of the dyed yeast paste. Use the toothpick to swirl the speck of yeast paste into the drop of *Paramecium* culture on the slide.

4. Place the cover slip over the well and put the slide on the microscope stage.

5. Focus on low power first. Adjust the lighting as needed to see the paramecia. Move the slide around to find one or two paramecia that are trapped in yeast paste.

6. Switch to medium power (100×). You can do most of your observations at medium power. If the paramecia you are observing are not moving around much, you can switch to high power to observe more details.

Advance Preparation

Two weeks before the lab
Order *Paramecium multimicronucleatum* or *Paramecium caudatum*, Congo red, and guar gum from a biological supply company.

If you would like to grow a larger *Paramecium* culture from a smaller purchased culture:
1. Add 10–15 grains of boiled wheat to 200 mL of bottled water.
2. Inoculate with 20 mL of *Paramecium* culture.
3. Grow for 7–12 days.

See the end of this lab for instructions to prepare the yeast paste.

Alternate Materials
If you don't have depression slides, use a roll-on lip applicator and apply a thin rope of petroleum jelly around the edge of the cover slips. After the students place a drop or two of the culture on a micrscope slide, they can gently drop the petroleum jelly side of the cover slip over the drops. This creates a chamber that is sealed and deep enough so it won't dry out.

Safety and Disposal
Remind students to wear safety goggles, gloves, and an apron when handling the dyed yeast paste. Tell students to handle the microscope and slides with care. Ask students to notify you of any broken glass and not to touch it. If the microscopes have lamps, review electrical safety rules and make sure that power cords are out of the way of foot traffic and water. Tell students to wash their hands thoroughly with soap after the lab. Used slides can be washed and reused.

7. Observe the yeast cells. How is the movement of the paramecium's cilia affecting them? Record your observations below.

Observations

_____

_____

_____

8. Look for red spots of dyed yeast inside a paramecium. Does the paramecium ingest the yeast one at a time or several at a time? Write your observations in the space provided.

Observations

Students will most likely observe that several yeast cells are ingested at the

same time.

_____

Part B: Observing Digestion of Yeast

1. Turn off the microscope light. Wait 5–10 min for the digestive enzymes to start to digest the yeast.

2. Look again for a paramecium that is stuck in the yeast paste. Look for any vacuoles in the cell that have turned blue. Draw a sketch of the paramecium using different colored pencils to distinguish the red yeast cells and blue vacuoles. Label the sketch appropriately.

Sketch

Expected Results
Students may not see the food vacuoles forming, but they should see red yeast cells being gathered in the oral groove. They will also soon see food vacuoles with clusters of yeast inside. After 10 min, some of the food vacuoles should have turned blue. If they have not, mix several mL of paramecia culture with some Congo-red-dyed yeast paste in a small plastic cup and leave them overnight. The next day, students can make slides of the mixture and view the blue food vacuoles.

Analysis and Conclusions

1. Describe how paramecia ingest and digest food.

Suggested answer: The paramecia gathered the yeast into the oral groove with their cilia. The yeast

cells appeared in red clusters inside the food vacuole. After about 10 minutes, the food vacuoles moved

through the paramecia and the reddish clusters of yeast cells turned blue.

2. Based on the action of the digestive enzymes in lysosomes, why do you think it is important that digestion take place within food vacuoles?

Suggested answer: The vacuoles separate the digestive enzymes from the rest of the cell. Otherwise,

the cell would digest itself.

3. Why did you focus on paramecia that were stuck in yeast paste? If you did not find any stuck in the paste, how did that affect your investigation?

Sample answer: I focused on the paramecia stuck in the paste because the others moved so fast and

so often they were too difficult to observe. If I didn't find one stuck in the paste, I would not have been

able to draw accurate sketches.

Extension

Not all protozoans ingest food in the same way as *Paramecium*. If your teacher makes available a culture of a protist that feeds on *Paramecium* you can compare the feeding method of this protist and the method of *Paramecium*. Place one drop of a *Paramecium* culture and one drop of the predator culture on a well slide. Place a cover slip on top. View the slide through a microscope and focus on low power. Once you have found paramecia and a predator in the same field of view, switch to medium power and observe what happens. Draw detailed sketches of your observations.

Extension
Organisms such as *Chaos* or *Didinium* commonly prey on *Paramecium*.

Resources
Anderson, R. O., and M. Druger. *Explore the World Using Protozoa.* National Science Teacher's Foundation, 1997.

Rainis, K. G., and B. J. Russell. *Guide to Microlife.* Orchard Books, 1997.

Prelab Activity based on:

Westover, Glenn. "The Jelly Bean Problem." Access Excellence, www.accessexcellence.org.

One week or less before the lab
Prepare the yeast paste:
  Put 1 envelope (7 g) of baker's yeast in 100 mL warm water (around 35°C). Add a couple of pinches (1/2 tsp) of sugar. Allow the yeast to incubate in the warm water for about 20 min. Pipette out 20 mL of the yeast into a small beaker and add 0.1 g Congo red. Heat in a microwave on 10% power for 3 min.
  The heating will cause the stain to penetrate the yeast. Washing the stained yeast with water is optional but recommended. If you do *not* wash the cells, this is the time to add about 1/8 tsp (a pinch or two) of guar gum to 1 mL of the stained yeast. This will make a paste. You can store this paste for a week or two. If you wash the cells, add the guar gum after washing.
  To wash the cells, follow the directions below to centrifuge the cells into a pellet and re-suspend them in water. You may have to wash the cells a few times.
  Clinical centrifuges: Put 2 mL of yeast solution in a 10 mL tube. Spin for 5 min. Discard supernatant (fluid). Re-suspend the pellet in 5 mL water.
  Microcentrifuge: Put 0.5 mL of yeast solution in a microcentrifuge tube and spin 1 min. Re-suspend in 1 mL of water.

Fishing for Protists

Sampling the Diversity of Protists

Questions What types of protists can be found in an aquatic ecosystem? How do the protists living near the surface of the water differ from those living near the bottom?

Lab Overview In this investigation you will collect aquatic protists by suspending sponges in a local body of water or an aquarium. After 2–3 days, you will retrieve the sponges and examine the collected protists in the laboratory with a microscope.

Introduction The microscopic world of protists includes incredible diversity. Protists differ not only in their shapes, structures, and sizes, but also in their habitats, motility, nutrition, and reproduction. During this lab, you will witness within a drop of water the variety and intricacy of organisms that cannot be seen with the unaided eye.

Prelab Activity A biologist collected protists from the bottom and the water surface of a pond. After viewing the protist samples through a microscope, the biologist made the sketches shown below. Use the photographs and diagrams in Chapter 17 of your textbook to help you identify these protists. Write the name of each protist in the space provided. Then, answer the Prelab Questions.

Objective to observe the characteristics and diversity of protists in two aquatic environments

Inquiry Skills
• observing
• classifying
• making inferences
• organizing data
• drawing conclusions

Time
• 15 min for Prelab Activity
• 20 min for Part A (once the destination is reached if taking a class trip to collect samples)
• 20 min for Part B (36–72 hours after Part A)
• 30 min for Part C
• 15 min for Analysis and Conclusions

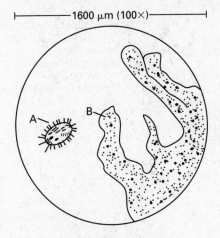

Slide 1 (pond bottom)

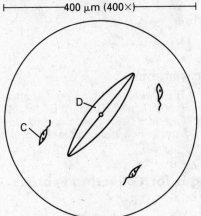

Slide 2 (pond surface)

Protist A: *Stylononychia*

Protist B: Amoeba

Protist C: Euglena

Protist D: Diatom

Prelab Questions

1. Based on your knowledge of how most autotrophs produce their food, predict which of these protist samples (1 or 2) is more likely to include autotrophs. Explain your prediction.

Suggested answer: The protists in Slide 2 are more likely to be autotrophs. Autotrophs would be

more likely to inhabit the surface of water where they would have access to sunlight for

photosynthesis.

2. Besides nutrition, what is another factor that could influence the habitat in which a protist lives?

Students' responses will vary.

3. Based on the biologist's sketches, list some characteristics that vary among these protists. What other differences would you look for if you were examining these protists under a microscope?

Sample answer: Locomotion and feeding methods differ among the examples in the sketches. Under

the microscope, I would look for color that cannot be seen in this sketch. Protists that contain green

coloring are most likely autotrophs.

Materials

- 2 sponge pieces (each about 2.5 cm^2)
- string
- scissors
- large metal washer
- 2 plastic containers with lids
- permanent marker
- 2 transfer pipettes
- 2 microscope slides with cover slips
- microscope
- colored pencils
- protist identification key

You can purchase cheap, cellulose kitchen sponges. However, do not use sponges containing any antimicrobial chemicals. These chemicals can kill organisms in an aquarium or a pond.

The Guide to Microlife by Kenneth Rainis and Bruce Russell (Orchard Books, 1997) offers excellent descriptions and photos of protists from which you can make a protist key.

Advance Preparation

A couple of weeks before the lab

- Decide on a plan for gathering the protists. You may want to organize a class trip, have several students collect protists from home freshwater aquaria, or collect the samples yourself. Samples should not be collected from private property without consent of the owner or from nature reserves or public water supplies.
- Gather plastic margarine or yogurt containers and lids.

Procedure

Part A: Preparing the Sponges for Collecting Protists

1. As directed by your teacher, decide on an aquatic ecosystem from which to gather protists. In the space provided on the next page describe your observations of the aquatic ecosystem.

Name _____ Class _____ Date_____

Observations:

_____

_____

Safety and Disposal
Do not allow students to go alone to set up or collect the sponges. Sponges tend to contain a high concentration of microorganisms, some of which may be harmful if ingested. Students should wash their hands thoroughly after handling the samples. You could have students return the water containing protists to the body of water from which they took their samples. However, they should not return this water to an aquarium. Pour bleach into the containers with the sponges before disposing of everything in the trash. Do not allow the trash to remain in the building overnight.

To secure the sponges in an aquarium, tape the free end of the string to the side of the aquarium.
To secure the sponges in a lake, pond, or marsh either use a pushpin to attach the free end of the sponge to a dock or pier, or securely tie the free end of the string around a rock.

2. Thread the end of the string around the washer several times and tie a knot to hold the string in place. Tightly tie the end of the string with the washer around a sponge. You will use this sponge to collect protists from the bottom of the ecosystem. The weight of the washer will cause the sponge to sink.

3. Tightly tie another piece of string around the second sponge. You will use this sponge to collect protists from the surface of the water.

4. Place the sponges in water as directed by your teacher. Leave the sponges in the water for 36–72 hours. Protists will collect on the surface of the sponges.

Part B: Gathering the Protists

1. With a permanent marker, label one plastic container "Surface." Label the other plastic container "Bottom." Take these containers and their lids with you to retrieve the sponges.

2. After retrieving the sponges, place each sponge with its string attached into the appropriately labeled container. Be careful not to squeeze the sponges. Place the lids on the containers. Wash your hands thoroughly after collecting the sponges.

3. Store the samples at room temperature until you are ready to observe them. Do not place the samples in a refrigerator or leave them in a warm car—many protists cannot survive such temperature changes.

Part C: Observing the Protists

1. In the laboratory, label one microscope slide "Surface" and the other microscope slide "Bottom."

2. Squeeze the water from each sponge into its container. Use a transfer pipette to place a drop of water squeezed from the "Surface" sponge onto the appropriately labeled slide. Cover the drop of water with a cover slip. Adjust the amount of light as needed.

3. Using a new transfer pipette, repeat Step 2 for the sample labeled "Bottom." Cover the water drop with a cover slip.

4. With a microscope, observe the "Surface" slide under low, medium, and high power. Make sure to move the slide around the stage to survey the entire area under the cover slip. Adjust the amount of light as needed.

Student samples also may contain micro-animals and plant debris. Give students hints to distinguish between these organisms and protists. Remind them that protists do not have appendages or specialized organs, such as a heart.

5. In Data Table 1 below, describe and sketch the protists you observe on the "Surface" slide. In your descriptions, note specific characteristics, such as method of locomotion (cilia, flagella, pseudopodia), color, shape, etc. Use a protist key to identify the different types of protists you observe. If you are unable to identify a protist, note that in the table.

Adding a drop of protist-slowing solution to the slide before placing the cover slip on it may help students with their observations.

Data Table 1: "Surface" Sample

Sketch	Description	Identification
	Has flagella for locomotion. It is long and green and can change shape.	*Euglena*
	No motility. A single chain of cells containing spiral chloroplasts	*Spirogyra*
	No motility. Jewel-box-like cells with intricate shapes	diatoms
	Cilia for locomotion. Oval-shaped; fast moving; bounces off objects	paramecium

6. Observe the "Bottom" slide under low, medium, and high power.

7. In Data Table 2 below, describe and sketch the protists you observe on the "Bottom" slide. If you are unable to identify a protist, note that in the table.

Data Table 2: "Bottom" Sample

Sketch	Description	Identification
	Pseudopodia for locomotion. Blob-like, oozes and changes shape slowly	amoeba
	No motility. Little springs with swirling green cups	*Vorticella*
	Cilia for locomotion. A large protist with a ribbon of cilia	*Stentor*

Analysis and Conclusions

1. Which sample contained a higher concentration of protists? Which sample contained a higher diversity of protists? Compare your answers to those of other lab groups. Do you observe any patterns? Explain.

Students will most likely observe that the sample collected from the bottom of the aquatic ecosystem

contained a higher concentration of protists, and the population was more diverse than the

"Surface" sample. Other responses will vary based on class results.

2. Did the protists living on the surface of the water share any of the same characteristics? Explain.

Students' responses will vary.

3. Did the protists living on the bottom share any of the same characteristics? Explain.

Students' responses will vary.

4. Describe any organisms or parts of organisms that you identified as non-protist. Explain how you concluded that you were not observing a protist.

Students' responses will vary, but might include that the organisms had organs or appendages.

Extension

With permission from your teacher, use new sponges to collect protists from a different type of aquatic ecosystem. Compare the protist samples from the second aquatic ecosystem with the first samples that you collected. Suggest possible explanations for the similarities and differences.

Extension
Reinforce safety information. Remind students not to collect samples alone.

Name _____ Class _____ Date _____

A Twist on Fermentation

Studying the Rate of Yeast Growth in Dough

Question How does sugar concentration affect the rate of yeast fermentation?

Lab Overview In this investigation you will make small batches of yeast dough containing varying amounts of sugar. Then you will measure and compare the rates at which the batches of dough rise in small cylinders.

Background Yeasts are single-celled fungi. Some yeasts live on the surface of plants (especially fruit), others live on animal tissue, and others live in the soil. In this lab you will work with *Saccharomyces cerevisiae,* called "baker's yeast," which is used to raise bread dough.

Yeast cells require sugar as a source of energy. In the presence of oxygen, yeast cells perform cellular respiration. However, when they are surrounded by bread dough, yeast cells do not have access to oxygen. As shown in the diagram below, the yeast cells perform fermentation instead of cellular respiration, producing ethyl alcohol, carbon dioxide gas, and the energy-storing molecule ATP. As the yeast cells release carbon dioxide, the gas is trapped in the dough. Bubbles form in the dough and cause the dough to rise.

Objective to measure the effect of sugar concentration on yeast fermentation

Inquiry Skills
- predicting
- observing
- making measurements
- calculating
- analyzing data
- controlling variables
- drawing conclusions

Time
- 15 min for Prelab Activity
- 10 min for Part A
- 30–60 min for Part B (depending on time available)
- 15 min for Analysis and Conclusions

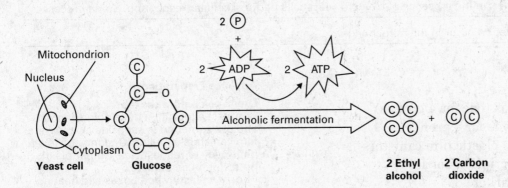

Prelab Activity In the lab you will measure the rate of fermentation by yeast in samples of bread dough containing different concentrations of sugar. You will place the dough samples into five small canisters and mark the initial levels of the dough. You will place the canisters in an "incubator" to warm the dough. (The heat from the incubator increases the reaction time of fermentation enzymes.) Then you will mark the levels to which the dough rises every 5 minutes. Complete the Prelab Activity, and then answer the questions.

Measuring the rate of the dough rising is an indirect way to measure the carbon dioxide production and thereby measure the rate of fermentation. Because the results in this lab are consistently linear (a rare characteristic in biology labs), the lab is an excellent exercise for students to practice gathering and graphing quantitative data.

Make a Prediction

Based on what you have read in the Background and Prelab, predict what will happen to dough samples containing varying concentrations of sugar. Do you think the dough will rise the fastest in the sample with the highest, the lowest, or a moderate concentration of sugar? Explain your prediction.

Prediction:

_____

_____

Prelab Questions

1. Based on the diagram of the yeast cell on the previous page, list two ways that these single-celled fungi are different from bacterial cells.

Suggested answer: Yeast cells have a membrane-bound nucleus and mitochondria, while

bacteria do not.

2. How do yeast cells benefit from fermentation?

Suggested answer: Fermentation generates ATP, which stores energy needed for cellular processes.

3. Since fermentation occurs in the cytoplasm of yeast cells, explain the role of mitochondria in yeast cells.

Suggested answer: In the presence of oxygen, yeast cells perform cellular respiration. Some processes

of cellular respiration occur in the mitochondria.

Materials

- plastic shoe box (one for 4 groups)
- heating pad (one for 4 groups)
- 5 clear (white) plastic film canisters or empty prescription bottles
- permanent marker
- masking tape
- dough   See end of lab for recipe.
- 1 g granulated sugar
- laboratory balance
- food coloring
- clock or watch
- metric ruler

Advance Preparation

One week before the lab
- Contact a local film developing center and ask someone to set aside clear (white) film canisters with lids. Or contact a local pharmacy to request clear amber plastic prescription containers.
- Borrow plastic shoe boxes and heating pads.

The day of the lab
Make the dough (see the end of this lab for the recipe). Make the dough right before the class or refrigerate until 2 hrs before class so that the dough is at room temperature for the lab. If the dough is cold, fermentation rates will be too slow.

Procedure

Part A: Setting up the Incubator and Preparing Dough Samples

1. To set up the incubator, turn on the heating pad to medium. Place the shoe box upside down on top of the heating pad.

2. With masking tape and a permanent marker, label each canister with one of the following labels: $1\times$, $\frac{1}{2}\times$, $\frac{1}{4}\times$, $\frac{1}{8}\times$, and 0. These labels indicate the approximate concentration of sugar in the dough of each canister compared to the $1\times$ container. For example, the canister labeled $\frac{1}{2}\times$ will contain dough with approximately $\frac{1}{2}$ the sugar concentration of the dough in the canister labeled $1\times$, and so on.

3. The diameter of the starting ball of dough should be about 6 cm. Divide this ball into 5 balls—four of equal size and one that is twice as big as the other four (see the diagram below).

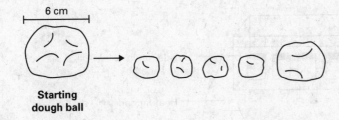

Starting dough ball

4. Use a laboratory balance to measure 1 g of sugar.

5. Mix 1 g of sugar into the large ball with your fingers. Divide this ball in half. Put one of the halves in the canister labeled "$1\times$." Use the diagram at right for guidance.

6. Combine a small ball from Step 3 with the leftover dough from Step 5 to make a ball with half the sugar concentration of the $1\times$ ball. Split this ball in half. Place one half in the canister labeled "$\frac{1}{2}\times$."

7. Combine another small ball from Step 3 with the leftover dough from Step 6 to make a ball with half the sugar concentration of the $\frac{1}{2}\times$ ball. Split this ball in half. Place one half in the canister labeled "$\frac{1}{4}\times$."

8. Combine another small ball from Step 3 with the leftover dough from Step 7 to make a ball with half the sugar concentration of the $\frac{1}{4}\times$ ball. Split this ball in half. Place one half in the canister labeled "$\frac{1}{8}\times$." Discard the leftover dough.

Safety and Disposal
Ask students to notify you of wheat allergies. Review electrical safety rules, and make sure that all power cords are out of the way of foot traffic. Have students wash their hands with soap after the lab. Film canisters can be placed in a bucket with bleach, then rinsed and air-dried for reuse. Dough can be baked to kill the yeast, then thrown in the trash. Remind students not to taste the dough.

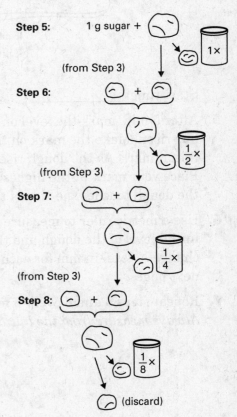

Step 5: 1 g sugar + (from Step 3) → $1\times$

Step 6: ∩ + ∩ (from Step 3) → $\frac{1}{2}\times$

Step 7: ∩ + ∩ (from Step 3) → $\frac{1}{4}\times$

Step 8: ∩ + ∩ → $\frac{1}{8}\times$ → (discard)

9. Place the remaining small ball from Step 3 in the canister labeled "0."

Part B: Testing Rates of Yeast Fermentation

1. Press down the dough ball in each canister so that the dough surface is relatively flat.

2. Place a drop of food coloring against the inside edge of each canister to help measure the dough level.

3. Use a permanent marker to mark the initial level of the dough on the outside of each canister.

4. Loosely place a lid on each canister. Place the five canisters in the "incubator," as shown in the diagram below. (**NOTE:** *The canisters should rest directly on the heating pad with the shoe box placed upside down over them.*) Record the start time below.

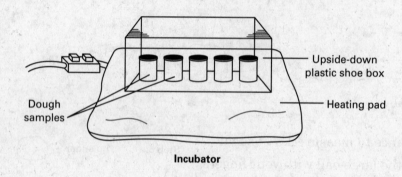

Incubator

Start time: _____

5. After 5 min, mark the level on each canister to which the dough has risen. Make the mark on the same side of the canister as the initial mark. As the dough rises it will form a rounded shape. Place your mark at the highest point of the colored dough where the dough touches the side of the canister.

6. Use a metric ruler to measure the distance (in mm) between the initial level of the dough and the level at 5 min. Record the change in level in mm for each canister in Data Table 1 on the next page.

7. Repeat steps 5 and 6 every 5 min for the next 30 min. (**NOTE:** *Always measure from the initial mark to the most recent mark.*)

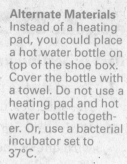

Alternate Materials
Instead of a heating pad, you could place a hot water bottle on top of the shoe box. Cover the bottle with a towel. Do not use a heating pad and hot water bottle together. Or, use a bacterial incubator set to 37°C.

To obtain consistent data, students should always mark the highest point where the dough touches the side of the canister (not the highest point of the dough surface).

Name _____ Class _____ Date _____

Data Table 1

Time	Change in Level of Dough from Initial Level (mm)				
	"0" Canister	"1/8×" Canister	"1/4×" Canister	"1/2×" Canister	"1×" Canister
5 min					
10 min					
15 min					
20 min					
25 min					
30 min					
35 min					

8. Plot 5 line graphs on the same grid. The *y*-axis of your graph should represent change in dough level (in mm) and the *x*-axis should represent time (in min). Be sure to label the different graph lines and axes, and title your graph.

Expected Results
The dough in the "0" canister will rise very slowly (some fermentation will occur because flour mixtures do contain some traces of sugar). Lower concentrations of sugar cause the most rapid rate of fermentation. At high sugar concentrations, the fermentation rate decreases probably because one or both of the following occurs: the high sugar concentration is hyperosmotic, which could cause the yeast to lose water and fail to thrive; the high sugar concentration could change the dough so that it no longer traps the carbon dioxide as effectively.

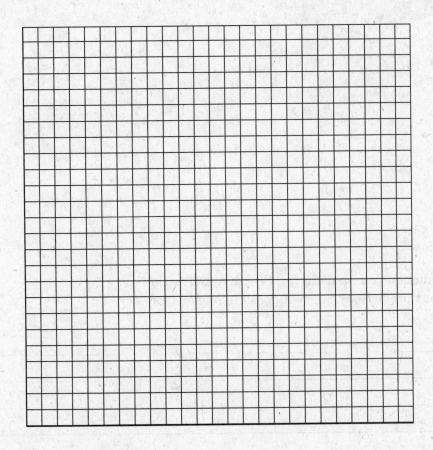

Analysis and Conclusions

1. Explain what the rising dough indicates.

The rising dough indicates that the yeast cells in the dough are performing fermentation. Carbon
dioxide is released during fermentation. The air bubbles become trapped in the dough, causing it
to rise.

2. The rate at which dough rises is calculated by dividing the distance the dough rises by the time period (mm/min). Calculate the *initial* rate of rising of each dough sample (the initial rate is the rate for the first 5 min).

3. Look back at the prediction you made in the Prelab Activity. Do your data support your prediction? Suggest possible reasons for any differences.

Students' answers will vary based on their predictions and data.

4. If you doubled the concentration of yeast in the dough, how do you think your results might change? Explain.

Sample answer: At first, the dough will rise twice as fast since twice as much carbon dioxide would

be released.

_____

5. Share data with two other lab groups. Do your data differ from the other groups? Suggest possible reasons for any differences.

Student responses will vary, but could include that dough balls were not separated the same, the

concentration of sugar among the different samples could have varied, or heating pads may differ in

temperature output.

_____

Extension

Do the experiment again, but change a different variable. For example, you could study the effect of temperature on the activity of the yeast, or the effect of adding different amounts of salt to the dough. Think of a question you would like to study, write a hypothesis, and design an experiment to test it. (**NOTE:** *Always check with your teacher before carrying out any experiments.*)

Dough recipe (15 groups)
(**NOTE:** *This requires a very large bowl.*)
1. Dissolve 2 packages of rapid-rising yeast in 2/3 cup warm water.
2. Use a large spoon to mix 6 cups flour with 2 cups water.
3. Add yeast solution and mix thoroughly.
4. Turn out onto a floured surface and knead for 5 min.
5. If necessary, add more flour or water to make a smooth ball of dough.

Extension
Review students' experimental designs for safety concerns. Fermentation rates should increase when the dough is warm. Small amounts of salt may stimulate yeast cells, but too much salt will inhibit fermentation.

Fungi Farming

Determining Optimal Conditions for Mushrooms

Question What amount of light will produce the fastest fungal growth and most appealing mushrooms?

Lab Overview In this investigation you will take on the role of a mycologist (a scientist who studies fungi) working for a company that grows and sells edible mushrooms. One of your jobs is to determine the amount of light that is ideal to grow the largest number of appealing mushrooms in the shortest time.

Introduction The fungus you will study in this investigation is in the phylum of fungi called Basidiomycota, commonly known as club fungi. Some club fungi are edible, including common white mushrooms, portabella mushrooms, shitake mushrooms, oyster mushrooms, and porcini mushrooms.

The "mushroom" part of a fungus that grows above ground is the fruiting body, the reproductive structure of the fungus. Spores are produced in the fruiting body. However, most of the cells of the fungus grow in the soil. The fungal cells that are in the soil or rotting wood grow in a network of fine, threadlike chains called hyphae. A mass of hyphae, called a mycelium, plays a key role in how a fungus obtains nutrients. The fungus secretes enzymes from its hyphae into the surrounding environment. The enzymes break down cellulose and other plant fibers, which are then absorbed through the hyphae. Under the right environmental conditions fruiting bodies grow from the hyphae. In this lab you will test how fruiting bodies develop in different lighting conditions. (Although club fungi do not perform photosynthesis, light may be needed for other reasons. For example, light may signal fungal cells that they are no longer underground.)

Fruiting bodies grow at different rates and look different under various growing conditions. The goal of your mushroom company is to grow the largest number of "appealing" mushrooms in the shortest amount of time. Your company's market research department has learned that mushrooms that are most appealing to shoppers are plump, tall, and have a uniform shape, rather than withered, small, and oddly shaped.

In the Prelab Activity on the next page, study an investigation performed by one of your colleagues at the mushroom company to test the optimal (ideal) amount of water for growing mushrooms. Then answer the Prelab Questions that follow.

Objective to observe fungal growth and determine optimal growing conditions

Inquiry Skills
• predicting
• observing
• collecting data
• making inferences
• controlling variables
• drawing conclusions

Time
• 15 min for Prelab Activity
• 15 min for initial set up; 5 min each class for 2–3 weeks for watering and observations; 20 min to gather data at the end of the lab
• 15 min for Analysis and Conclusions

Club fungi grow best in moist, cool conditions with moderate light. With the right amount of moisture, the fungi can grow either in the dark or in bright light, but the shape of the fruiting bodies and the rate of growth will vary. Most of the time, fruiting bodies will not grow if the fungus has not been exposed to light at all. Just opening a cabinet or box to make observations should provide the fungi with enough light.

Prelab Activity Another mycologist at the mushroom company performed an experiment to determine the amount of water required for optimal mushroom production—growing the largest number of appealing mushrooms in the shortest amount of time. The researcher supplied water to the fungi by misting them and grew the mushrooms at room temperature. Study the results of the experiment below. Then answer the Prelab Questions that follow.

Misted once every other day · Misted once a day · Misted twice a day

Prelab Questions

1. Based on the data above, how often do you think the growing fruiting bodies should be misted? Explain.

   Suggested answer: Twice a day. This amount of misting produced the most and plumpest mushrooms.

   (Students may also note that misting more often than twice a day might produce even better results.)

2. Misting by hand hundreds of fungi in their individual growing containers would be far too costly. Draw a rough sketch of an automated misting machine that would work in your mushroom growing facility. Describe how it would work.

   Students' responses will vary.

3. Besides water, what else do you think fungi need to grow fruiting bodies? Explain.

Suggested answer: Moderate temperature, light, and nutrients to enable the fungi to carry out their

life processes.

See the end of this lab for **Alternate Methods**.

Materials

- mushroom growing kit
- spray bottle with water
- metric ruler

Advance Preparation

A couple of weeks before the lab
Order three mushroom growing modules. This lab was tested with inexpensive modules from Gourmet Mushrooms (www.gourmetmushroomsinc.com). Many biological supply companies also offer mushroom modules. See the front of this Laboratory Manual Teacher's Edition for supplier information.

Procedure

1. As directed by your teacher, follow the instructions included with your mushroom growing kit to set up the fungal growing module.

2. Predict which of the following lighting conditions will yield the greatest number of appealing mushrooms in the shortest amount of time. (Review the Introduction for the qualities that customers consider appealing in mushrooms.)

- Darkness (inside a cupboard or box)

- Classroom light (away from windows)

- Direct light (sunny windowsill or fluorescent light bank)

Predictions:

_____

_____

_____

Safety and Disposal
Do not allow students to consume the mushrooms. Although the mushrooms produced from the Gourmet Mushrooms modules are edible, a laboratory is not an appropriate environment to grow food. Remind students to wash their hands after handling the modules. Mushrooms can be disposed of in the trash.

3. Place the growing module in one of the above conditions based on your teacher's instructions.

4. Each day, use the spray bottle to mist your growing module. Always be sure that the nozzle is set to "Spray." Spray the bottle four times at each "misting."

5. After about 10 days, you should see bumpy growths forming on the surface of the module. Inform your teacher when you notice the growths. Now the module needs two mistings a day.

6. Observe and count the developing fruiting bodies each day. Record your observations in Data Table 1 on the next page. Also measure the height of the tallest fruiting body each day, using a metric ruler. Record the height in Data Table 1.

Most mushroom growing kits arrive inoculated with spores. Once the growing medium is hydrated, the spores will germinate into hyphae. A mycelium will establish itself throughout the growing medium before forming a fruiting body. This takes 1–2 weeks. Once bumpy structures form on the surface of the growing medium, it is critical to mist the developing fruiting bodies twice daily. If the module is not kept moist, fruiting body growth will stop and the fruiting bodies will shrivel. Be sure to spray extra water on the fungi to last through weekends.

Data Table 1

Day	Number of Fruiting Bodies	Height of the Tallest Fruiting Body (cm)

7. The fruiting bodies will mature in about 4–6 days. You will know when they are mature when the "gills" underneath the mushroom cap are fully formed ridges. When they have matured, compare the number, size, shape, and color of the fruiting bodies in your growing module with those of the other lab groups. Record this information in Data Table 2 below.

Data Table 2

Lighting Condition	Number of Fruiting Bodies	Overall Description of Fruiting Bodies	Tallest Fruiting Body (cm)
Darkness			
Classroom light			
Direct light			

Analysis and Conclusions

1. Did fruiting bodies appear in all three lighting conditions?

Sample answer: Yes, fruiting bodies grew in all three lighting conditions.

2. Describe any differences in the shape, color, and height of the fruiting bodies among the different lighting conditions.

Students' responses will vary based on the type of fungi that were used in the lab.

_____

_____

3. Under which lighting conditions did the most fruiting bodies grow? Did these mushrooms also have the most appealing appearance? Explain.

Students' responses will vary based on the type of fungi that were used in the lab.

_____

_____

Extension

When the fruiting bodies have matured, you can observe the fungal spores by making "spore prints." First, remove the cap from a fruiting body and place it "gill" side down on a piece of black construction paper. Place the paper with the fruiting body in an area where it is unlikely to be disturbed. Cover it with a box to keep drafts from blowing away the spores. As the fruiting body dries, the spores will be released. You should be able to see the spores against the black background.

Extension
You may wish to have students view the spores under a microscope. Students can collect some spores with a damp toothpick and scrape the spores onto a microscope slide. Have students sketch their observations.

Additional Resource
Brennerman, J. A., and M. C. Guttman. "The Edibility and Cultivation of the Oyster Mushroom." *The American Biology Teacher* vol 56, no 5 (May 1994): 291–293.

Alternate Methods
• Rather than ordering several modules, you could grow one or two modules as a class demonstration. Students can make observations each day. Or, see the article referenced in the Additional Resource above, which explains how to make your own modules.
• If you do not have a windowsill in your classroom, you can use a fluorescent light bank. However, do not use incandescent lights, or the fruiting bodies will dry out.
• To maintain the moisture between mistings, a plastic tent should be placed over the modules. If the growing module you have purchased does not come with a tent, make tents from plastic bags. Poke small holes in the bags and place them over the growing modules.

Seeds, Spores, and Sperm

Comparing Fern and Angiosperm Life Cycles

Questions How do seeds, spores, and sperm differ in structure and function? Which types of plants have these structures, and what are they used for?

Lab Overview In this investigation you will compare seeds and spores, sow them, and observe the results. You will sketch your observations over several weeks to compare fern and angiosperm life cycles. After three weeks, you will observe swimming sperm produced by the fern gametophyte.

Introduction The fern spores you will sow in this lab will develop into two types of gametophytes (the gamete-producing plant generation): male gametophytes and hermaphrodite gametophytes. Male gametophytes produce sperm. Hermaphrodites (hur MAF roh dyts) are animals or plants that possess both male and female organs. Therefore, hermaphrodite gametophytes produce both sperm and eggs. After a fern sperm fertilizes an egg, the resulting zygote may grow into a sporophyte that is capable of producing more spores. In the lab you will also observe the behavior of sperm released from a fern gametophyte and the development of a fern sporophyte.

In contrast to the fern life cycle, angiosperms do not release their spores. Instead, gametophytes develop in the stamens and carpels of sporophyte flowers. Male gametophytes, or pollen grains, are carried away from the sporophyte by wind or animals. If pollen grains reach the carpels of another plant, a pollen tube and two sperm cells may develop. The pollen tube extends to the female gametophyte (the embryo sac) and deposits the two sperm cells into the embryo sac where they fertilize two cells. The result of this double fertilization is a seed containing an embryo, nourishing materials, and a protective coat. Under the right conditions, this seed will grow into a sporophyte. You will begin your investigation of the angiosperm life cycle at this point by sowing angiosperm seeds and observing their development into sporophytes.

Prelab Activity Based on the information you read in the Introduction section, on the next page develop a graphic organizer that describes the life cycle of a fern and a separate organizer that describes the life cycle of an angiosperm. Begin both life cycles at the "spore" stage.

Objective to observe fern and angiosperm life cycles and compare form and function in seeds, spores, and sperm

Inquiry Skills
• predicting
• observing
• classifying

Time
• 20–25 min for Prelab Activity
• 40 min for Part A (Day 1)
• 10–15 min every few days for Part B (Days 3–14)
• 20–30 min for Part C (Day 21)

C-ferns® (Ceratopteris) are water ferns that have a fast life cycle. The hermaphrodites produce a hormone that causes surrounding germinating spores to develop into male gametophytes, better ensuring cross-fertilization.

When the male sexual organs have matured after about three weeks, contact with water will cause sperm release. A chemical substance produced by the female sexual organs attracts the sperm to the egg. The fertilized egg will grow into the fern sporophyte.

Fast Plants™ are in the crucifer family. They have very quick life cycles. The seeds germinate in just 48 hours and flowers form in three weeks.

Life Cycle of a Fern Student organizers will vary.

Life Cycle of an Angiosperm Student organizers will vary.

Prelab Questions

1. The dominant generation of a plant is the generation that is the most prominent—the one that is most likely to be seen. Which generation—the gametophyte or sporophyte—is dominant in ferns? In angiosperms? Explain your response.

Suggested answer: In both angiosperms and ferns, the sporophyte generation is the dominant

generation. Fern gametophytes are tiny compared to mature sporophytes, and angiosperm

gametophytes are contained within flowers.

2. Describe one difference between spores and seeds.

Sample answer: Seeds grow into sporophytes, while spores grow into gametophytes.

3. Match the plant part with the letters that describe it. (*Hint:* Each plant part has two letters that describe it. Some letters will be used more than once. Refer to Chapter 19 in your text, if needed.)

c, e ____ Spore

b, d ____ Pollen

a, d ____ Seed

a. contains an embryonic sporophyte and stored food

b. contains two sperm nuclei and a structure that can grow into a pollen tube

c. contains a cell that can grow into a gametophyte

d. found only in angiosperms and gymnosperms

e. found in all plant life cycles

Name _____ Class _____ Date _____

Materials

- vial of *C-fern*® spores
- sterile water
- transfer pipette
- microscope slides and cover slips
- marker
- agar plate
- plastic spreader
- Fast Plant™ or radish seeds (5)
- growing container(s) filled with soil (10-cm-wide plastic pot or 2 plastic film canisters)
- vermiculite
- metric ruler
- plastic container
- water
- growing box
- colored pencils
- unlined white paper
- microscope
- well slide
- 2 toothpicks
- section of an apple
- plastic spoon

Procedure

Part A: Sowing Spores and Seeds, Day 1

1. Examine the vial of spores. The spores should look like specks of dark dust on the side or bottom of the vial. Compare the size of the spores to the size of the seeds.

2. Use a transfer pipette to add 1 mL of sterile water to the vial.

3. Use the same transfer pipette to place one drop of the spores suspended in water onto a microscope slide. Cover the slide with a cover slip and label it "Spores."

4. Mix the remaining spores in the vial by using the transfer pipette to gently draw them up and replace them in the vial several times. Then, use the pipette to add 1 drop of the liquid to the surface of the agar plate. Use the plastic spreader to gently spread the liquid over the top of the agar to distribute the spores. Do not dig into or press down on the agar as it is soft and will tear.

5. Next you will sow the seeds. Place 4 of the seeds about 1 cm apart from each other on top of the soil in the growing container. Cover the seeds with about 0.5 cm of vermiculite. Follow your teacher's instructions to water the soil.

Advance Preparation

A few days before the lab
Order *C-fern*® spores and growth medium from Carolina Biological. See the front of this Laboratory Manual Teacher's Edition for contact information. Order small petri dishes if needed for the growth media. Order the wild-type Fast Plant seeds from Carolina Biological or purchase radish or turnip seeds from a local retailer (radish and turnip plants take longer to flower than Fast Plants).

See the end of this lab for Fast Plant and *C-fern*® growing instructions.

One day before the lab
Melt and pour *C-fern*® growth medium.

Day of the lab
Have students complete Part A, Step 2, or rehydrate the spores just before the lab. Dry spores can be stored for up to a year. Once they are rehydrated they only survive a couple of days.

Safety and Disposal
Tell students to handle glassware with care. Remind students to wash their hands after handling soil. The growing box contains a fluorescent light source. Remind students about electrical shock hazard and to avoid spilling water. Ask students to notify you of broken bulbs. Tell students not to pick up broken glass or touch or inhale dust particles from the broken bulb. To clean plastic containers for reuse, soak in a 10% bleach solution for 20 min, rinse with water, and air-dry. Allow the agar plate to dry out before disposal of the *C-ferns*®.

6. Place both the agar plate with the spores and the growing container with the seeds under the light in the growing box as directed by your teacher.

7. Observe the slide labeled "Spores" under the microscope. Sketch the spores below.

8. Observe the remaining seed under the microscope. Sketch the seed below.

Part B: Observing the Plants, Days 3–14

1. Observe the developing plants and spores every few days from Day 3 to Day 14 as directed by your teacher. Each time you make observations, make a colored sketch of the plants developing from the spores and seeds. Date each sketch and keep them together in your notebook. With the sketches, record differences you see in the structures and shapes of the developing gametophytes and sporophytes.

2. To observe a developing spore, carefully use a toothpick to transfer a developing spore onto a microscope slide. After sketching the spore, wipe your slide with a dry paper towel then rinse the slide in the sink.

Part C: Observing Sperm, Day 21

1. Observe the surface of the agar plate. The tiny green oval-shaped specks on the agar are male gametophytes. The larger green spots shaped like mittens, are hermaphrodite gametophytes. An egg is located at the notch of the hermaphrodite gametophyte. Use a toothpick to transfer several male and hermaphrodite gametophytes from the agar plate to a well slide. Do not put a cover slip on the slide.

2. Observe the gametophytes under low power through a microscope. Use dim light, but be sure that you can clearly see a male gametophyte.

3. Add one drop of water to the slide and observe the male gameto-phyte again. Adjust the lighting and focus, if needed. In a few moments, you should observe the release of sperm into the water. Once you see the sperm, switch to the medium- and then to the high-power objectives to observe them more closely. Describe your observations below.

Observations:

_____

_____

_____

4. The structure on a hermaphrodite gametophyte that holds the egg also releases chemicals that attract sperm. Apples contain a chemical that is structurally similar to the chemical released by the hermaphrodite gametophyte. Push a toothpick into a piece of apple and remove it. Switch back to low power. While looking through the eyepiece, bring the toothpick into view above the slide. Touch the end of the toothpick that has apple juice on it to the water. Observe the sperm. Describe your observations below.

Observations:

_____

_____

_____

5. Use a transfer pipette to add a thin layer of sterile water to the agar dish. This will allow for the release of sperm and fertiliza-tion among the gametophytes remaining on the dish. Replace the agar dish in the growing container to allow the sporophytes to grow.

Analysis and Conclusions

1. Summarize the life cycle of a fern from spore to spore.

Suggested answer: Spores develop into gametophytes. Gametophytes produce gametes.

Sperm fertilizes an egg and the resulting zygote develops into a sporophyte. Sporophyte matures

and produces more spores.

2. Summarize the life cycle of an angiosperm from spore to spore.

Suggested answer: Spores produce gametophytes (pollen grains and embryo sacs). Pollen grains

travel by wind or animals to embryo sacs where the male gamete (sperm) fertilizes the female gamete

(egg). A seed develops containing an embryo, nourishing material, and a protective coat. The seed

germinates and becomes a sporophyte, containing more spores.

3. Describe one major difference between the spores of a fern and the spores of an angiosperm.

Sample answer: Spores of a fern are dispersed, while spores of an angiosperm are not.

4. Do all male gametophytes produce motile sperm? Explain.

Suggested answer: No, the male gametophytes of angiosperms do not produce motile sperm. Cells that can develop into sperm are carried in pollen grains. When pollen grains land on the carpel of another plant, a pollen tube develops through which sperm are deposited into the female gametophyte.

Extension

Continue observing the life cycle of a fern by planting a sporophyte. Use a plastic spoon to transfer one or two healthy-looking sporophytes from the agar dish to a pot of soil. Eventually, the sporophytes should develop spores.

You can also continue to observe the life cycle of an angiosperm. By the time you complete Part D, flowers should be growing on the angiosperms you planted. Use a bee stick or chenille stem to transfer pollen from the anther of one flower to the stigma of another flower on a different plant. If fertilization occurs, seeds with a developing embryo may develop. You will be able to observe the seeds within the pods left behind after the flower falls away.

Extension
You can have students continue to grow their plants in the classroom or take them home and report their progress to you.

Fast Plant Growing System
Film canisters: Poke a hole in the bottom of the canisters and insert felt wicks. Fill the canisters with 1 : 1 peat moss to vermiculite and a few pellets of slow-release fertilizer. Place four canisters in a plastic margarine or deli container. After the seeds are planted, have students add water to the plastic containers. Go to www.fastplants.org for more details.

The same procedure can be used if you decide to use 4-inch pots. Use large plastic freezer containers instead of deli containers.

See the front of this Laboratory Manual Teacher's Edition for lighting instructions.

C-fern® Growing and Lighting System
You can use the same growing boxes for *C-ferns*® that you use for Fast Plants. However, the *C-ferns*® prefer less light and more heat. The preferred growing system is to use a soft-drink cooler bag. Line it with foil. Place the petri dishes in it in stacks of five. Place a 1/4-inch sheet of clear acrylic on top of the petri dishes. Suspend a utility light with a 15-watt fluorescent bulb over the box so that the internal temperature is about 28–30°C.

Leave Impressions

Comparing the Structures of Leaves

Questions What differences can you observe in cells on the lower surfaces of leaves from different types of plants? How do these differences reflect the environments in which the plants live?

Lab Overview In this investigation you will compare certain structures of leaves from a pteridophyte, a gymnosperm, and an angiosperm. You will make impressions of the leaf surfaces to examine the shape, arrangement, and number of certain cells.

Introduction Carbon dioxide enters a plant's leaves through tiny openings called stomata. Water vapor also exits a plant through the stomata. In hot conditions, losing some water protects a plant through evaporative cooling. However, if more water is lost than can be replaced by the roots, the plant can become dehydrated. Water loss is partly controlled by the opening and closing of stomata. Two guard cells surround each stoma. The movement of certain ions in the leaf causes the guard cells to swell, opening the stoma, or causes the guard cells to sag together, closing the stoma. The opening and closing of stomata is influenced by temperature and wind.

The stomata of different types of plants vary depending on the plant's vulnerability to water loss. For example, plants in windy environments may have stomata that are set into the leaf, shielding them from the wind. Plants that live in moist and shady environments may have a relatively high density of stomata (stomata per cm^2) on their leaves. These plants benefit from increased access to carbon dioxide since their risk of excess water loss is relatively low.

In this lab you will make impressions of leaves using clear fingernail polish. You will observe the guard cells and stomata of each leaf and draw conclusions about how their structure and number fit the environment for which each plant is adapted. In the Prelab Activity, read more information about the plants you will study and analyze a cladogram. Then answer the Prelab Questions that follow.

Prelab Activity The leaves of pteridophytes, gymnosperms, and angiosperms are adapted to various environments. In the table on the next page, read the information about these types of plants and their characteristic habitats. Then analyze the cladogram that follows.

Objective to observe the shape, arrangement, and density of guard cells and stomata in different plants

Inquiry Skills
• predicting
• observing
• making measurements
• collecting data
• making inferences

Time
• 15–20 min for Prelab Activity
• 45 min for Procedure
• 15 min for Analysis and Conclusions

Plants have many adaptations that limit water loss. For example, the lower surface of most leaves consists of a layer of epidermal cells that secrete a waxy cuticle. The waxy cuticle reduces evaporation from the leaf. Some plant leaves have very little wax, but have hair-like projections extending from the epidermal cells. These hairs help to keep the moving air from directly contacting the surface of the leaf, thereby limiting evaporation.

Type of Plant	Environment
Pteridophyte (fern)	Most pteridophytes are found in moist, shady habitats such as forest floors. The bottoms of the gametophyte leaves must remain moist for sperm to be able to swim to and fertilize the eggs.
Gymnosperm (conifer)	Gymnosperms are generally found in northern forests or mountain forests. They are adapted to stormy winters and dry summers. The sperm of gymnosperms are contained in dry pollen grains.
Angiosperm (flowering plant)	Angiosperms thrive in a variety of environments from deserts to rain forests. You will examine leaves of a monocot or dicot angiosperm or both. One difference between them is that monocot leaf veins are parallel to each other, while dicot leaf veins are branched.

For this lab, you can choose to use either monocot or dicot leaves, or both. The venation differences between these two types of angiosperms will also show up in the leaf impressions.

Below are some key structures that plants gained during their evolutionary history. Referring to the cladogram below, write the letter for each plant structure on the appropriate line. Then write the number for each plant group on the appropriate line.

Students can refer to Chapter 19 in the textbook to review these adaptations.

Structures (match with letters)

<u>C</u> Flowers (attract pollinators)

<u>A</u> Lignin-hardened vascular tissue (transports water)

<u>B</u> Pollen (transports sperm)

Plants (match with numbers)

<u>2</u> Gymnosperms (conifers and relatives)

<u>1</u> Pteridophytes (ferns and relatives)

<u>3</u> Angiosperms (flowering plants)

Prelab Questions

1. Explain the role of stomata in a plant.

Suggested answer: Stomata allow carbon dioxide into the plant leaves where it can be used in photosynthesis. The stomata also regulate water loss from the leaf.

2. Predict which of the plant leaves you examine will have the greatest number of stomata. Explain your prediction.

Sample answer: The fern frond will have the highest density of stomata. Ferns are often found in moist habitats and can have more stomata without being affected by water loss.

3. Which pair of plants in the list below do you predict will have the most similar leaf structure? Explain.

a. a rose and a sunflower   **b.** a fern and a redwood tree (conifer)

c. a Jefferson pine and a cherry tree

Suggested answer: The answer is **a**. A rose and sunflower are both flowering plants (angiosperms); therefore, they will most likely have a more similar leaf structure than any of the other pairs.

Name _____ Class _____ Date _____

Materials

- fast-drying clear fingernail polish
- fern frond
- pine needle
- angiosperm leaf or leaves
- masking tape
- permanent marker
- paper towel
- metric ruler
- clear mailing tape   (do not use regular cellophane tape)
- scissors
- microscope and 3 or 4 microscope slides

To help the nail polish dry faster, you could provide students with hair dryers or fans.

Advance Preparation
The day of the lab
Gather one type of leaf for each lab group. Choose fern fronds that are not covered with spores. Choose thick pine needles. Onion and daffodil leaves work well for monocot samples. Fruit tree leaves work well for dicot samples. Do not choose hairy or soft leaves.
If you gather leaves the day before, place them in small plastic bags. Spray water inside the bags to prevent wilting.

Procedure

1. Place a small piece of masking tape on the top sides of the fern and angiosperm leaves. Label the tape on the fern "F" and the tape on the angiosperm "A." If you are observing a monocot and a dicot, label them "A: M" and "A: D."

2. Paint about a 1-cm^2 section of the underside of the fern and angiosperm leaves with clear fingernail polish. For the pine needle, paint one side. Place each leaf, painted side up, on a paper towel to dry. Allow the polish to dry for about 10 min.

3. Cut four 2-cm^2 pieces of mailing tape. **CAUTION:** *Handle sharp instruments with care to avoid injury.* Stick the tape on the painted section of each leaf. Carefully pull the tape off. With the permanent marker, label one corner of the tape with the appropriate leaf letter.

4. Stick each piece of tape on a separate microscope slide.

5. Put the first slide on the microscope stage and focus on low power. Switch to medium power to observe the impressions of the stomata, guard cells, and surrounding epidermal cells. For reference, see the photograph of stomata, guard cells, and epidermal cells in Figure 19-3 on page 421 in your textbook.

6. In the first circle below, sketch and label the stomata, guard cells, and epidermal cells you observe. Describe the leaf impression in the data table on the next page.

Safety and Disposal
Avoid using poisonous leaves such as oleander or foxglove. Students with allergic skin conditions should wear gloves while handling the leaves. The room should be well ventilated while students are using the fingernail polish. Remind students to handle the microscope slides with care and to notify you immediately if any should break. Students should not handle broken glass. Remind students to wash their hands before leaving the laboratory. Remove the tape and wash the slides for reuse. Plant parts can be placed in the trash after the lab.

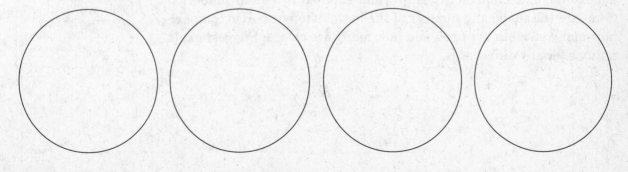

_____ _____ _____ Date _____

7. Now observe the slide at high power (400×). Count the total number of stomata (open and closed) you see in this field of view. Record the total in the data table below.

8. Repeat steps 5–7 for the remaining leaf impressions.

Data Table

Type of Plant	Description of Guard Cells and Stomata	Number of Open and Closed Stomata (400×)
Pteridophyte	**Expected Results** Fern fronds will most likely have the highest density of stomata. The stomata of pine needles are recessed in the needle and lie parallel to each other. In angiosperms, it is interesting to see the differences in the shape of the stomata.	
Gymnosperm		
Angiosperm: monocot		
Angiosperm: dicot		

Analysis and Conclusions

1. Describe how the stomata are arranged in the gymnosperm leaf.

Sample answer: The stomata in the pine needle are parallel and recessed.

2. Which of the leaves contained the most stomata per cm^2? Do these data support the prediction you made in Question 2 of the Prelab Activity? Explain.

Students' responses will vary.

3. If you and your classmates observed both monocot and dicot leaves, describe any differences in their cell arrangement.

Sample answer: The stomata are parallel in the monocot just as the veins are.

Extension

Make impressions of two leaves from the same plant. For example, you could make an impression of an older leaf (darker green) and younger leaf (lighter green). Or make impressions of a leaf exposed to a lot of sun and a leaf on the same plant exposed to a lot of shade. Compare the shape and number of the leaves' stomata. Also compare how many stomata are open and how many are closed. Suggest explanations for any differences.

Extension
Students should try to explain the differences in terms of a plant's need to take in carbon dioxide for photosynthesis, while avoiding excess water loss. Remind them of the safety precautions.

Bees, Birds, and Botanists

Exploring Flower Structure and Adaptations

Question How do the parts of a flower attract pollinators and produce seeds?

Lab Overview In this investigation you will discover how flowers attract different types of animal pollinators. Then you will dissect a flower to observe reproductive structures and learn how they produce a seed.

Introduction Flowers, which are unique to angiosperms, function in reproduction. The flowers of many angiosperms have adapted in ways that attract pollinators (animals such as birds or insects that carry pollen between flowers). As a bird or insect feeds on a flower's nectar or pollen, pollen sticks to the animal. When the pollinator moves on to another plant of the same species, it pollinates the second plant. Pollination may lead to fertilization and the development of a new generation of plants.

In the Prelab Activity you will learn about the various features of flowers that attract hummingbirds and bees. During the investigation you will "think like a botanist" as you dissect flowers and examine the parts that are involved in pollination and the production of seeds.

Prelab Activity Study the table below. Then complete the activity on the next page.

Flower Feature	Hummingbirds	Bees
Shape	Hummingbirds prefer flowers with a tubular shape that fit their long, slender beaks.	Bees prefer cup-shaped flowers in which they can nestle while gathering pollen or nectar.
Color	Hummingbirds as well as many other birds, are most attracted to red flowers, but will also drink nectar from flowers with colors that contain red such as orange or pink.	Bees, as well as other insects, respond mostly to blue and yellow flowers. They cannot detect red.
Pattern	Hummingbirds respond to color and shape, rather than patterns.	Bees are attracted to flowers with "runway" lines or dashes that lead to the bee to pollen or nectar.
Scent	Hummingbirds have a limited sense of smell. Smell has little impact on food choice.	Bees have a strong sense of smell and are attracted to fragrant flowers.

Objective to explore the relationships between plants and pollinators, and to study flower anatomy

Inquiry Skills
- observing
- predicting
- classifying
- asking questions
- formulating hypotheses
- drawing conclusions
- communicating conclusions

Time
- 20 min for Prelab Activity
- 10 min for Part A
- 10 min for Part B
- 20–30 min for Part C
- 15 min for Analysis and Conclusions

Honeycreepers and orioles are other types of birds that drink nectar from flowers.

Flowers that have shapes that attract hummingbirds often have adaptations that keep insects from robbing the nectar. For example, many hummingbird flowers have a thickened base near the sepals that prevent insects from fitting through the flower opening.
   Some patterns on flowers can only be seen by insects with ultraviolet vision.

Based on the information in the table on the previous page, use colored pencils to sketch a flower that you think would attract a hummingbird and a flower that you think would attract a bee.

Sketches:

Advance Preparation
Purchase flowers or collect them from flowering trees and shrubs. For 30 students, you'll need about 100 flowers for parts A and B. Some flowers that attract hummingbirds are penstemon, honeysuckle, columbine, fuchsia, trumpet creeper vine, palo verdé, hibiscus, Sweet William, and cardinal flower. Some flowers that attract bees are *Ceanothus*, lavender, alfalfa, red clover, rosemary, rose, bottlebrush, butterfly bush, and aster.

For 30 students, you'll need about 15 large flowers with easy-to-identify reproductive parts for Part C. Flowers that work well for dissection include gladiola, blue hibiscus, azalea, daffodil, iris, canna lily, and camellia.

Be sure to tell students the name of the flowers they are observing (or assign A, B, and C labels) so students can refer to flowers throughout the lab.

Prelab Questions

1. Explain why you think the flower in your first sketch would attract hummingbirds.

   Students' responses will vary based on their sketches, but should include characteristics that were

   described in the Background such as red-colored and tubular-shaped.

2. Explain why you think the flower in your second sketch would attract bees.

   Students' responses will vary based on their sketches, but should include characteristics that were

   described in the Background such as blue- or yellow-colored and cup-shaped.

3. Hummingbirds need to feed several times an hour. Flowers that attract hummingbirds typically contain a lot of nectar. This keeps the hummingbird at each flower longer before it moves on to another source. Flowers that attract nectar-feeding bees typically contain smaller amounts of nectar, and therefore a bee has to visit several flowers to obtain enough nectar. Explain how both adaptations lead to better chances of successful pollination.

   Suggested answer: If hummingbirds spend more time at a flower, they are more apt to pick up more

   pollen to distribute to other plants. If a bee must visit more than one flower to gather enough food,

   the bee is more apt to distribute pollen to more plants.

Materials

- flowers of varying color, size, and scent
- large flower for dissection
- forceps (optional)
- scissors (optional)
- stereomicroscope (optional)

Safety and Disposal
Ask students with plant allergies to notify you before starting the lab. Do not use highly poisonous plants such as foxglove or oleander. You may want to have students wear gloves and aprons because some types of pollen can stain skin or clothes. Have students wash their hands with soap after handling plant materials and before leaving the laboratory. Flowers can be thrown away after the lab.

Name _____ Class _____ Date _____

Part A: Thinking Like a Hummingbird

CAUTION: *Notify your teacher of any plant or pollen allergies before starting this lab.* Compare your various flowers. (Remember to use your senses as a hummingbird would.) Which of these flowers do you think would most attract a hummingbird? Describe the flower and explain your prediction.

Students' descriptions and predictions will vary.
_____

_____

_____

Part B: Thinking Like a Bee

Compare your various flowers. (Remember to use your senses as a bee would.) Which of these flowers do you think would most attract a bee? Describe the flower and explain your prediction.

Students' descriptions and predictions will vary.
_____

_____

_____

Part C: Thinking Like a Botanist

One reason botanists study flower parts is that these structures help to classify flowers. The number of flower parts (petals or sepals) and their shape and position are key to flower classification. Botanists also ask questions about how pollination occurs in different flowers. They may study how a flower's shape aids in pollen from an anther becoming attached to a pollinator and then being transferred to another flower's stigma.

1. Your teacher will give you a large flower with prominent parts to study. Use the diagram of the generalized flower below to help you identify the parts in steps 2 and 3.

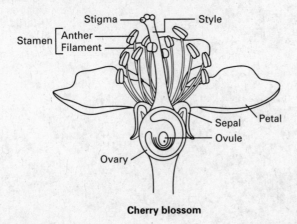

Cherry blossom

Alternate Methods
Instead of having students describe their choices in Parts A and B, you might have each group tape their "hummingbird flower" and "bee flower" onto index cards with their initials and justification. Group the class's cards together and have students look for common themes.

2. You may recall from Chapter 19 that angiosperms are classified in several evolutionary branches. Monocots and dicots are two groups of angiosperms. One way to recognize monocots is to count the number of sepals or petals. If this number is a multiple of three, the plant is a monocot. If the number is a multiple of four or five, and if the leaves contain branched veins, the plant is a dicot. If the flower does not fit the monocot or dicot description, it likely belongs in one of the other several groups of angiosperms. Observe your flower. Is it a monocot, dicot, or neither? Explain your classification below.

_____

_____

_____

3. Flowers have structures with specialized shapes that allow sperm in pollen to reach the eggs in the ovaries. Follow the directions below to take the flower apart and identify its reproductive structures.

a. Gently pull off the petals and set them aside. Look for the yellow, dusty pollen. (**CAUTION:** _You may want to wear goggles, gloves, and an apron for steps a and b. Pollen can irritate the eyes and some types of pollen may stain skin or clothing._)

b. Identify a stamen. A stamen consists of a stalk called the filament and a structure at the tip called the anther. Pollen is produced in the anther. Sketch the stamen in the space below.

You may wish to have students tap some pollen onto a microscope slide and view it under a microscope (dry mount). Pollen from different flowers has different appearances.

Instead of making sketches, you could have students tape the flower structures directly to their Laboratory Manual pages or to index cards that they label.

c. The stigma, style and ovary make up the carpel—the female part of a plant. Identify the style and stigma. Look for a centralized stalk (the style) with a sticky end (the stigma). In most flower species, there is only one style. Pollen carried by pollinators or wind sticks to the stigma and absorbs fluid. Then a tube called the *pollen tube* grows from the stigma through the style, toward the ovary. A cell in the pollen divides, and two sperm nuclei travel down the pollen tube toward the ovary. Sketch the style in the space below.

d. Remove the stigma and style from the flower and locate the ovary. Using forceps, or your thumbnails, pull open the ovary to observe the ovule or ovules. Each ovule contains an egg cell. If available, use a hand lens or stereomicroscope to observe the ovule(s). One sperm that travels down the pollen tube fertilizes the egg cell and forms a zygote. The other sperm fertilizes a large central cell in the ovule, which develops into a tissue called endosperm that nourishes the growing embryo. After this double fertilization takes place, the ovule develops into a seed with the embryo and endosperm inside. Sketch the ovary and ovule in the space below.

Your students may wonder why a plant that contains both a stigma and anthers does not pollinate itself. Explain to students that plants have certain mechanisms that prevent self-fertilization. In most plants, if a pollen grain from an anther lands on a stigma of a flower on the same plant, the plant emits a chemical that blocks the pollen from completing its development. In some plants the stamens and carpels mature at different times. These types of mechanisms contribute to genetic variety by ensuring that plants cross-fertilize.

Analysis and Conclusions

1. Describe the structures you observed. Which structures are involved in the formation of male gametophytes? Which structures are involved in the formation of female gametophytes?

Students' descriptions will vary. The part that is involved in the formation of male gametophytes is the stamen. The part that is involved in the formation of the female gametophyte is the ovary.

2. Through what part of the flower does the pollen tube grow?

Suggested answer: the style

3. If a flower has 8 ovules and the egg cell in each is fertilized, how many seeds will the flower produce?

Suggested answer: 8 seeds

4. Summarize the pathway of pollen from where it is produced to where it is deposited in another flower.

Suggested answer: Pollen is produced in the anther. A pollinator or wind picks up the pollen and

may carry it to a flower on another plant. There, the pollen may stick to the stigma, possibly leading

to fertilization.

5. A bird watcher wants to attract more hummingbirds to a feeder. He decides to add fragrance to the hummingbirds' food supply. Do you think this will attract more hummingbirds to the feeder? Explain your response.

Suggested answer: Hummingbirds have a limited sense of smell. Adding fragrance to a food supply

will not attract more hummingbirds.

6. A woman wearing a blue and yellow dress and strong perfume attends a party outside on a warm summer day. What problem do you anticipate that she may encounter?

Sample answer: The colors of the woman's dress and the fragrance of the perfume may attract bees.

Extension

Based on the information you have learned in this lab, describe how you would design a hummingbird feeder. Describe in detail why you think your feeder would work. With your teacher's permission, build the feeder, place it in an approved location, and observe it to see if it attracts hummingbirds.

Extension
Student designs should consider some basic characteristics that would attract hummingbirds such as the color red and perhaps the shape of the feeder. If you allow students to build their feeders and place them for observation, tell students how to make food for the hummingbirds. Hummingbirds should be provided with a solution of 4 parts water and 1 part white table sugar. Boil the water. Then add the table sugar. Allow the solution to cool completely before adding it to the feeder. Check with your local Audubon Society for information on local hummingbird species and migration patterns.

Predicamint

Exploring Asexual Reproduction in Plants

Question What parts of a mint plant can reproduce asexually?

Lab Overview In this investigation you will make predictions about which mint plant parts can regenerate (grow into new plants) and which parts cannot. Then, you will perform an experiment to test one or more of your predictions. After performing your own experiment, you will share results with other lab groups that tested different plant parts.

Introduction Mint plants, such as spearmint (*Mentha spicata*), water mint (*Mentha aquatica*), and peppermint (*Mentha piperita*), are members of the angiosperm family Labiatae. Mint plants typically live in temperate climates and are characterized by square stems and pink or purple flowers. They produce fragrant oils that are used in many food and health products.

Gardeners who have grown mint learn quickly that it is very invasive—it will crowd out and take over the resources of many other plants. Not only do mint plants reproduce sexually by flowering and producing seeds, they also reproduce asexually. For example, mint plants have underground horizontal stems from which new shoots can grow at a distance from the parent plant. Also, some parts of mint plants that have been separated from a plant can produce new cells that allow the parts to grow into a new plant (a *clone*).

Sexual and asexual reproduction both offer different advantages to plant species. Sexual reproduction ensures genetic variation in a population. Seeds can survive harsh conditions and grow once the conditions have improved. Asexual reproduction allows for rapid growth. Typically, a clone is not as frail as a seedling emerging from a seed.

Prelab Activity A gardener seeking advice from a gardening expert wrote the following letter. Read the letter and then answer the Prelab Questions on the next page.

Dear Dr. Botanist,

This spring I transplanted peppermint from a small pot into my garden. By early summer it had grown to take up half my garden area. I used my hoe to tear up the mint, hoping to save my other plants. To my dismay, I noticed even more mint popping up all over the place. Now it is all over my garden! I don't understand how this could have happened. The plants have not even flowered and produced seeds yet! Please help explain this.

Sincerely,

Jamie Spear

Objective to perform an experiment to determine which parts of a mint plant have the ability to regenerate into new plants

Inquiry Skills
- observing
- predicting
- drawing conclusions
- communicating conclusions

Time
- 15 min for Prelab Activity
- 20 min for Part A
- 5 min, twice a week for 3 weeks for Part B
- 15 min for Part C
- 15 min for Analysis and Conclusions

Prelab Questions

1. Write a letter to respond to Jamie. Based on what you have learned about mint reproduction, explain what may have happened in the garden.

Dear Jamie: The mint took over your garden because it grew horizontal stems that produced new shoots.

Your hoeing cut the mint into pieces and some of these pieces have the ability to form new plants. Mint,

like many plants, can reproduce asexually, as well as sexually. Sincerely, Dr. Botanist

2. What do you think that Jamie could have done differently to prevent the mint plants from taking over the garden?

Suggested answer: The gardener could have protected the garden by removing whole mint plants,

including the roots. Or, the gardener could have kept the mint plant in the pot.

Materials
- mint sprigs
- plastic cups
- marker
- masking tape
- scissors
- water

Advance Preparation
Obtain mint plants from a local nursery. Call ahead to make sure they are available. You will need about 4 plants in 4-inch pots per class of 30 students.

Safety and Disposal
Remind students never to eat or drink in the laboratory. Students with allergic skin conditions should wear gloves when handling the mint. All students should wash their hands after handling the mint. Remind students to use caution when handling water near electrical devices. Remind students to use care when handling sharp objects. Allow the mint plants to dry up before disposing of them in the trash.

Procedure

Part A: Testing the Plant Parts

1. Before you begin, study the list of mint plant parts below.
- stem with leaves
- stem with no leaves
- root
- a whole leaf
- a piece of a leaf

Which mint plant parts do you think can become a new plant when completely separated from the original plant? Explain your predictions.

Students' predictions will vary.

Which plant parts do you think will not be able to regenerate when completely separated from the original plant? Explain your predictions.

Students' predictions will vary.

_____

_____

2. Choose a plant part to study. (To make sure all of the plant parts are tested, your teacher might assign your group to a particular plant part.) Discuss your prediction about the plant part with your group.

3. Label two plastic cups with your group's initials and the name of the plant part you are testing. Fill the cups about three-quarters full of water.

4. Use scissors to cut the plant part you are testing from the mint sprig. **CAUTION**: *Use caution when handling sharp objects to avoid injury.* Place one sample of the appropriate plant part in each plastic cup. Then place the cups in a sunny location as directed by your teacher.

Part B: Observing the Plant Parts

Every couple of days for the next few weeks, observe your mint pieces. Record your observations in Data Table 1 below.

Encourage students to think of other specific parts of a plant to test. Encourage them to ask or test other questions. For example, are the roots that grow closest to the stem more likely to regenerate? Does the size of the stem influence how long it takes to grow new roots? How would the results be different if the plant pieces were placed in soil instead of water?

To ensure that the mint plants thrive, make sure that the temperature of your classroom does not drop below 10°C (50°F). Place the cuttings near a window.

Data Table 1 Part of Mint Plant: _____

Day	Observations

Part C: Sharing Results

After three weeks, compare results with other groups. Record the class results, including your own group's results, in Data Table 2 below.

Data Table 2

Mint Plant Part Tested	Results
	Expected Results Mint root pieces will produce shoots, and stem pieces will produce roots in a few weeks. A stem or root piece is needed for regeneration because they contain cells that remain totipotent (capable of differentiating into different types of cells). Just a piece of a leaf or a leaf without a stem will not produce roots or shoots.

Analysis and Conclusions

1. Which parts of the mint plant regenerated?

   Students' answers will vary based on the part of the mint plant they tested.

2. Were there any parts of the mint plant that did not regenerate?

   Suggested answer: Yes, pieces of leaves did not regenerate.

3. How does the ability to reproduce sexually and asexually benefit a plant?

   Suggested answer: The benefits of sexual reproduction include increased genetic variation and

   the production of seeds that can withstand harsh conditions. The benefits of asexual reproduction

   are rapid growth and the production of clone plants that are typically stronger than seedlings.

Extension

Experiment with other plants such as geraniums, coleus, or African violets. Snip off a small stem with a few leaves and place the cut end of the stem in water. Change the water every few days. When roots appear, transplant the new plant into soil.

Extension
Encourage students to ask questions about these plants as well. Do roots grow faster from older or younger stems? Will new roots grow from stems that are planted in well-watered soil?

Zip Up the Xylem

Measuring Transpiration Rates

Question How do plants control the rate at which water is transported through the xylem?

Lab Overview In this investigation you will perform an experiment to measure and compare the transpiration rates of leaves under varying environmental conditions such as intense light, wind, or humidity. You will also make imprints of the bottom surfaces of some of the leaves to observe the guard cells and stomata.

Introduction Stomata (openings in plant leaves) enable carbon dioxide to enter a plant. The openings also allow evaporative cooling, which keeps plant enzymes from breaking down in hot conditions. Environmental conditions influence the number of stomata that are open. For example, low carbon dioxide levels in a leaf cue the guard cells to actively accumulate potassium ions. Due to osmosis, water follows the potassium ions into the guard cells, causing them to swell until gaps (the stomata) open between them. When more water has been lost through transpiration than can be replaced from the soil, the guard cells lose pressure and sag together. The stomata close, preventing more water loss.

Prelab Activity You will make a device called a potometer (puh TAWM ih tur) to measure transpiration rates in the lab. To make it, you will fill four transfer pipettes with water and seal the tips to prevent water loss. Next you will cut off the tops of the bulbs so that a leaf petiole (stalk) can be inserted into each pipette. As water transpires from the stomata, more water will be drawn up through the petioles of the leaves (see diagram below).

Objective to measure transpiration rate under different environmental conditions, and discover which conditions cause stomata to open or close

Inquiry Skills
- predicting
- making measurements
- observing
- calculating
- formulating testable hypotheses
- organizing data
- analyzing data
- evaluating hypotheses

Time
- 10 min for Prelab Activity
- 15–20 min for Part A
- 30 min for Part B
- 20 min for Part C (Part C can be performed during the next class meeting)
- 15 min for Analysis and Conclusions

See the Procedure, Part B section for alternative methods to measure transpiration.

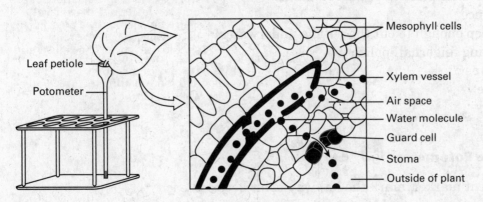

Leaf petiole

Potometer

Mesophyll cells

Xylem vessel

Air space

Water molecule

Guard cell

Stoma

Outside of plant

You will keep two potometers in "normal" classroom conditions and place two potometers in a different condition such as high humidity, wind, or bright light. You will record how long it takes for water to leave the potometer and calculate the transpiration rate of each sample.

Prelab Questions

1. Explain how the opening and closing of stomata are controlled.

Due to osmosis, water follows potassium ions into guard cells, causing them to swell until gaps

(the stomata) open between the cells. When more water has been lost through transpiration than

is replaced from the soil, the guard cells lose pressure and sag together, closing the stomata.

2. Compared to average environmental conditions, predict how the conditions below would affect a plant's rate of transpiration. Rate each condition using the following scale: 1 = greatly decrease, 2 = slightly decrease, 3 = no effect, 4 = slightly increase, 5 = greatly increase. Explain your predictions on the lines below.

____ High humidity   ____ Moderate light

____ Light wind   ____ Bright light

____ Heavy wind

Students' predictions will vary.

Materials

- 2 permanent markers of different colors
- 4 disposable transfer pipettes
- plastic cup of water with food coloring
- safety pin
- petroleum jelly in lip applicator tube
- scissors
- test-tube rack
- large leaves with long petioles or narrow stems
- laboratory balance
- plastic bowl (deep enough to cut the petiole underwater)
- clear, rapid-drying fingernail polish
- clear mailing tape
- microscope slide
- microscope

Advance Preparation

A couple of days before the lab
Locate a plant or vine with large leaves and long petioles (such as ivy). If it is a potted plant, bring it to class and have the students cut fresh stems. Otherwise, take cuttings the morning of the lab and keep them in water until they are needed.

Leaves with larger surface areas will lose water through transpiration at a faster rate than leaves with a smaller surface area. For best results, each lab group should use leaves of a similar size.

The day of the lab
Add food coloring to water in plastic cups.

Procedure
Part A: Making the Potometers

1. With a permanent marker, mark the halfway point between each graduation (marking) on a transfer pipette. For example, between the 0.75 and 1 mL marks, make a mark to represent 0.875 mL. Repeat on the other three transfer pipettes.

2. Place a transfer pipette in colored water and draw up water past the 1 mL mark. Let go of the bulb before taking the pipette out of the water.

3. Open the petroleum jelly and squeeze the air out of the tip. Place the petroleum jelly tube under the tip of the pipette. Squeeze about 3 mm of petroleum jelly into the pipette to seal it.

4. Without squeezing the pipette bulb, use a safety pin to poke a hole in the bulb. (This keeps pressure from building up in the bulb.) With scissors, cut off the top of the pipette bulb. Repeat steps 1–4 for the other three pipettes. Then place the potometers in a test-tube rack.

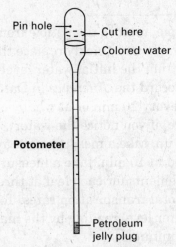

5. Find the mass of each leaf using a laboratory balance. Enter the mass of each leaf in Data Table 1 on the next page.

6. Place Leaf 1 in the bowl of water so that its petiole or stem is underwater. Cut off the end of the petiole or stem underwater. Repeat with the other three leaves.

7. Place a leaf petiole or stem in each potometer. Label the leaf samples 1–4 on the remaining portion of the pipette bulb.

8. In Part B you will need to remove the leaves from the potometers to measure how much water has transpired. Because you are starting with only about 1 mL of water in each potometer, the water that sticks to the leaf petioles will affect your measurements. Therefore, you need to know how much water remains in the potometers when the petioles are removed. Remove the leaves and record the initial water levels of each potometer below.

Leaf 1 potometer initial water level: _____ mL

Leaf 2 potometer initial water level: _____ mL

Leaf 3 potometer initial water level: _____ mL

Leaf 4 potometer initial water level: _____ mL

9. Replace the leaves. Mark the water level on the pipette with a marker of a different color than the one you used before. This mark will help you notice when the water level changes.

Safety and Disposal
Do not use oleander or other poisonous leaves for this activity. Advise students with allergic skin conditions to wear plastic gloves when handling plant materials. Remind students to handle glassware carefully and to use care when handling sharp instruments. Make sure that the room is well-ventilated and that students wear goggles when fingernail polish is used. Have students wash their hands with soap before leaving the laboratory. No special disposal is required.

The following are suggestions for setting up the different conditions:
High humidity: Drape a plastic bag over the leaf setup. Spray water under the bag before taking measurements.
Windy: Use a fan. If you place the fan within 15 cm of the leaf it will generally cause the stomata to close. If the fan is further away so that it is just blowing gently on the leaf, it will generally increase the transpiration rate.
Bright light: Use a fluorescent light. If you must use an incandescent light, put a large glass container of water between the light source and the leaves to prevent an increase in temperature (a second variable).

Part B: Measuring Transpiration Rates 🌿 🧪

1. Place Leaf 1 and Leaf 2 in ambient conditions (existing classroom conditions—no special treatment). These two leaves will be your experimental controls. (Testing two leaves in each environment will help verify your results.) Record the time below.

   Start time for Leaf 1 and Leaf 2: _____

2. You will be assigned to test the effect of intense light, wind, or humidity. Record the variable you are testing in Column 1 of Data Table 1. As directed by your teacher, place Leaf 3 and Leaf 4 in your assigned environmental condition. Record the time below.

   Start time for Leaf 3 and Leaf 4: _____

3. To take a measurement on a leaf sample, remove the petiole from the potometer. Read the level of the water and quickly replace the petiole. Subtract the new water level from the initial water level that you recorded in Part A, Step 7. Record the *difference* in Data Table 1. You can take measurements every 10 min or at whatever intervals are appropriate. For instance, if you notice the water level has decreased before 10 min are up, take a measurement and note the time. If nothing has happened in 10 min, take a measurement at 15 min instead. Take measurements for each leaf at three time intervals before calculating the total transpiration rates. To calculate the rate, divide the third water level reading by the mass of the leaf and by the total number of minutes.

Alternate Methods
The easiest method to measure transpiration rate is the least accurate: Place a stem (cut while underwater) in a graduated cylinder or test tube of water and measure the rate at which the water level decreases. Since the amounts of water are measured in mL, it takes several hours to get a measurable difference in water level.

The most accurate method is a potometer consisting of a 1-mL pipette and aquarium tubing, but note that it is difficult to get a good seal between the stem and the tubing without introducing air bubbles. This method can provide an accurate transpiration rate in about 30 min.

Data Table 1

	Mass of Leaf (g)	Water-Level Difference at ___ min	Water-Level Difference at ___ min	Water-Level Difference at ___ min	Total Transpiration Rate $\left(\dfrac{mL/g}{min}\right)$
Leaf 1 (control)		____ mL	____ mL	____ mL	
Leaf 2 (control)		____ mL	____ mL	____ mL	
Leaf 3 Variable: _____		____ mL	____ mL	____ mL	
Leaf 4 Variable: _____		____ mL	____ mL	____ mL	

4. Plot 4 line graphs on the same grid on the next page. The *x*-axis should show time (in min) and the *y*-axis should show amount of water transpired (in mL). Be sure to label the different lines and axes and title your graph.

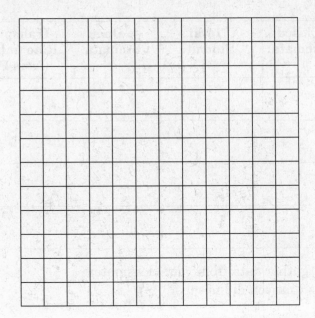

Part C: Observing Stomata and Guard Cells

Students could apply the nail polish to the leaves after finishing Part B and then perform the rest of Part C during the next class meeting.

1. Apply clear fingernail polish to a 1-cm^2 section of the underside of Leaf 2 to make an impression of the stomata and guard cells. Repeat with Leaf 4.

2. Follow your teacher's instructions to allow time for the fingernail polish to dry. When it is dry, cut out two 2-cm^2 pieces of clear mailing tape. Place the sticky side of the tape over the dry polish on each leaf and then gently pull it off. With a permanent marker, label one corner of the tape with the corresponding number of each leaf.

3. Place both pieces of tape sticky side down on a microscope slide.

4. Focus first on low power, then switch to medium power to observe the impression of the leaves' epidermal cells and guard cells. Draw and label sketches of the impressions of both leaves below.

5. Count the numbers of open and closed stomata in Leaf 2 that you can see in a field of view at 100× power (medium power on most microscopes). Record the numbers of open and closed stomata and the total number of stomata in Data Table 2 on the next page. Repeat with Leaf 4. Calculate the percentage of open stomata by dividing the number of open stomata by the number of total stomata. Then multiply by 100%.

Data Table 2

	Open Stomata	Closed Stomata	Total Stomata	% Open Stomata	Transpiration Rate (mL/g/min) (from Part B)
Leaf 2 (control)					
Leaf 4 (wind)					
Leaf 4 (humidity)					
Leaf 4 (bright light)					

6. To fill in the rest of the table, gather data from your classmates about leaves in the conditions that you did not test.

Analysis and Conclusion

1. Compare the predictions you made in the Prelab Activity to the data. Do the data support your predictions? Explain.

Students' responses will vary based on their predictions and results.

2. What can you conclude about the response of plants to wind and humidity?

Students' responses will vary based on how close the fan was placed to their plants. From a distance, the fan will cause transpiration rates to increase. If it is too close, the stomata will close.

Transpiration rates on humid days are slower than the rates on normal days.

3. A gardener noticed that her plants were more wilted on sunny days even when it wasn't very hot. Explain why this might have occurred, based on the results of your experiment.

Suggested answer: Stomata open in response to light, therefore, on a sunny day more water may

transpire even if it is not hot.

Extension

With permission from your teacher, repeat the procedure in Part C to make impressions of leaves from plants adapted to specific conditions, such as drought-tolerant plants that are adapted to very dry conditions (smooth-leaved species such as aloe, cape honeysuckle, and Indian hawthorne). First predict how you think the results will compare to what you observed in this lab. Then count the numbers of open and closed stomata in one field of view under 100× power, and compare the number with your previous observations.

Extension
Students observing drought-tolerant plants may note that the stomata are concentrated on the lower leaf surfaces, or recessed in tiny pits, which helps prevent water loss in dry, windy conditions.

Name _____ Class _____ Date _____

Farms of the Future?

Learning About Plant Nutrition Through Hydroponics

Questions Can plants be grown without soil? Will plants grow better if their roots are aerated?

Lab Overview In this investigation you will try to grow plants without soil by submerging their roots in a mineral solution, a method called *hydroponics*. You will determine which gas (carbon dioxide or oxygen) the roots absorb. Then you will perform an experiment to test the effect on the plants of adding air to (aerating) the mineral solution.

Introduction Besides the sunlight, carbon dioxide, and water that plants require for photosynthesis, plants also require several minerals for the production of DNA and proteins. In this investigation you will discover whether a plant can grow as well in a solution containing mineral nutrients as it can in soil. You will also investigate whether roots take in carbon dioxide as plant leaves do, or whether they require oxygen.

Background Hydroponics is usually used in greenhouses on commercial farms in areas where the soil is poor or water is scarce. Tomatoes and lettuce plants are common hydroponic crops. There are several benefits of hydroponics. Growers do not have to use herbicides and pesticides to fight weeds and pests that live in the soil. The growers control the type and amount of nutrients the plants receive by adjusting the makeup of the nutrient solution. Another benefit is that less water is needed to maintain the plants since water is not lost to runoff. A drawback of hydroponics is that the equipment and labor are more expensive than growing plants in soil. Also, not every type of plant responds well to hydroponics.

In the Prelab Activity on the next page, you will observe what happens when carbon dioxide is added to a solution containing bromothymol blue (a pH indicator). You will need the information from this activity to perform the lab investigation. After completing the Prelab Activity, answer the questions that follow.

Objective to examine alternative methods of growing plants, learn about plant nutrition, and practice evaluating plant health

Inquiry Skills
• predicting
• observing
• collecting data
• drawing conclusions

Time
• 15 min for the Prelab Activity
• 30 min for Part A
• 20 min for Part B (about 6 days after Part A)
• 15 min for Part C (1–2 weeks after Part B)
• 20 min for Analysis and Conclusions

Students often think that plants absorb soil. When students grow plants in a solution, they realize that roots only need to absorb minerals and water from soil.

When carbon dioxide is added to an aqueous solution, it forms a weak acid with water. The acid causes the bromothymol blue to turn green and then yellow. When carbon dioxide is removed from the solution, the solution will turn from yellow to blue. Therefore, bromothymol blue can be used in this lab to detect whether carbon dioxide is being used or produced by the plant's roots.

Prelab Activity Begin your test of the effect of carbon dioxide on bromothymol blue by filling a clear plastic cup half full with bromothymol blue solution.

Next, blow up a balloon, but do not tie the end. While tightly pinching a straw, place the open end of the balloon over a straw as shown in the diagram below. Keep pinching the straw and balloon to prevent air from escaping the balloon.

Place the straw's open end into the cup with the solution. Slowly release your pressure on the straw to allow the exhaled air containing carbon dioxide gas to escape from the balloon, through the straw, and into the cup. Observe the changes that occur to the solution as it is aerated (supplied with air). The carbon dioxide will dissolve in the water.

For this Prelab Activity you will need bromothymol blue solution, balloons, straws, and plastic cups. Students should wear goggles, gloves, and aprons when working with bromothymol blue. To ensure students do not ingest the bromothymol blue, do not allow students to add carbon dioxide to the solution by blowing through the straws.

Do a trial run of this activity. If your tap water is slightly acidic, the water will turn green as soon as the bromothymol blue solution is added. In this case, add a drop of very dilute ammonia or bleach (1:100) to the cups.

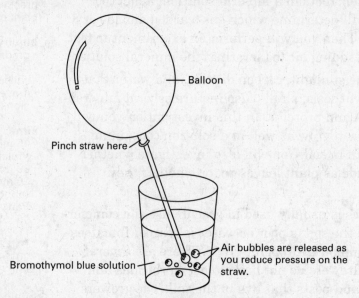

Balloon

Pinch straw here

Bromothymol blue solution

Air bubbles are released as you reduce pressure on the straw.

Prelab Questions

1. The pH indicator bromothymol blue has a blue color in a basic solution but turns yellow in an acidic solution. What can you conclude happens to a basic solution when carbon dioxide is introduced? Explain.

   Suggested answer: When carbon dioxide is introduced, a basic solution becomes acidic. After I added

   carbon dioxide to the solution, the bromothymol blue turned from blue to yellow, indicating that the

   solution was acidic.

2. Suppose you placed plant leaves in a cup of bromothymol blue solution containing dissolved carbon dioxide and placed the cup under a bright light. Based on what you know about photosynthesis, predict what would happen to the color of the solution. Explain.

   Suggested answer: The solution would turn back to blue. Leaves would use the carbon dioxide for

   photosynthesis.

3. Now suppose you placed plant roots in a cup of bromothymol blue solution and left the cup under a bright light. Based on what you know about photosynthesis, predict what would happen to the color of the solution. Explain.

Suggested answer: Roots do not perform photosynthesis, so they would not take

up carbon dioxide. The solution would remain yellow.

Materials

- 3 plants in plastic six-pack pots
- plastic knife
- hydroponic solution
- clean plastic gallon milk container
- bromothymol blue solution
- 2 transparent 16-oz plastic cups
- 2 plastic lids with holes for straws
- labels
- marker
- transfer pipette
- vinegar
- bucket of water
- potting soil
- 4-inch pot
- single-hole punch
- aquarium pump
- aquarium tubing
- aerating stone (optional)

You'll need 1 aquarium pump for every 5 groups. You'll also need several multivalve connectors.

Alternate Material
You could substitute other soluble plant food, such as Miracle-Gro®, for the hydroponic solution; however, it is critical to make the solution very dilute.

Advance Preparation

A couple of weeks before the lab
Order the concentrated hydroponic solution from a biological supply company such as Carolina Biological. See the front of this Laboratory Manual Teacher's Edition for contact information.

A couple of days before the lab
Purchase plants from a local nursery in plastic six-packs. Pansy plants work well.

Safety and Disposal
To prevent students from accidentally ingesting the hydroponic medium and bromothymol blue, do not allow students to blow through the straws to add carbon dioxide to the solution. Students should wear goggles, gloves, and an apron when working with bromothymol blue. Students with allergic skin conditions should wear gloves when working with the plants. Promptly clean up any spills so that students do not slip. Make sure that the aquarium tubing is out of the way of all foot traffic. Bromothymol blue and the hydroponic medium can be poured down the drain. Plant materials can be disposed of in the trash.

Procedure

Part A: "Replanting" Plants Into Hydroponic Medium (Day 1)

1. In the milk container, make 1 quart of the hydroponic solution according to your teacher's directions.

2. Remove three plants from the soil by squeezing the plastic of the six-pack container.

3. Use a plastic knife to make a vertical slice through the root clumps of each of the three plants to loosen the roots.

4. In a bucket of water, use your fingers to loosen the roots and carefully remove the soil from two of the three plants.

Soil removal may be very messy. Consider removing the soil from the plants before class and placing the plants in a bucket of water. If you have access to an outdoor hose, you could use that to remove the soil.

5. Once the soil is removed, place these two plants in the plastic lids as shown in the diagram below. First, widen the straw holes in the plastic lids. Then carefully push the clumps of roots through so that the roots hang out the bottom of the lids and the leaves emerge through the top.

6. Fill two transparent plastic cups with hydroponic solution. Leave approximately 2 cm of space at the top of each cup.

7. Add just enough bromothymol blue to turn the solution in both cups blue. Label one cup "Start blue" and set it aside.

8. Aerate the solution in the other cup by repeating the Prelab Activity. Blow up a balloon, attach it to a straw, and then allow carbon dioxide to "bubble" into the solution. (**NOTE:** *Because of the minerals in the hydroponic solution, it may be necessary to add a drop or two of vinegar to make the solution turn yellow.*) Label this cup "Start yellow."

9. Place a lid with a plant on each cup. Place the plants under a fluorescent light bank as directed by your teacher.

10. Transplant the remaining plant from Step 3 into a 4-inch pot with potting soil and water it. This plant is your control.

Part B: Observing the Plants (Day 7)

1. Approximately 6 days later, observe the color of the hydroponic solution in each cup. Record the colors in Data Table 1 on the next page.

2. The general health of plants is indicated in part by leaf color. Dark green leaves usually indicate that a plant is healthy. If the leaves have a yellow, light green, or purple tint, then the plants are probably not obtaining adequate nutrients or are otherwise under stress. Count the discolored leaves on your group's plants. Do your plants have signs of new growth? Record the information in Data Table 1. Then, examine all of the plants in the class and record the information in Data Table 1.

Name _____ Class _____ Date _____

Data Table 1

Sample plant	Color of hydroponic solution after 6 days	Number of discolored leaves: Group data	Signs of new growth: Group data	Number of discolored leaves: Class data	Number of plants with new growth: Class data
"Start blue"					
"Start yellow"					
Control plant	—				

Part C: Aerating Plants in a Hydroponic Solution

1. Replace the hydroponic solution in your two cups with fresh solution that does not contain bromothymol blue. Place one of the plant's roots back into the solution. Use the single-hole punch to make an additional hole in the other lid. Then, place the other plant's roots back into the solution.

2. Slide the aquarium tubing, which is connected to an air pump, into the hole you made with the single-hole punch. According to your teacher's instructions, attach the aerating stone to the end of the aquarium tubing.

3. Place the plants under fluorescent lights. Let them grow for another 1–2 weeks as directed by your teacher. Check the cups over this period of time and replace lost liquid with more hydroponic solution as needed. Also, continue to monitor and water the control plant.

4. After the growing period, compare the color of the leaves and check for new growth on the plants. Record this information in Data Table 2.

Expected Results
The plants grown in hydroponic nutrients should do at least as well as the ones grown in soil. Although aeration is widely used in hydroponic growing systems, you may not see any difference for a few weeks.

Data Table 2

Sample plant	Number of discolored leaves: Group data	Signs of new growth: Group data	Number of discolored leaves: Class data	Number of plants with new growth: Class data
Aerated				
Non-aerated				
Control				

Analysis and Conclusions

1. Based on the color change you observed, do roots perform photo-synthesis? Explain.

   Suggested answer: The solution that was originally blue turned yellow, indicating that carbon dioxide

   was being released. This indicates that root cells do not perform photosynthesis.

2. Did you observe any differences in the health of the plants grown in hydroponic solution and those grown in soil? Explain.

   Sample answer: Yes, the leaves of the plants grown in the hydroponic solution are greener than the

   leaves of the plant grown in soil.

3. Did you observe any differences in the health of the plants grown in aerated hydroponic solution compared to the plants grown in non-aerated hydroponic solution or in soil?

   Sample answer: Yes, the leaves of the plant grown in the aerated hydroponic solution have grown

   faster.

4. Suggest a possible reason why roots need oxygen.

   Suggested answer: Roots need oxygen to perform cellular respiration.

5. When soil is saturated with rain, all the air spaces become filled with water. If the soil were to remain saturated for many weeks, what do you think would happen to plants? Explain.

   Suggested answer: Plants may begin to die because their roots need oxygen.

6. Why do you think this investigation involved comparing all the plants in your classroom, rather than just the ones your lab group prepared?

   Suggested answer: Collecting data from multiple similar experiments provides more reliable results.

Extension

Research the pros and cons of hydroponics. Use valid and dependable sources for your research. Based on your research findings, conclude if you think that hydroponics will be the future of farming. Write a report to explain your conclusion.

Extension
Students' conclu-sions will vary. Check that they used reliable resources to make their conclu-sions.

How Do Plants Grow Up?

Exploring Gravitropism

Inquiry Challenge How do plants respond to gravity?

Lab Overview In this inquiry investigation you will explore how plants respond to gravity. You will develop and test your own hypotheses about the effects of gravity on young plant stems. Then you will perform an experiment of your own design using film canisters and seedlings.

Introduction Plant hormones cause chemical changes in certain cells in response to environmental factors such as light, wind, temperature, touch, and gravity. In the Prelab Activity you will examine a diagram of two-day-old radish seedlings grown in an upright petri dish. Note that the "leaves" you observe are the cotyledons or "seed leaves." Based on your observations of root growth, you will make and test predictions about stem growth.

Prelab Activity Seedlings typically emerge from buried seeds that are not exposed to light. No matter what the position of the seed is, a healthy seedling's root usually grows downward into the soil. Study the diagram below of two-day-old radish seedlings growing in an upright petri dish. The seedlings are held in place on a wet paper towel. Then answer the Prelab Questions on the next page.

(NOTE: *Because this lab is designed as an open-ended inquiry investigation, it will be most effective and motivating if assigned before students read Chapter 22.*)

Objective to formulate hypotheses based on observations of how a young stem responds to gravity, and test the hypotheses with simple experiments using seedlings

Inquiry Skills
• predicting
• observing
• formulating testable hypotheses
• designing experiments
• controlling variables
• drawing conclusions

Time
• 15 min for Prelab Activity
• 20 min for Part A
• 20 min to set up Part B, 1 day for response
• 30 min to set up Part C, 1 day for response
• 15 min for Analysis and Conclusions

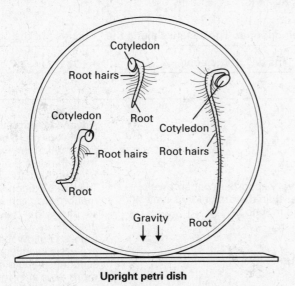

Upright petri dish

Prelab Questions

1. Record your observations below of the two-day-old seedlings in the diagram on the previous page.

Sample answer: Roots and stems have emerged from the seeds. On some of the seedlings,

you can see the cotyledons, or "seed leaves."

2. An organism's response to gravity is called gravitropism. If an organism grows toward a source of gravity, it is exhibiting *positive gravitropism*. If an organism grows away from a source of gravity, it is exhibiting *negative gravitropism*. Which type of gravitropism do plant roots exhibit? Explain.

Suggested answer: Positive gravitropism. They grow downward, toward gravity.

3. Examine the diagram below. As the root of this seedling bends, which side of the root is getting longer: the side labeled "A" or the side labeled "B"? Explain.

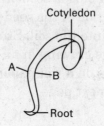

Suggested answer: Side "A" is getting longer. The distance along the "outside" of the bend is

greater than the distance along the "inside" of the bend.

Materials

- black film canister
- marker
- heavy-duty paper towel   Use very absorbent paper towels, rather than the brown ones typically found in schools.
- scissors
- water
- transfer pipette
- Fast Plant™ or turnip seedlings

Advance Preparation
A week or more before the lab
Order wild-type Fast Plant seeds from Carolina Biological. See the front of this Laboratory Manual Teacher's Edition for contact information. (You can also grow turnip seedlings, but the cotyledons do not stick as well to the wet paper towels.) Follow the directions to grow the seedlings in soil. The seedlings should grow about 4 more days after they emerge from the soil, or until the cotyledons have flattened. Cut the seedlings at the surface of the soil.

Gather black plastic film canisters with lids. Ask a local photo processer to save them for you.

Procedure

Part A: Making a Prediction

In the Prelab Activity you looked at how plant roots respond to gravity. Now you will make predictions about how young stems respond to gravity and perform an experiment to test the predictions. Discuss the following questions as a group.

1. Normally, as a seed germinates the young stem grows upward toward the light. But in what direction do you think young stems will grow in the dark? Could gravity also influence in which direction a stem grows? Record your thoughts below.

_____

_____

_____

2. Make your prediction.
In the dark, a plant's stem will grow _____.

Part B: Observing Plant Stem Gravitropism

1. Use a marker to label the outside of the film canister's lid with your initials.

2. Use scissors to cut a 1-cm-wide strip of paper towel. Place the paper towel strip against the inside surface of a film canister. Use a pipette to add a few drops of water to the paper towel strip. Leave no more than a couple of extra drops of water on the bottom of the canister.

3. Gently pull the wet paper towel strip about halfway out of the canister. Then position the seedling so that the cotyledons are resting on the middle of the strip as shown below. The water will hold the seedling in place, and when the canister is upright, the young stem will be in a position parallel to the ground (horizontal). Note that the seedling does not have a root. Your teacher removed the root because it would make the seedling too heavy to stick to the paper towel.

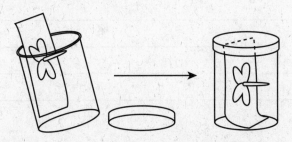

4. Slide the paper towel strip and seedling into the canister. Snap on the lid. Place the canister in an area designated by your teacher.

Safety and Disposal
Advise students with allergic skin conditions to wear plastic gloves when handling plant materials. Remind them to handle scissors with care. Have students wash their hands with soap after the lab. Film canisters and plastic pots can be washed for reuse. No special disposal required.

The seedling can survive and grow for several days in the dark because cotyledons contain nutrient reserves. Once these nutrients are used up, the seedlings will require light for photosynthesis.

5. The next day, open the film canister and observe the stem. Sketch the stem in the space below.

Expected Results (Part B)
The stem will bend upwards. This will surprise many students, who may assume that the "root end" of the stem will grow down.

Do the results of this experiment support your prediction? Explain.

_____

_____

_____

Part C: Designing Your Own Experiment 🌱 🔪 ✋ ⚠️

1. List two or three questions that you have in response to the results of Part B.

_____

_____

_____

_____

2. Design an experiment to answer one of your questions. Have your teacher approve your procedure before you start.

Question:

Some questions students could ask are: "Which environmental factor has more influence—light or gravity?" "If a tiny bit of the root were left attached to the young stem, which direction would the stem bend in the film canister?" "Do seedlings and mature plants respond to gravity in the same way?"

_____

Hypothesis:

_____

_____

_____

_____

Name _____ Class _____ Date_____

Prediction:

_____

_____

_____

Procedure:

_____

_____

_____

_____

_____

_____

_____

Observations:

_____

_____

_____

_____

Analysis and Conclusions

1. Why was it necessary to grow the plants in the dark for Part A?

Suggested answer: to make sure that only the effect of gravity was tested.

_____

_____

2. What type of gravitropism do plant stems exhibit? Explain.

Suggested answer: Plant stems exhibit negative gravitropism. Stems grow in the direction opposite of

gravity's pull.

3. Discuss the results of your experiment in Part C. Did the results support your hypothesis? If not, revise your hypothesis and record it below.

Students' responses will vary based on their experiments and results.

_____

_____

_____

Extension

What is the mechanism behind the ability of stems to bend in response to gravity? Most researchers believe that the plant hormone auxin may play a role. To demonstrate auxin's effect on stem growth, obtain another stem and cotyledons from your teacher. Place a small piece of wet paper towel in the lid of a film canister. Then place the cotyledons on the piece of paper towel. With a flat toothpick apply auxin paste to one side of the stem. **CAUTION:** *Wear goggles when working with the auxin paste.* Mark the paper towel on the side of the stem where you placed the auxin (see the diagram below). Place the film canister over the lid and allow the stem to sit at least overnight. Did the stem bend toward the side with the auxin paste or away from it? What does this tell you about the effect of auxin?

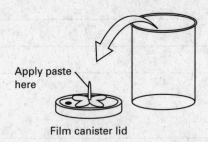

Apply paste here

Film canister lid

Extension
You and your students should wear goggles when working with the auxin paste.

Some researchers think that auxin accumulates in cells in the lower side of a stem and weakens the cell walls. The water pressure in the cells causes them to elongate. The lower side grows longer than the upper side, causing the stem to bend and the plant to continue to grow up.

You can order auxin paste from a biological supply company. If you have auxin powder, you can make paste by mixing 100 g auxin powder with 25 g lanolin, which you can purchase at a pharmacy.

Source: Wisconsin Fast Plants™ Program. *Spiraling Through Life With Fast Plants.* Kendall Hunt, 2001.

Falling Leaves

Testing the Effects of Auxin on Leaf Drop

Question What role does the plant hormone auxin perform in the regulation of leaf drop?

Lab Overview In this investigation you will experiment with bean plants to discover the influence of the plant hormone auxin on the attachment of a leaf to a stem at the base of the petiole. You will cut two leaf blades from a plant, while leaving the petioles intact on the plant. Then you will apply auxin to one petiole and observe the plant for 7–14 days.

Introduction Leaf drop in plants occurs for various reasons. In the fall, deciduous plants drop their leaves in preparation for the long, cold winter when the ground will be too frozen to obtain water and nutrients to support the leaves. Leaves also may be dropped because harsh temperatures have damaged them, or because they have aged and are no longer functioning correctly.

Two hormones—auxin and ethylene—regulate leaf drop. When these hormones are in balance, a leaf remains attached to the plant stem at the base of the petiole. However, if the level of one of these hormones drops and the other one rises, reactions occur in a layer of cells near the base of the petiole that cause the cell walls to weaken. A strong wind, or, eventually, the weight of the leaf, will cause the leaf to drop. In this lab, you will perform an experiment to determine what role auxin plays in leaf drop. First read about various reasons that agriculturists might be interested in controlling leaf drop and "fruit drop" in the Prelab Activity. Then answer the Prelab Questions that follow.

Prelab Activity Agriculturists may alter the levels of plant hormones for many reasons. For example, some cotton farmers spray their crops with hormones that cause leaf drop because cotton is easier to harvest when the leaves are gone. The morning dew dries faster, allowing harvesting to begin earlier. Less time is needed to clean the cotton because the leaves have already been removed.

Plants drop their fruit in a way that is similar to how they drop their leaves. Fruit farmers may spray their fruit trees or plants with hormones that prevent fruit drop, ensuring that the fruit ripens on the plant rather than on the ground.

NOTE: You may wish to have the class do this lab before students read Concept 22.1, which discusses the roles of hormones in leaf drop.

Objective to discover the role of auxin in leaf drop

Inquiry Skills
• predicting
• observing
• making inferences
• controlling variables

Time
• 15 min for Prelab Activity
• 15 min to set up plants on Day 1; 5 min to make observations each class period for 1–2 weeks
• 15 min for Analysis and Conclusions

When ethylene levels are high and auxin levels are low, enzymes such as cellulases are produced that break down cell walls in the abscission zone (area at the junction of stem and petiole). The abscission zone weakens and narrows, causing the leaf to fall off the plant.

There are many types of defoliants used by agriculturists. Some defoliants damage leaves, causing the rise of ethylene levels and fall in auxin levels that lead to leaf drop. Other defoliants produce ethylene, stimulate ethylene production by the plant, or inhibit auxin production.

Examine the art below of a leaf on a deciduous tree and an apple on an apple tree. Then answer the Prelab Questions that follow.

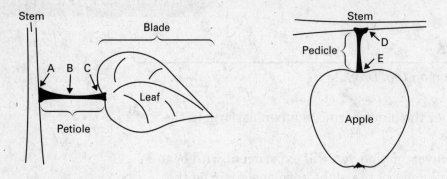

The stalk of a leaf is called the petiole. The stalk of a fruit is called the pedicle.

Prelab Questions

1. Which letters in the diagram represent the points at which a leaf and a piece of fruit typically separate from a plant? Explain.

Suggested answer: A leaf separates from a plant at the base of the petiole (A), and a fruit separates

at the base of the pedicle (D).

2. Give two reasons why it might be easier and more economical to harvest certain crops after the plants have lost their leaves.

Sample answer: Harvesting can begin earlier in the day. Less time is needed for cleaning the crop if the

leaves have already been removed.

3. One effect of auxins is to cause cells to elongate (grow in length). Seeds also produce auxins that stimulate the development of the surrounding ovary into fruit. Based on this information, predict whether low or high levels of auxin are more likely to lead to leaf drop. Explain your prediction.

Students' predictions will vary.

Name _____ Class _____ Date _____

Materials

- bean plant in 4-inch plastic pot
- masking tape
- permanent marker
- scissors
- toothpick
- auxin paste
- twist tie or piece of string
- water

Procedure

1. Use masking tape and a permanent marker to label the plastic pot with the initials of your lab group.

2. With scissors, carefully cut off the *blade only* (not the petiole) of two bean leaves.

3. With a toothpick, apply auxin paste to the cut end of one petiole.

4. To remind you which petiole is treated with auxin, loosely attach a twist tie or a piece of string around the treated petiole.

5. Place your bean plant near a light source as directed by your teacher.

6. Over the next 2 weeks, water the bean plant as directed by your teacher. During each class period, observe the petioles. Record changes you observe and the day that you observe them in the data table below.

Data Table

Day	Observations
	Expected Results: The petiole not treated with auxin will drop off the plant.

Advance Preparation

A few weeks before the lab

- Order IAA (indoleacetic acid) paste from a biological supply company or make the paste following the directions in the **Alternate Materials** section at the end of this lab.

- Contact a local nursery to inquire if they have bean plants or *Coleus* in plastic six-pack pots. If you decide to start bean plants from seed, you will need to sow the seeds at least 3 weeks before you plan to do the lab. See **Alternate Materials** at the end of this lab.

Day of the lab

If you purchased bean plants in six-packs, transplant the plants into 4-inch plastic square pots. Place each 4-inch pot into a plastic freezer container. When the bean plants are watered, extra water will flow into the plastic container, which serves as a reservoir. Only a small amount of excess water is needed. Placing the bean plants under a bank of fluorescent lights is recommended, but not required.

Safety and Disposal

Students should wear goggles when working with the auxin paste. Remind students to wash their hands with soap after applying the auxin paste. Students with allergic skin conditions should wear gloves when working with the plants. Remind students to use the scissors with care to avoid injury. Auxin paste may be flushed down the drain. Plants and soil may be placed in the trash.

Analysis and Conclusions

1. Describe the changes that occurred to the petioles during the time you observed the plants.

Suggested answer: The petiole that was not treated with auxin fell off the plant.

2. What do your results suggest about the effects of auxin on leaf drop? Did your results support the prediction you made in the Prelab Activity? Explain.

Suggested answer: Auxin prevents leaf drop. (Students' responses will vary based on their prediction.)

3. Why do you think a step in the lab was to remove the blades from the leaves? What does this imply about one possible location in a plant where auxin is produced?

Sample answer: We had to add auxin paste after removing the blades. This implies that some auxin

may be produced within leaves.

4. Some chemicals that cause leaf drop work by damaging leaves, causing one plant hormone level to increase and another to decrease. Do you think ethylene or auxin levels increase after a leaf is damaged? Suggest a reason why a decrease in one hormone level might be followed by an increase in another.

Suggested answer: Auxin levels decrease after a leaf is damaged, while ethylene levels increase. This

suggests that one hormone may influence the level of another hormone.

Extension

Are leaves on a plant independent of each other, or can products produced in one leaf influence other leaves? To test this question in relation to leaf drop, you will need two bean plants. Remove all of the leaf blades from one plant. Take care not to remove the apical bud. Remove half of the leaf blades from another plant (remove some leaf blades from both sides of the main stem). Over the next couple of weeks, record when petioles drop from each plant. Compare the rates at which the petioles fall from each plant. Discuss your conclusions.

Extension
Students may observe that the petioles drop from the plant with all of the blades removed at a faster rate than the petioles from the plant with only half the blades removed do.

Alternate Materials
If you have IAA powder, you can make your own paste by mixing 100 mg IAA with 25 g lanolin. You can purchase lanolin from a pharmacy.

Not all plants will drop their petioles in the absence of auxin. If bean plants or *Coleus* plants are not available, try another plant that comes in six-pack containers and has strong petioles 1–2 cm long. Cotton plants are a good choice if you can get some from a local agricultural extension or university.

You can grow your own bean plants from seed in any season. Soak the bean seeds overnight. Then rinse them in a 1% bleach solution. Plant one or two seeds per 4-inch pot in sterilized potting soil. Place pots under a fluorescent light bank. Keep the light within 8 cm of the top of the leaves. The main problems encountered in growing beans from seed are seed rot and etiolation (blanching from lack of sunlight). The bleach treatment, sterile soil, and growing the plants in plenty of light should prevent these problems. Bean plants are mature enough for the lab once they have two sets of true leaves.

Mapping a Mollusk

Squid Dissection

Question What are the anatomical features of a squid? How do these features allow a squid to hunt, avoid predators, and carry out basic life functions?

Lab Overview In this investigation you will explore mollusk form and function as you dissect a squid, observe features of its external and internal anatomy, and make sketches based on your observations.

Introduction Squid are a member of the class of mollusks called cephalopods. Cephalopods are much more agile and active than the other classes of mollusks. Squid have unique features that enable them to move quickly and respond rapidly to stimuli. One example of such a specialized structure is the siphon, which the squid can use to propel itself in any direction. You'll observe the action of the siphon in the Prelab Activity. Another specialized structure is the ink sac. When threatened by a predator, a squid can release murky, black ink from its ink sac, concealing the squid. For hunting, squid have two long tentacles that can extend out quickly like whips and grasp the squid's prey tightly. These tentacles, along with eight grasping arms, make up the foot of the squid.

The mantle, an outgrowth of the body surface that drapes over the animal, is a distinctive feature of mollusks. A squid's internal organs are exposed to the external environment as seawater circulates through the mantle cavity (the space between the mantle and the squid's body). When squid reproduce, the male squid reaches an arm into its mantle cavity, obtains sperm, and transfers them to the female squid's mantle cavity.

Prelab Activity Rinse your squid under running water before beginning your dissection. As you rinse the squid, you can observe the action of the siphon. **CAUTION:** *Wear safety goggles, gloves, and an apron at all times when working with the squid.*

Hold the squid vertically in the stream of water with the tentacles pointing upward so that water flows into the mantle cavity. Tilt the head back away from the siphon and stand back! Record your observations below.

Observations:

_____

_____

Objective to learn about the complex adaptations of a mollusk

Inquiry Skills
- observing
- classifying
- making inferences

Time
- 10 min for Prelab Activity
- 10 min for Part A
- 30 min for Part B
- 15 min for Analysis and Conclusions

Prelab Questions

1. The name cephalopod means "head-foot." How do you think the squid got this name?

Sample answer: Its eyes are located near its foot.

2. What are some general characteristics of mollusks that you might expect to see while observing the squid in the lab?

Sample answer: A mantle, radula, shell, gill, and foot.

3. Identify at least three structures found in squid, and describe their functions.

Sample answer: Squid use a structure called a siphon to propel themselves in different directions.

They can release ink from their ink sacs, which hides them from predators while they escape. Squid

have two tentacles that they use to catch prey.

Materials

- one fresh or preserved squid
- large paper plate or dissection tray
- small scissors
- dissecting probe or bamboo skewer
- hand lens or stereomicroscope
- dissecting pins (optional)

Procedure

Part A: Studying the Squid's External Anatomy

1. Sketch the squid and describe its external anatomy.

Suggested answer: The squid has a long mantle with fins. It has two eyes, eight arms, and

two tentacles.

Advance Preparation
A week before the lab
Locate a source for frozen or fresh squid. You may be able to find whole frozen squid sold in 1-lb blocks in a supermarket's frozen seafood section. Many bait shops near the ocean also sell frozen squid. Seafood and Asian markets sell fresh squid. Often seafood markets cut up squid before selling it. Call ahead to ask them to reserve whole squid for you.

Day of the lab
If frozen, thaw squid just before class. Rinse frozen or fresh squid just before the lab to reduce the odor.

Safety and Disposal
To prevent illness caused by microorganisms, remind students to wear plastic gloves, goggles, and lab aprons during the dissection. Remind students to handle sharp instruments carefully to prevent cuts or wounds. Afterward, have students use soap to wash all working surfaces, dissection trays, scissors, probes, pencils and any other items they handled during the lab, then wash their hands thoroughly. Squid and used paper plates should be placed in a waste container lined with two plastic trash bags. Close both bags securely for disposal and remove promptly from the building.

2. The squid should have eight arms of about the same size, known as grasping arms. The squid should also have two longer arm-like structures called tentacles. How do the tentacles differ from the grasping arms?

Suggested answer: The tentacles have suckers at their ends.

_____

_____

_____

3. Use the scissors to remove one of the squid's tentacles. Observe the suckers with a hand lens or stereomicroscope. **CAUTION:** *Handle sharp instruments with care to avoid injury.* Look for tiny, tooth like structures in the suckers that snag prey. Record your observations below.

_____

_____

4. Observe the squid's skin. Look for spotted areas. These spots contain color-producing pigments (called *chromatophores*) that allow the squid to change its color and pattern. Pull off a section of this thin layer of skin and observe it with a stereomicroscope. What do you think might be the benefit to the squid of being able to change its appearance?

Sample answer: The squid can hide from predators or sneak up on prey.

_____

_____

_____

5. Sketch the sucker and chromatophores below.

Part B: Studying the Squid's Internal Anatomy

1. Locate the squid's siphon. Place the squid so the siphon is on top and the fins lie flat against the plate (the ventral [abdominal] side of the squid should be facing up). With scissors, make a cut along the mantle toward the pointed end of the squid. Cut only the mantle—take care not to damage the organs beneath it.

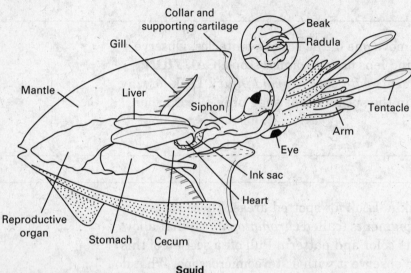

Squid

2. Pull the mantle open to study the internal organs. If you are using a dissection tray, you can use dissection pins to hold the mantle open. Notice the ridges of supporting cartilage on the inside of the mantle. This part of the mantle is called the collar. Now you can see how the siphon is attached. Locate the long tough white muscles on either side of the siphon. Carefully cut these muscles and gently pull the siphon out so you can better see the organs below it. The actions of these muscles move the siphon, changing the angle at which the water is pushed out. This propels the squid in different directions.

NOTE: Squid may vary considerably in appearance from the example depicted here. It may be difficult for students to identify the various organs. Encourage them to make their best inferences and to identify any structures they can.

3. The digestive system extends from the esophagus into the stomach. Food then passes into a long pouch off the stomach called the cecum. Most absorption occurs in the cecum. From the cecum, the intestines go back towards the head and end in the anus near the mantle collar. Wastes exit from the opening of the mantle. To begin your exploration of the digestive system, first locate the liver. The large, white liver consists of two side-by-side lobes. Underneath the liver is the stomach, which is also white. Carefully remove the liver without removing the stomach or any other organs. Be careful also not to remove the ink sac, which looks like a silver pouch.

If you wish, you can have students puncture the ink sac, dip their probe into the ink, and write with the squid ink. Or, later have them remove the pen and use the pen to pierce the ink sac to write with.

4. Next locate the mouth. At the point where all of the arms meet, look for a tiny black structure. This is part of the beak. Squid use their sharp beaks and the radula located inside of the beak to crush or rip prey apart. To access the esophagus, pry the beak apart and gently insert the probe into the beak. When you slide the probe down the esophagus, you should be able to see the probe inside of it. Remove the beak by pulling on it and observe how the two halves fit together. Sketch the beak and the radula in the space below.

5. On either side of the stomach, look for the almost transparent, feathery gills. As water circulates through the mantle, it washes over the gills. Oxygen diffuses through the gills and enters the squid's blood. Two hearts (called *branchial hearts*) pump blood from the gills. One branchial heart is located at the base of each gill (the end furthest from the head). Gently remove one gill by snipping it with scissors. Observe the gill with a stereomicroscope. Sketch the gill in the space below.

How do you think the shape and texture of the gill relate to its function?

Suggested answer: There is a lot of surface area for gas exchange.

_____

_____

_____

6. Squid have a flexible internal shell called a *pen* that gives a squid its shape. To find the pen, gently remove the rest of the internal organs. Look for the pen lying along the whole length of the mantle.

7. Cephalopods (squid, octopus, and their relatives) have very complex nervous systems and keen vision. Examine an eye with the

hand lens and note the cornea (a disk-shaped structure). Sketch your observations below.

Analysis and Conclusions

1. Most mollusks have a mantle, mantle cavity, foot, radula, and a shell. Describe these structures in a squid.

Suggested answer: The mantle drapes over the squid's body like a coat. The mantle cavity is the

space between the mantle and the rest of the squid's body. The squid's foot is divided into eight

arms and two tentacles. The radula is contained in its beak. A squid's "shell," called the *pen,* is

internal and flexible.

2. Identify at least three squid adaptations you observed and explain how they help the squid's survival.

Sample answer: Squid use a structure called a siphon to propel themselves in different directions

away from danger. They can release ink from their ink sacs, which hides them from predators while

they escape. The body surface of squid contains chromatophores, which change the color and pattern

of the squid's skin.

3. Which squid feature did you find most interesting? Why?

Students' answers will vary.

4. Which features that you observed in the squid would you also expect to find in a snail? Which would you not expect to find?

Sample answer: Would expect to find a mantle, mantle cavity, radula, heart, and gill. Would not

expect to find tentacles, a beak, and an ink sac.

Extension

Squid have the largest nerve cells of any animals in the world. The cells can be 100 times wider than mammalian nerve cells, but they function in much the same way. Scientists have used the long nerves in a squid's body to study how a brain sends signals through nerve cells and how nerve cells repair themselves. Research and write a report describing squid nerve cells and what researchers have learned from studying them.

Extension
You may wish to go over the basic structure of a nerve cell (neuron) with your students. This will help them understand more of the information that they research.

Wanted Worms

Exploring the Adaptations and Behavior of Flatworms and Segmented Worms

Question How are the adaptations and behavior of flatworms and segmented worms suited to their lifestyles and environments?

Lab Overview In this investigation you will closely observe a living flatworm (planarian) or segmented worm (*Lumbriculus*). You will study the anatomy of the worm and discover how it moves and responds to stimuli. You will research the type of worm you are observing, then create a "wanted poster" describing it.

Introduction Planarians, like all flatworms (phylum Platyhelminthes), have bilateral symmetry. They have a distinct head, tail, back surface, and bottom surface. The eyes and other sense organs are located toward the head. Planarians have a highly branched digestive sac (gastrovascular cavity) with one mouth opening. Food is ingested and wastes are excreted through the same mouth opening.

Lumbriculus (phylum Annelida) are segmented worms. Internal walls divide the body of *Lumbriculus* into distinct sections. The digestive tract is one continuous tube with two openings—a mouth and an anus. Like planarians, *Lumbriculus* are also bilaterally symmetrical.

In this lab and in your further research, you will learn more about the characteristics of planarians and *Lumbriculus*, such as their habitats, sources of food, and methods of locomotion. In the Prelab Activity you will construct a simple device to test your worm's reaction to stimuli.

Prelab Activity In this lab, you will test how your worm moves in response to touch. For the test you need a tool to gently touch the worm without harming it.

1. Cut a 2.5-cm piece of a thin rubber band with scissors.

2. Cut off the bottom 2.5 cm of a transfer pipette tip. Then cut off the narrow portion of the tip.

3. Bend the piece of rubber band in half. Thread it through the pipette tip so that the rounded end sticks out of the tip. See the diagram for guidance.

4. Place the toothpick into the piece of pipette so that the rubber band is lodged in place.

Toothpick and rubber band inside pipette piece

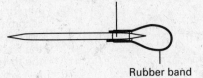

Rubber band

Objective to compare and contrast the adaptations and behavior of flatworms and annelids

Inquiry Skills
• predicting
• observing
• making inferences

Time
• 15 min for Prelab Activity
• 20 min for Part A
• 20 min for Part B
• 30 min for Part C (finishing posters can be assigned for homework)
• 15 min for Analysis and Conclusions

See the end of this lab for more information on *Lumbriculus* and planarians.

Each group will need a rubber band, scissors, a transfer pipette, and a toothpick for the Prelab Activity.

Prelab Questions

1. What are two differences between flatworms and segmented worms?

Suggested answer: Segmented worms are divided into distinct sections. Flatworms have a digestive

sac with one opening, while segmented worms have a digestive tract with two openings.

2. Do you predict that touching the head of either worm would initiate the same response as touching the tail end of the worm? Why or why not?

Sample answer: I predict that touching the head end of a worm and touching the tail end will produce

different responses because a worm's sense organs are located near its head.

Materials

- file folder
- markers or colored pencils
- large sticky notes
- flatworm (planarian) or segmented worm (*Lumbriculus*)
- petri dish
- stereomicroscope
- testing tool (see Prelab Activity)

Procedure

Part A: Starting the Wanted Poster

On the front of a manila file folder, write the word "WANTED" in large letters. Underneath the word "WANTED" record the genus and species name of the worm you will observe, followed by the worm's "aliases" (common names) and "crime." See the diagram below for guidance. Later you will draw in "mug shots" of the worm and record its length. On the inside of the folder, you will place sticky notes with various descriptions of the worm.

Advance Preparation

A couple of weeks before the lab
Order *Lumbriculus variegatus* and planarians from a biological supply company such as Flinn Scientific to be delivered the day before the lab. See the front of this Laboratory Manual Teacher's Edition for contact information.

Lumbriculus can be easily maintained and cultured in a small aquarium or a plastic shoe box. Cover the bottom of the container with torn pieces of brown paper towel. The towel serves as a fibrous substrate of decomposing material for the worms and for microscopic organisms. Fill the container with about 2–3 inches of bottled water. Do not use tap water. To transfer the worms, cut off a bit of the tip of a transfer pipette to enlarge the opening and gently draw up the worms. Every few days, feed *Lumbriculus* a tiny piece of a sinking fish food pellet about the size of a sesame seed. Do not overfeed, or you will foul the water. Aerating the water is recommended, but not critical. Replace the water and half of the toweling every few weeks.

Safety and Disposal
Remind students to handle the stereomicroscopes with care. Students should wash their hands after the lab. Follow the disposal guidelines supplied by the biological supply company from which you ordered the worms.

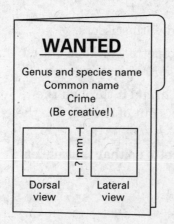

WANTED

Genus and species name
Common name
Crime
(Be creative!)

Dorsal view — Lateral view

Part B: Observing Body Plans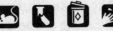

1. Label one sticky note "Identifying features" and label a second one "Distinguishing features." Open the file folder. Place the notes on the left side.

2. Place the petri dish with your worm on the stage of the stereomicroscope and observe the worm closely. Record your observations on the appropriate sticky note. You will add to these lists as you do more research.

   Identifying Features: In this category, provide detailed descriptions of the "suspect's" appearance, including size, color, shape, segmentation, any visible blood vessels, and so on.

   Distinguishing Features: In this category, provide descriptions of any unique or "peculiar" features that distinguish the suspect from its relatives.

3. Draw the "mug shots" on the front of the folder. Sketch the dorsal (top—the worm's "back") and lateral (side) views of the worm. Between the dorsal and lateral sketches, draw a line showing the worm's length in mm. See the diagram on page 276.

Part C: Observing Locomotion

Use the testing tool you made in the Prelab Activity to touch the anterior (head) end and posterior (tail) end of the worm. Touch the worm with the rubber elastic portion of the testing tool only. Use your observations to prepare a "Means of Getaway" sticky note.

Means of Getaway: In this category, describe the worm's movement. How did the worm respond when you touched its head? How did it respond when you touched its tail?

Part D: Researching and Preparing the Poster

1. To fill in the rest of the wanted poster, you will need to learn more about the habitat and adaptations of the worm you were assigned. Use the Internet, library, and other resources provided by your teacher to find information. Prepare sticky notes for the following categories and place them on the right side of the open folder.

   Suspect's Last Whereabouts: Describe the suspect's specific microhabitat (where you would find this type of worm in the wild).

   Preferred Hangouts: Describe the suspect's biological community. What populations of plants and animals tend to live in the same environment as the suspect? What is the suspect's niche?

   Suspect Last Seen Heading Toward: Describe the possible destinations within the suspect's habitat.

Planarians are difficult to keep alive very long in the classroom. To maintain the planarian culture, first place several rocks (about 5 cm in diameter) and 5 cm of bottled water in a plastic shoe box. Carefully add the planarians. The planarians will probably attach themselves to the underside of the rocks. Aerate the water gently with an aquarium pump and aerating stone. You can feed them a piece of cooked egg yolk (the size of a grain of rice) or a fragment of *Lumbriculus*. After they have had an hour to eat, remove any uneaten food so that the water doesn't foul. Change the water often. Keep the box in dim light. Planarians are very sensitive to temperature and oxygen level. If the water temperature rises above 23°C or if the water is not aerated, they will die.

If you wish, you could provide students with information on the feeding methods of planarians with a demonstration of predation. First, make a safety blade by cutting out a 1-cm by 2-cm piece of transparency acetate and covering one edge with masking tape. Place a *Lumbriculus* on a moist paper towel on a hard surface. With the safety blade, cut the worm into three pieces. The worm will not bleed. Place the *Lumbriculus* segments and a planarian in a petri dish half full of water. Place the petri dish in an area where students can observe the worms.

Caution When Apprehending: What makes this organism dangerous to its predators or prey? Describe the suspect's capture and defense mechanisms.

2. Review the descriptions you have posted on the inside of the file folder and revise as needed.

Analysis and Conclusions

1. Compare the habitats of planarians and *Lumbriculus*.

Suggested answer: Both types of worms are typically found in fresh water. *Lumbriculus* live in the

sediment of muddy, shallow water. Planarians live in shallow and deeper waters. They usually

hide under rocks.

2. Which of the two worms do you think would be more likely to capture and eat another worm? Explain your reasoning.

Suggested answer: Planarians, because they are carnivores. *Lumbriculus* consume mainly plant parts

and microscopic organisms.

3. Describe the most intriguing fact that you learned about the worm you observed.

Students' responses will vary.

Extension

Switch posters with a classmate who observed the type of worm you did not observe. Describe the poster. Note the characteristics of the worm that are much different from those of the worm you observed.

Extension
See the descriptions of the worms below for many of the differences that students will note.

Adapted from: "America's Most Wanted Invertebrates" (2001) by Lori Ihrig and Charles Drewes from www.eeob.iastate.edu/faculty/ DrewesC/htdocs/. Used by permission.

Lumbriculus variegatus are a member of the phylum Annelida and the class Oligochaeta. Common names are California blackworms or mudworms. They live in many areas of the world in the muddy sediments of shallow waters where they consume decaying plants, bacteria, algae, and protists. Blackworms crawl through the mud with the aid of rough bristles on their ventral side. They can also swim, but only for short distances. Respiration occurs through the skin, especially through the dorsal side of the tail. In shallow water, blackworms push their tails through the surface of the water. Students will observe the pulsating dorsal vessel that brings blood from the head toward the tail. Although each blackworm contains male and female reproductive organs, sexual reproduction is not common. Fragmentation is the usual method of reproduction.

Flatworms with the common name planaria are members of the phylum Platyhelminthes, of the class Turbellaria, and the genus *Dugesia* (species vary). Planarians live in fresh water. They are predators, but will also feed on decaying meat. To feed, planarians move their pharynx and attach it to their prey. They wrap their body around their prey as they digest the prey. Planarians have a head and two eyespots. The lateral flaps on their heads detect smell. Planarians move by gliding along a layer of mucus, propelled by the cilia that line their ventral surface. Planarians can reproduce asexually by fragmentation. They are hermaphrodites, but cross-fertilization does occur during sexual reproduction. Planarians have no circulatory or respiratory systems. Chemical and gas exchange occurs by diffusion through their flat bodies.

The Life of WOWBugs

Observing WOWBug™ Behavior

Question How do WOWBugs interact and communicate with each other?

Lab Overview In this investigation you will observe an active culture of WOWBugs, identify the males and females, and compare their behaviors. Then, you will perform an experiment to discover how WOWBugs communicate over a distance.

Introduction To start the investigation, you'll learn about differences between male and female WOWBugs and about WOWBug behavior. In the lab activity, you will observe male and female WOWBugs separately. Then, you will observe them together. Next you will conduct an experiment to determine how male and female WOWBugs communicate and find each other.

Prelab Activity Read the information below about WOWBugs, then complete the Prelab Activity.

WOWBugs (*Melittobia digitata*) are tiny wasps that live as parasites on the larvae of other insects. There are many differences between female and male WOWBugs. Females can fly, while males just have stubby wings and cannot fly. Females have reddish, compound eyes. Males have tiny pits where their compound eyes would be. They have three simple eyes on their foreheads that allow them to sense light, but they are essentially blind. Only females have stingers (though the stingers are too small to penetrate human skin). Females have black bodies. Males have light brown bodies. Females have thinner antennae than males.

When an adult female and male mate, up to 95% of the female's hundreds of eggs are fertilized. Female larvae with two sets of chromosomes (diploid) hatch from the fertilized eggs. From the unfertilized eggs hatch male larvae with only one set of chromosomes (haploid). Therefore, female WOWBugs have twice the amount of DNA as males.

Female WOWBugs leave their colony to start a new colony. If a female has mated before she leaves her original colony, she will lay fertilized eggs on other insect larvae. If she has not mated, she will lay a few unfertilized eggs. When male larvae hatch from these eggs and mature, the female mates and the new colony begins.

Male WOWBugs are very aggressive in the presence of other males. In the lab, males must be kept separate because they will fight to the death. Since such a small number of male eggs are laid in each batch, you will need to take extra care in the lab to be sure that the males are not harmed.

Objective to observe insect behavior and design an experiment to discover how male and female WOWBugs communicate and locate each other

Inquiry Skills
- predicting
- observing
- asking questions
- designing experiments
- formulating testable hypotheses
- drawing conclusions
- evaluating and revising hypotheses

Time
- 15 min for Prelab Activity
- 20–30 min for Part A (optional)*
- 15–20 min for Part B
- 30–40 min for Part C
- 50 min for Part D
- 15 min for Analysis and Conclusions

(*Note that students do not have to complete all of the parts. Part A is the least essential part of the lab. You can separate the males and females prior to the lab.)

WOWBugs develop from egg to adult in 17–21 days. Adults do not need food or water. They survive for about two weeks.

Based on what you have read about WOWBugs, make predictions about how you think males and females find each other. Do you think that WOWBugs communicate through vision, sound, smell, or touch? Do you predict that males search for females or that females search for males? Explain your predictions.

Predictions:

_____

_____

_____

Prelab Questions

1. Given that WOWBugs are insects, what types of characteristics do you expect to observe?

   Suggested answer: A head, thorax, and abdomen and three pairs of walking-legs.

   _____

2. List two ways that the female and male WOWBugs differ in appearance.

   Sample answer: Females have reddish compound eyes, while males only have pits where the eyes

   would be. Males have stubby wings, while females have wings capable of flight. Females have black

   bodies. Males have light brown bodies. Females have thinner antennae.

3. Explain the reason that female and male WOWBugs have different amounts of DNA.

   Suggested answer: Females develop from fertilized eggs containing DNA from another female

   and a male. Males develop from unfertilized eggs containing one set of DNA from a female.

   _____

4. Do WOWBugs undergo complete or incomplete metamorphosis? Explain.

   Suggested answer: Complete metamorphosis. WOWBug adults look and function very differently

   from larvae.

   _____

   _____

Materials

- WOWBug pupae culture
- 2 small acrylic boxes
- hand lens or stereomicroscope
- toothpicks
- small paintbrush
- labels

- marker
- aluminum foil
- 3 5-cm pieces of aquarium tubing
- T or Y tubing connector
- cotton balls
- cotton swabs

Name _____ Class _____ Date_____

Procedure ⬛ ⬛ ⬛ ⬛

Part A: Sorting the Female Pupae

1. Use a hand lens or stereomicroscope to examine the WOWBug pupae culture. At this stage you will be able to identify females by their reddish eyes. Use a toothpick to gently push several female pupae into an isolated clump.

2. Touch the end of the paintbrush to the clump of female pupae. Some will become trapped in the bristles. Transfer them to a new acrylic box by gently tapping the brush on the side of the container. Label the container "Unmated females." Later, your teacher will transfer each male into a separate container.

3. Sketch a female WOWBug pupa in the space below.

Alternate Methods
To sort the females before the lab, allow the adults to emerge. Then place several adults in small self-sealing plastic bags, and pass them out to students. Some bags may contain a male mixed in with the females. You can use these mated females to make more cultures. Place four or five mated females in a container with three blowfly pupae.
   Instead of acrylic boxes, you could use depression slides to house the males. Place a male into a depression. Cover the depression with another, upside-down depression slide. Tape the slides together so that the male cannot escape.

4. Check the pupae every day to see if they have emerged as winged adults.

Part B: Observing Female WOWBug Behavior

1. Once the female WOWBugs have matured, observe them closely with a stereomicroscope or hand lens. **CAUTION:** *Do not open the container during your observations. The WOWBugs may escape.* Every 3–5 min for about 15 min, record your observations in the space below. During the observation period, tilt the container to see how the WOWBugs respond. Cover about half of the container with aluminum foil to see how they respond to light and dark.

Observations:

_____

_____

_____

_____

Advance Preparation
Order WOWBug cultures from Carolina Biological. See the front of this Laboratory Manual Teacher's Edition for contact information. The cultures will arrive within blowfly pupae and with extra blowfly pupae you can use as hosts to maintain the cultures. When the cultures arrive, break open the blowfly pupae cases with a toothpick. See the annotation next to Part D for descriptions of the pupae at different stages. It is best to sort the cultures in the late pupal stage.

Safety and Disposal
Review guidelines for the use of live animals. Remind students to take care when using sharp instruments and to handle slides, microscopes, and hand lenses with care. After the lab, have students wash their hands with soap. Freeze insects overnight in a plastic bag before disposal. Acrylic boxes and paintbrushes can be washed for reuse. Other materials can be thrown away.

2. Sketch one of the adult female WOWBugs below.

In most insect species, females attract males by emitting pheromones. However, in WOWBugs males attract the females with pheromones. The male WOWBug often lifts his wings during courtship, which may be a way of releasing the pheromones. When the female WOWBug contacts the male WOWBug, he climbs on her back. The male WOWBug touches the female WOWBug's antennae with his antennae and her legs and abdomen with his legs and abdomen. In nature, courtship and mating occur inside the host nest in the dark.

Part C: Observing WOWBug Courtship and Mating Behaviors

1. Observe the male WOWBug provided by your teacher. Note how its behavior is different from the female WOWBugs' behavior. Record your observations below.

Observations:

_____

_____

_____

2. Carefully open the container holding the male WOWBug. Remove the lid from the container labeled "Unmated females." There should be several females crawling on the lid. Quickly but gently, tap the lid over the container holding the male until several females drop into the box with him. Immediately re-cover both containers.

3. Observe the behavior of the male WOWBug in the presence of females over the next 15–20 min. These pre-mating behaviors are called a *courtship ritual*. Record your observations below.

If several unmated females are placed with one male, the females sometimes surround and harass the male. If he attempts to mate with one female, the other females may knock him off. Sometimes the females line up to mate with the male. Possibly the females are more aggressive if several days have passed since they emerged as adults and they have not mated.

Observations:

_____

_____

_____

4. Go back to the Prelab Activity and review your predictions. Based on your observations in parts B and C, would you now like to revise your predictions? If so, explain your revisions below.

Revised Predictions:

_____

_____

_____

Part D: Discovering How WOWBugs Communicate

1. Now you will perform an experiment with a "choice chamber" to find out how male and female WOWBugs communicate and find each other. To construct a choice chamber, insert aquarium tubing into the T or Y connector (see diagram below). Construct Chamber 3 first. Use a toothpick to insert a small piece of cotton about 2.5 cm into the tube. Use scissors to cut off one end of a cotton swab and use that to plug the chamber.

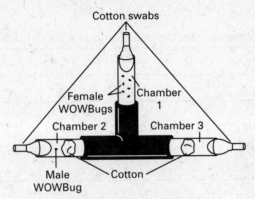

Sample Choice Chamber

2. To construct Chamber 2, use a toothpick to insert a small piece of cotton about 2.5 cm into the tube. Place the open end of Chamber 2 over a male WOWBug. The insect will crawl up the side of the tube. Seal the chamber with another cut-off cotton swab.

3. Next, place the open end of Chamber 1 over the female WOW-Bugs. Once you have about 10 females in the tube, quickly seal it with a cut-off cotton swab.

4. Observe the female WOWBugs. Do they wander aimlessly or in a particular direction? Based on your observations, can you rule out vision, touch, sound, or smell as senses that female and male WOWBugs use in locating each other? Explain.

   Sample answer: Yes, the female WOWBugs move toward Chamber 2, which contains the male.

   Since the females and male are separated by cotton, WOWBugs must use another sense other than

   touch or vision to locate each other.

5. Experiments have shown that if a dead male WOWBug is placed in Chamber 3, females are attracted toward both Chamber 2 and Chamber 3. Based on this information, which sense do you think WOWBugs use to commumnicate? Explain.

   Sample answer: If females are attracted to a male WOWBug that cannot produce sound, then females

   must be attracted by the scent of a male WOWBug.

Determining WOWBug Pupal Development
Early pupal stage: Some larvae are still present. They look like tiny white worms. In 1–2 weeks, you will have adults.
  Middle pupal stage: Light colored pupae that look like tiny flies trapped in a clear case. If you can see red eyes on most of the pupae, they are almost in late stage.
  Late pupal stage: Dark colored pupae. Once some of the pupae are dark colored, it is possible to find the males. Look for pupae without eyes. If your students are carrying out Part A, have the students separate out clumps of females at this stage.
  If some adult males have emerged before you separate the males and females, remove the males and place them in separate containers (otherwise the males will kill each other). If some females have also emerged, separate out the females that are still pupae. When the separated females emerge, you will have unmated females for parts C and D of this lab.

Analysis and Conclusions

1. Describe the WOWBugs' behavior in the choice chamber.

   Answers will vary.

2. Discuss the results of your experiment(s). What conclusions do the results lead you to make about how WOWBugs communicate in seeking a mate?

   Answers will vary, but students should conclude that the bugs communicate through smell produced by the male.

3. Share your findings with other lab groups. Did other lab groups draw similar conclusions? Explain.

   Answers will vary.

4. What are some of the challenges you faced working with live WOWBugs?

   Sample answer: Extra care had to be taken to make sure the bugs did not escape or become harmed.

   Live organisms can be unpredictable.

5. Discuss some possible sources of error in your conclusions about how WOWBugs behave in nature.

   Sample answer: The females could have been searching for a way out, rather than searching for males.

   We didn't test to see if females would respond to the smell of other females.

Extension

You can use the choice chambers to design experiments to study many other questions. For example, you could observe how mated females behave in the choice chamber with just a male or in the presence of unmated females. You could also use the choice chambers to test the reaction of WOWBugs to different environmental conditions such as temperature and light. Choose one of these examples or come up with a new question of your own and devise an experiment. Check with your teacher before carrying out any experiments.

Extension
Challenge students to determine the rate at which females move toward the male. Does this change with the number of days since emergence? Do the females race toward the male faster when they have fewer days left to live?

Name _____ Class _____ Date _____

Crustacean Formation

Observing Brine Shrimp Growth and Development

Question What are the stages of brine shrimp development?

Lab Overview In this investigation you will observe the growth and development of brine shrimp, crustaceans of the genus *Artemia*. To begin, you will adhere cysts—eggs containing a dormant embryo—to a miniature grid. You will observe specific cysts as they develop and hatch and then observe the *Artemia* as they mature into adults.

Introduction Despite their common name, "brine shrimp," *Artemia* are not closely related to decapod shrimp. *Artemia* inhabit saltwater wetlands and are a major food source for many shorebirds and fish.

Female *Artemia* can release either thin-shelled eggs or thick-shelled cysts. Thin-shelled eggs contain embryos that develop rapidly and hatch quickly. Thick-shelled cysts contain dormant embryos—embryos that have stopped developing. The *Artemia* cysts you will study can survive for over a decade. Under the right environmental conditions, embryo development will begin again and a larva will hatch from a cyst. At this stage, the larva has a head with two pairs of antennae, one eye, and mandibles. In the lab, you will observe *Artemia* go through multiple stages of molting before becoming adults with the typical characteristics of arthropods.

Prelab Activity Read the information below. Use the sketch of an *Artemia* as a guide to construct a model demonstrating its feeding mechanism. Use a paper plate to represent the body, small paint-brushes for the appendages, and rice grains to represent food particles. Use your model to show how food is filtered and directed toward the mouth.

Brine shrimp use their appendages for locomotion, respiration, and feeding. Movement of the appendages produces a water current that pulls food particles, such as algae, toward the brine shrimp's body. Hair-like projections on the appendages trap the food against the body. The food is slowly pushed along a groove on the ventral side toward the mouth. Once the food gets close to the mouth, the brine shrimp secretes a sticky substance that holds the food together. The brine shrimp then ingests the ball of food through its mouth.

Objective to observe hatching and development of the arthropod *Artemia*

Inquiry Skills
• observing
• classifying
• collecting data
• calculating

Time
• 15 min for Prelab Activity
• 30 min for Part A
• 10–15 min for Part B, days 1–5, Day 7, and Day 14
• 15 min for Analysis and Conclusions

The bodies of *Artemia* average 8 mm in length.

Prelab Questions

1. What are the three functions of *Artemia's* appendages?

Suggested answer: The appendages are used for locomotion, respiration, and feeding.

2. Would you characterize *Artemia's* method of feeding as hunting or filtering? Explain.

Suggested answer: Filtering. As water moves through the appendages, food is "collected."

3. Learning that *Artemia* are arthropods, what characteristics would you expect to observe in adult *Artemia*?

Suggested answer: *Artemia* should have segmented bodies, jointed appendages, and exoskeletons made of chitin.

Materials

- transparency grid
- forceps
- double-sided tape
- scissors
- *Artemia* cysts
- small paintbrush
- paper towel
- microscope or stereomicroscope
- petri dish
- graph paper
- artificial sea water
- blended yeast powder

Advance Preparation

A few weeks before the lab
Obtain brine shrimp cysts and Instant Ocean® from a biological supply company or from a pet store. See the front of this Laboratory Manual Teacher's Edition for supply company information. Cysts die if they are not stored properly, so it is best to obtain them from a pet store that gets new stock often. The cysts should not be more than a year old. Buy new cysts each year.

The day before the lab
- Mix 36 g of Instant Ocean® with 1 L of dechlorinated or bottled water to make the artificial sea water.
- Prepare grids. See the template at the end of this lab.

After students complete Part A
Prepare the powdered yeast to feed the larvae. Grind a few tablespoons of dry baker's or brewer's yeast with a mortar and pestle until it is a fine powder. Transfer the powder to microcentrifuge tubes. Push pushpins through the bottom of the tubes. To feed the larvae, pull out the pin and dust a tiny amount of yeast on the surface of the water.

Procedure

Part A: Placing the Cysts (Day 1)

1. Position your transparency grid so that the numbers are on the left and the letters are across the top.

2. Use forceps to pull on the end of the double-sided tape. Use scissors to cut off a 1-cm piece of tape. **CAUTION:** *Handle sharp objects with care to avoid injury.* Place the tape on top of the grid and push gently with the forceps to stick it down. Avoid touching the tape with your fingers.

3. Pick up several *Artemia* cysts by very gently touching the cysts with the tip of a paintbrush.

4. You need to adhere about 50 cysts to the grid so that they are spaced evenly. You should not have more than 2 cysts in a square.

Safety and Disposal
Remind students to handle the forceps with care. Students should wash their hands with soap after setting up the grids and observing the brine shrimp. To dispose of the brine shrimp you can feed them to fish. Or, heat the water or add bleach to the water. Then dispose of them in the trash. Wash petri dishes with a 10% bleach solution and store for reuse.

Gently brush cysts onto a tiny section of the grid. Lift the brush from the grid and place the brush on a different section. Use the brush to gather more cysts as necessary. If you end up with more than 50 cysts on the tape, or if the cysts are clumped together, you will need to start over.

Camel hair paintbrushes work best for transfer of the cysts.

Students may need a few tries to get the grids set up correctly.

5. Gently brush the paintbrush over the surface of the grid so that any unattached cysts will roll onto a sticky area.

6. Holding the grid over a paper towel, flick your finger against the side of the grid without the tape to remove loose cysts.

7. Pull off another piece of double-sided tape and place it in the middle of a petri dish. Use forceps to transfer the grid to the petri dish and stick the side without the cysts onto the tape.

8. Gently brush the paintbrush back and forth over the grid to re-adhere any cysts that have come loose.

9. Observe the cysts with a microscope or stereomicroscope on low power. If you see that there are too many cysts on the grid, you will need to repeat steps 1–8.

10. Label a piece of graph paper to match the grid with numbers on the left and letters across the top. Record the number of *Artemia* you see in each square of the grid in the corresponding square on the graph paper. If a square on the grid is blank, leave the corresponding square on the graph paper blank.

11. Choose five cysts to observe closely during their growth and development. Record their coordinates in Data Table 1 below. Also, sketch the cysts and write a general description.

Data Table 1

Cyst Coordinate	Initial Sketch and Observations	Day 1 Sketch and Observations	Day 2 Sketch and Observations
	Expected Results Initial: cysts look like table tennis balls that are dented in one spot		
	12 h: cysts have swelled and are spherical 16 h: cysts have cracked 18 h: hatching begins; bulge forms out of cyst 72 h: nauplius larvae are swimming		
	Days 4–5: metanauplius larvae, trunk has elongated Development of the thoracic appendages depends on the temperature of the room but will occur in 7–14 days.		

12. Add artificial sea water to the petri dish until it is half full.

Part B: Observing Development of *Artemia*

Days 1–2

On days 1 and 2, use the microscope or stereomicroscope to observe the five cysts. Record your observations and sketch the cysts in Data Table 1 on the previous page.

Days 3–4

1. By Day 3, several of the *Artemia* may have hatched. Record your observations and draw sketches of the five larvae (called *nauplius larvae* at this stage) in Data Table 2 below. Note the moving antennae and undeveloped appendages.

Data Table 2

Day 3 Sketch and Observations	Day 4 Sketch and Observations	Day 7 Sketch and Observations	Day 14 Sketch and Observations

2. On Day 4, record your observations and draw sketches in Data Table 2. At this point, you may observe some larvae (now called *metanauplius larvae*), which have molted their exoskeleton. They have developed an elongated trunk (thorax) from which the thoracic appendages will eventually develop.

3. To feed the metanauplius larvae, pull the pushpin out of the microcentrifuge tube containing yeast powder. Tap a tiny amount of powder onto the surface of the water in the petri dish.

Day 7 and Day 14

1. Observe the metanauplius larvae again on Day 7. Record your observations and make sketches in Data Table 2.

2. Feed the *Artemia* again by dusting a few specks of powdered yeast on the surface of the water.

3. Repeat steps 1–2 on Day 14.

Nauplius larvae do not need to be fed because they obtain energy from the yolk that is still attached to them.

Male *Artemia* can be distinguished from females by the males' large grasping secondary antennae.

Name _____ Class _____ Date _____

Analysis and Conclusions

1. What characteristics of *Artemia* make it a crustacean?

Suggested answer: *Artemia* have a hardened shell, multiple pairs of appendages, legs on abdomen, and two pairs of antennae.

2. Do adult *Artemia* have a cephalothorax or a head, thorax, and abdomen?

Suggested answer: *Artemia* have a head, thorax, and abdomen.

3. Compare and contrast the adult *Artemia* and the fossil trilobite shown in Figure 24-4 on page 526 in your textbook.

Suggested answer: They both have numerous legs and appendages on their heads. *Artemia* have smaller heads and have an abdomen, whereas the trilobite appears to have only a large head and a thorax.

4. Summarize the growth and development of *Artemia*.

See **Expected Results** in Part A of the lab.

Extension

Design an experiment using transparency grids to test the rate at which *Artemia* cysts hatch and develop in artificial sea water versus distilled or tap water. Obtain permission from your teacher before carrying out any experiments.

Extension

Students can use the coordinates on the transparency grids to monitor the number of cysts that hatch. Some cysts will hatch in the distilled or tap water, but many more will hatch in the artificial seawater.

Adapted from: "Stuck on *Artemia*" (1999) by Charles Drewes from www.eeob.iastate.edu/faculty/DrewesC/htdocs/

Template for Transparency Grids

Transparency grid instructions:

Photocopy this master onto a piece of transparency film made for photocopiers. Cut out the individual "slides" and distribute them to your students.

Voyagers and Acrobats

Comparing Fish Body Shapes

Question What body shapes can be observed in cartilaginous and bony fishes? How does body shape affect the way a fish moves?

Lab Overview In this investigation you will study examples of fishes with different body shapes and learn how each body shape is an adaptation for survival in a specific environment. You will make a model of one of the fish body shapes and test how fast the model can move across an aquarium.

Introduction The amount of effort a fish uses as it moves through the water depends directly on the resistance that the water exerts on the fish. In general, the more streamlined the body of the fish, the less water resistance there is. In this lab, you will determine which of two body shapes enables a fish to swim forward at a faster rate by dragging model fish through the water at a constant degree of resistance. You will measure the "fitness" of a particular fish body shape in regards to moving forward through the water.

Prelab Activity The ability to move quickly forward through the water is an important adaptation for many types of fishes. However, there are other types of fishes that do not spend much of their time moving forward through the water. For example, some fishes lie in wait for their prey. Other fishes make quick, precise movements in all directions to evade predators.

The body shapes of fishes are adaptations that allow them to move through the water in different ways. Read the descriptions below and on the next page of various types of fish shapes. Then, match the letter of the description with the correct diagram on the next page. Afterward, answer the Prelab Questions.

a. Fishes with a streamlined body shape and pointed head encounter little water resistance as they swim. Fishes with this body shape usually have a narrow, forked tail, which helps to generate forward power. They are the long-distance voyagers of the sea. Examples of this type of fish body shape include the tuna, mackerel, and anchovy.

b. Fishes with compressed, disklike bodies can maneuver in all directions like acrobats. These fishes are adapted to capture tiny floating prey, and have rippling, waving fins that allow for control of precise movements. Examples of this type of fish body shape include the butterfly fish and angelfish.

Objective to make predictions about fish based on body shape, then design and test clay models of fish shapes

Inquiry Skills
- making measurements
- using models
- collecting data
- controlling variables
- analyzing data
- drawing conclusions

Time
- 15–20 min for Prelab Activity
- 5–10 min for Part A
- 10–15 min for Part B
- 20 min for Analysis and Conclusions

c. Fishes with flexible bodies and large, traplike mouths are adapted to move forward quickly and "pounce" on their prey. Their bodies bend into a curve, which provides quick forward motion over a short distance, and their large heads have powerful jaws to clamp prey. Examples of this type of fish body shape include the bass and kelp rockfish.

d. Fishes with long, snakelike bodies can easily hide in rock crevices. These fishes have very small fins or no fins at all and move by undulating their bodies (moving in a wavelike motion). They lurk in narrow spaces and lie in wait for prey. Eels are an example of this type of fish body shape.

e. Fishes that rest on the ocean floor usually have flat bodies. These fishes often have eyes on the top of their head so that they can see while lying on the ocean floor. These fishes move by making wavelike motions with their bodies. Many have body coloring that allows them to blend in with the ocean floor. They sometimes partially cover their bodies with sand, which makes them even less visible. Examples of this type of fish body shape are the ray, flounder, and sand dab.

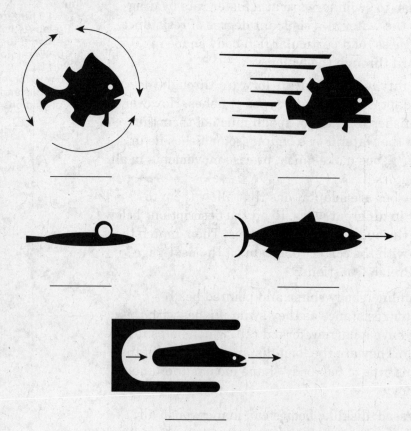

Name _____ Class _____ Date_____

Prelab Questions

1. Which body type do you think a fish that migrates to different areas of the ocean would have? Explain.

Suggested answer: Voyager. This body shape allows a fish to travel for long distances with little

water resistance.

_____

_____

2. Which body type is best for a fish that ambushes its prey? Explain.

Suggested answer: Fish with flexible bodies and large traplike mouths. These fish can bend

their bodies in a curve and then lunge forward to grab prey.

_____

_____

3. Which body type is best for a fish that feeds on tiny, floating zoo-plankton? Explain.

Suggested answer: Acrobat. This body shape allows a fish to move in all directions with precise

movements, which allows them to capture tiny prey.

_____

_____

Materials

- modeling clay two lumps of clay, 25 g each (about 1 tbsp)
- copper or brass wire (0.5 m, 28 gauge)
- protractor
- large aquarium or large, shallow plastic box (clear)
- water
- pencil or tape
- stopwatch

Procedure

Part A: Setting Up the Tank

1. Fill the aquarium or storage box half full of water.

2. Place the meter stick across the top of the length of the aquarium or storage box as shown in the diagram on the next page.

3. With a pencil or a small piece of tape, mark the "start" point on the meter stick, 8 cm from the left edge of the container.

For success it is critical to use 28-gauge wire. Do a trial run so that you know the appropriate length of the wire.

Safety and Disposal
Remind students to handle the wire with care to avoid wounds to the skin. If a student is cut with a wire, he or she is at risk for a tetanus infection. Ask students to take care not to splash water on the floor when testing their fish models. Keep water away from any electrical equipment. Promptly wipe up any spilled water to prevent slips and falls. Modeling clay and wire can be saved for reuse.

4. Mark the "finish" point on the meter stick, 8 cm before the end of the right edge of the container.

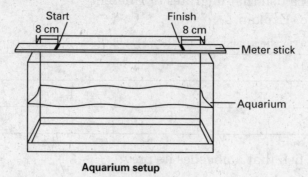

Aquarium setup

Part B: Preparing the Fish Models

1. With one piece of modeling clay make a model of a streamlined, long-distance voyager fish.

2. Use the second piece of clay to make a model of a compressed, disklike acrobat fish. The two fish must have the same mass, so use all of the clay to make the models.

3. Attach one end of the wire to the center of the straight edge of the protractor as shown below. To attach it, wrap the wire once around the protractor and then twist the wire end around the rest of the wire.

4. Wrap the other end of the wire around the middle of one of your fish shapes. Twist the wire end around the rest of the wire. Adjust the wire so that the fish hangs down straight. You may need several practice tries to get the fish model to hang straight and parallel (horizontal) to the ground.

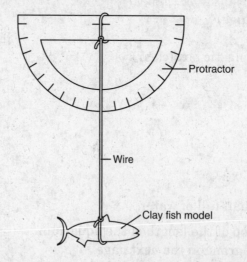

Expected Results
The voyager-shaped fish will travel across the water about twice as fast as the acrobat with the same amount of deflection. It is difficult to keep the acrobat fish from changing direction, whereas the voyager fish naturally speeds forward.

5. Predict which fish you think you will be able to move across the tank faster. Explain your prediction.

_____

_____

Part C: Testing the Fish Models

1. Position the first fish in the water so that it is fully submerged and its "head" is at the "start" mark on the meter stick. See the diagram below for guidance. Hold the protractor upside down so that the straight edge is at the top. Note that the wire is taut and hangs straight down so that it crosses the 90° mark on the protractor. Use the meter stick as a guide to keep the protractor level as you pull the "fish" through the water. Notice that the wire is no longer hanging straight down. The resistance of the water causes the fish to "lag" behind your hand. The faster you pull the fish, the more the wire deflects. Practice adjusting your movement to keep the wire deflected only 5° so that the protractor reads 95°.

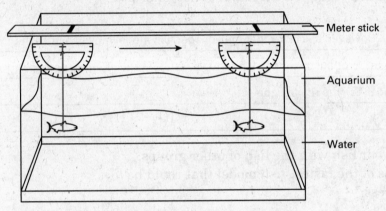

Hold the protractor at about the level of the meter stick as you pull the fish through the water.

2. Once you feel comfortable moving the fish through the water at a constant rate of deflection, bring the fish back to the "start" mark and start the stopwatch. Move the fish so that the wire deflects 5° during the entire distance of the tank. Remember to use the meter stick as a guide to be sure that the top of the protractor remains level. Stop the stopwatch when the head of your model fish reaches the "finish" point marked on the meter stick.

3. Repeat Step 2 three times for each fish. Record your data in the data table below.

Data Table

Voyager Model	Time (sec)	Acrobat Model	Time (sec)
Trial 1		Trial 1	
Trial 2		Trial 2	
Trial 3		Trial 3	

Analysis and Conclusions

1. Calculate the average time it took for each of your fish to reach the end of the tank.

   Voyager: _____ sec   Students' answers will vary. Depending on the size of
                                  the tank or plastic container used, it could take 5–15 sec
   Acrobat: _____ sec   to drag a "fish" from one end to the other.

2. Which of your fish moved through the water faster? Were the results of your investigation what you expected? If not, offer possible explanations.

   Students' answers will vary. However, it is likely that the voyager fish model moved across the

   tank about twice as fast as the acrobat fish model. If a group's results were different, perhaps

   they did not make the voyager fish the right shape.

3. Compare the times of your fish with the fish of other groups. Describe characteristics of the fastest fish model that could have contributed to its "success."

   Students' answers will vary.

Extension

Make another fish from 25 g of clay. See if you can improve on the streamlined shape or test another fish body shape and see how it compares to the ones you tested in this activity.

Additional Resource
The following book has good drawings and information about fish locomotion (pages 43–52).
Niesen, Thomas M.
The Marine Biology Coloring Book.
HarperResource, 2000.

Extension
Students should test additional models in a supervised environment. If students choose to test other fish shapes keep in mind that a model with an "eel" shape will appear to be a better forward swimmer than a voyager. This is only because an artificial force is moving the fish. A real eel would have to undulate its body, and change its overall shape.

Frog Features

Observing Amphibian Body Structures and Adaptations

Question What body structures and adaptations allow frogs to live both in the water and on land?

Lab Overview In this investigation you will explore amphibian structure and function as you dissect a frog, observe features of its external and internal anatomy, and make sketches based on your observations.

Introduction Frogs (order Anura) make up one of the three orders of amphibians. The other two orders are salamanders (order Urodela) and caecilians (order Apoda). Like most amphibians, frogs live part of their life cycle in water and part on land. Although adult frogs are primarily land organisms, their habitats are usually close to the water. Frogs release and fertilize their eggs in the water. Frog eggs do not have shells and therefore would dry out if they were laid on land. After hatching, tadpoles live in the water until metamorphosis is complete and they are capable of surviving on land. In this lab, you will investigate various structures of a frog's anatomy and explore how they support this "double life."

Prelab Activity Follow the procedure below to examine the frog's external anatomy. Then answer the Prelab Questions that follow.

1. Examine the frog's skin. Find an area of skin where you can use your fingers to easily pull the skin away from the muscle layer beneath it. Feel the thickness and texture of the skin. The skin of a frog contains many glands. Some glands excrete mucus that prevents the skin from drying out. Other glands secrete toxins that deter predators from eating the frogs.

2. Pull the skin up again. Cut and remove a large piece of skin with scissors. **CAUTION:** *Handle sharp instruments with care to avoid injury.* A frog's skin is permeable to oxygen and carbon dioxide, allowing for gas exchange through its skin. Compare the external and internal sides of the skin. Record your observations below.

_____

3. Compare the size and webbing of the frog's front and hind feet. Then, compare the front feet of your group's frog to the front feet of other groups' frogs. Generally, male frogs have larger and more muscular "thumbs" on their front feet than females. Do you think your frog is male or female? Record your inference below.

_____

Objective to examine adaptations that enable amphibians to survive on land and in the water

Inquiry Skills
- observing
- classifying
- measuring
- making inferences

Time
- 20 min for Prelab Activity
- 20 min for Part A
- 40 min for Part B
- 15 min for Analysis and Conclusions

Have an alternate activity available for students who do not wish to participate in this dissection. Many virtual frog dissections are available online and on CD-ROM. One example of an online virtual frog dissection can be found at http://www.froguts.com.

Lab groups of 2 or 3 students work well for this Prelab Activity and lab. Students can take turns dissecting and taking notes. If students switch roles during the investigation, remind them to remove and dispose of used gloves and wash their hands thoroughly.

4. Examine the outside of the frog's head. The location of a frog's eyes, ears, and nose on the upper part of its head allow the frog to hide from land predators in the water. Only a small part of the frog's head needs to stay above the water. Find the transparent nictitating membrane below the eye. The nictitating membrane flicks over the eye, keeping it clean (on land and in the water) and moist (on land), while still allowing the frog to see. Nictitating membranes are found in many amphibians, reptiles, and birds, and also in some mammals.

5. Press down on the eyes and observe how they can sink into the frog's head. When a frog swallows, its eyes bulge into its mouth cavity. The inward bulges caused by the eyes help the frog hold on to large moving prey.

6. Locate the circular eardrums behind the eyes. These eardrums are called tympanic membranes. Attached to the underside of each tympanic membrane are tiny bones that transmit to the brain the vibrations caused by sound waves.

7. Locate the nostrils, called external nares, leading into the frog's mouth. Gently push the nares open with a narrow, blunt probe. When a frog inhales, the nares open and allow air to travel into the mouth. Then the nares shut and the frog's mouth contracts, forcing air into the lungs. The nares also function in the frog's sense of smell, which is generally keen in frogs and other amphibians. Many slow-moving amphibians such as salamanders rely on their sense of smell to find food.

The pink bump (called a caruncle) in the corner of the human eye is thought to be the remnant of a nictitating membrane.

Prelab Questions

1. Explain how nictitating membranes are helpful to land animals.

   Suggested answer: Nictitating membranes sweep away debris and keep eyes moist. Since they are

   usually transparent, the organism can still see when the membranes are closed.

2. What are two adaptations you have examined or read about so far that allow adult frogs to survive in the water?

   Suggested answer: skin that can absorb oxygen; webbed feet; sense organs located at the top of

   the head

Materials

- preserved frog
- dissection tray
- scalpel
- scissors
- dissecting probe
- dissecting pins
- paper plate
- plastic dropper or transfer pipette
- metric ruler

Name _____ Class _____ Date_____

Advance Preparation

A couple of weeks before the lab
• Check the condition of your scalpels and other dissection instruments. Purchase new blades and order new pins, trays, etc. as needed.
• Order non-injected, preserved frogs from a biological supply company. See the front of this Laboratory Manual Teacher's Edition for contact information. Larger frogs are more likely to be sexually mature and to have eggs or larger, more identifiable testes than smaller frogs.

Procedure

Part A: Observing the Mouth Cavity

1. To see all the structures in the mouth, you will need to open it fully. Pry the frog's mouth open with your finger and use scissors to cut the bone at the corner of each side of the mouth.
CAUTION: *Handle sharp instruments with care to avoid injury.*

2. Oxygen can be absorbed into the frog's blood through the thin, moist mouth lining. There are six small openings in a female frog's mouth and eight small openings in a male's mouth. Use a thin, blunt dissecting probe to locate the openings and read the information below to identify them. Gently push the probe into each opening to see where it leads. Sketch the mouth cavity in the space below and label the openings.

a. Male frogs have two vocal sac openings located on the sides of the mouth toward the back. Male frogs croak to attract female frogs. Female frogs cannot make vocal sounds.

b. Two Eustachian tube openings are located on the sides of the mouth, opposite the tympanic membranes. They maintain pressure inside the frog's mouth equal to the outside air pressure, preventing the membranes from stretching.

c. The internal nares are the inside openings of the external nares.

d. The glottis is an oval, raised valve that is most likely closed. It is the opening to a tube that leads to the lungs. Why might the opening to the lungs have a valve that can open and close?

Sample answer: to keep water or food from entering the passageway to the lungs

e. Just above the glottis is a smaller opening to a tube called the esophagus that leads to the stomach.

Sketch:

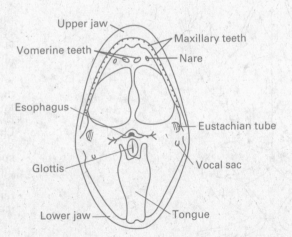

Upper jaw — Maxillary teeth
Vomerine teeth — Nare
Esophagus
Eustachian tube
Glottis — Vocal sac
Lower jaw — Tongue

3. Feel along the frog's upper jaw for a rough ridge of maxillary teeth (*maxillary* means "upper jaw"). Between the internal nares, feel for the two vomerine teeth (*vomerine* means "between the nostrils"). Frogs cannot chew because they do not have teeth on their lower jaw. Their teeth, along with their inward-bulging eyes, function in holding food as it is pushed into the esophagus. Add the teeth to your sketch on the previous page.

4. Pull up on the tongue and record your observations below. How might the tongue's shape and attachment help frogs capture prey?

   Sample answer: It is long and flexible and may trap prey.

5. Gently push down on the eyes again from the outside of the frog's head. Notice the soft pads on the inside of the mouth that stretch as the eyes bulge inward.

6. Place the frog on its back (dorsal) side. Note the small hole between the hind legs located toward the dorsal side of the frog. This is the cloaca, the common exit for urine, feces (digestive waste), and gametes (sperm or eggs). Many amphibians, as well as fish, birds, and reptiles, have a cloaca.

7. If you will be exploring the frog's internal anatomy another day, wrap the frog in a wet paper towel and place it in a self-sealing plastic bag. Label the bag with the initials of your lab group.

Part B: Observing the Internal Anatomy of the Frog

1. Lift up the skin of the belly (ventral) side with forceps. Cut *only the skin* of the frog up the center as shown in the diagram below (1). Next make two horizontal incisions (cuts) through the skin at the top (2 and 3) and bottom (4 and 5) of the belly. Pull the skin back to reveal the abdominal muscles.

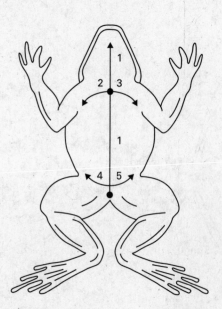

Safety and Disposal
Remind students to wear plastic gloves, goggles, and aprons to prevent exposure to microorganisms and preservative chemicals. Afterward, have students use antibacterial soap to wash all working surfaces, dissection trays, scissors, pencils, and any other items they handled during the lab, then wash their hands thoroughly. To prevent wounds remind students to handle scalpels carefully. Good ventilation is critical for the health and comfort of students. Open windows and doors and use a powerful fan to circulate the air. Although present preservation methods do not use as much formaldehyde as in the past, the specimens will likely still have an unpleasant smell. For disposal, double-wrap the frogs in paper and place in a tightly sealed plastic bag. Check with the supplier for any other specific disposal information. Do not allow the trash to remain in the building overnight.

2. Following the same pattern of incisions (1–5) as you did for the skin, carefully make shallow incisions through the muscle layer. Keep the incision shallow to avoid damaging the internal organs.

3. To reveal the organs in the chest cavity, you need to cut through the breastbone without puncturing the heart. As you cut the breastbone, twist the scissors so that they are parallel to the frog (as if you were going to lay them flat on the table).

4. Pull the skin and muscle layers to each side to reveal the internal organs. Pin down the flaps of skin and muscle to the dissection tray as shown. Also pin down the frog's front and back legs as shown in the diagram below.

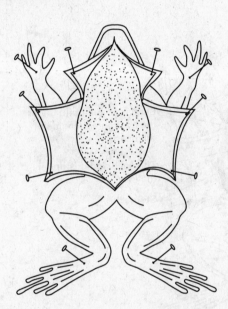

5. If you have a male frog, go to Step 6. If you have a female frog, you may see clusters of black and white eggs in the ovaries. Sometimes the clusters of eggs may take up more than half the space in the body cavity. Carefully remove the eggs by cutting the connective tissue that attaches them to the rest of the body cavity. Be careful not to cut any other organs. Place the eggs on a paper plate and set them aside.

6. In both males and females, look for fat bodies—yellow, finger-like projections on the sides of the frog's body cavity. The fat stored in the fat bodies can be used as an energy source when a frog is hibernating. Remove the fat bodies carefully to expose the other organs.

7. The prominent dark brown organ with three lobes is the liver. Lift up the liver to see how it attaches to the frog's digestive system. Under the liver, between the middle and right lobe, look for a greenish sac. This is the gallbladder. One of the liver's functions is to produce bile, a digestive juice that is stored in the gallbladder. The bile is secreted into the upper part of the small intestine. Bile helps the frog digest fat.

8. Remove the liver by cutting the connective tissue that holds it in place as well as the duct that connects the liver to the upper part of the small intestine.

9. Using the diagram below, identify the stomach, small intestine, and large intestine. (Remember that "small" and "large" refer to the width of the intestine rather than the length.) The stomach mixes food with digestive juices as its muscular wall churns the contents. In the first section of the small intestine, digestive enzymes and bile are added to the liquefied food. In the rest of the small intestine, the broken-down food is absorbed into the blood. The large intestine reabsorbs the water from the juices secreted into the digestive tract.

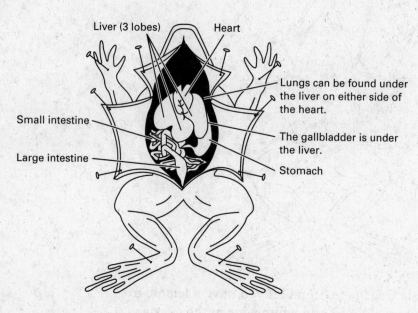

Liver (3 lobes) Heart

Small intestine

Large intestine

Lungs can be found under the liver on either side of the heart.

The gallbladder is under the liver.

Stomach

Note that the preserved frogs your students dissect may differ in appearance from the example depicted here.

10. Cut the esophagus (the tube that runs from the mouth to the stomach) where it enters the stomach. Remove the entire digestive tract in one piece by carefully cutting away the membranous connective tissue that attaches the organs to the body wall. Gently stretch the digestive tract into one long tube.

11. Measure the length of each digestive organ. Circle the longest organ.

    Stomach: _____ cm

    Small intestine: _____ cm

    Large intestine: _____ cm

    Student responses will vary, but the small intestine should be the longest.

12. Cut open the stomach with your scalpel and observe the inside lining. You may find an insect or other small prey inside the stomach. Record your observations below.

_____

_____

13. Locate the heart. It is covered in a saclike membrane. Remove the heart by carefully cutting the arteries and connective tissues that hold it in place.

14. Slice off the front of the heart to reveal its three chambers. With a blunt probe, find the two upper chambers, each called an atrium, and the lower chamber, called the ventricle. The left atrium receives oxygenated blood from the lungs and the right atrium receives deoxygenated blood from the rest of the body. The atria contract and fill the single lower ventricle. The heart then pumps the blood to the rest of the body. (Refer to Figure 25-15b on page 553 in your textbook to see how the three-chambered heart works.)

15. Locate the lungs. Amphibian lungs are more saclike than the spongy lungs of birds and mammals.

16. Identify the bronchi, tubes coming from the top of the lungs. Cut the bronchi and gently remove both lungs. Place a plastic dropper into a lung and depress the bulb to inflate the lung.

17. Identify the kidneys—long, red structures attached to the lower back of the body wall.

18. Identify the frog's reproductive structures. If your frog is a female, you should see the tiny, curled tubes called oviducts that run from the bottom tip of the lungs along the sides of the frog. If your frog is a male, look for the testes—yellow bean-shaped structures located on top of the kidneys. The sperm produced in the testes pass through the kidneys before exiting out the cloaca.

19. Find another lab group that is studying a frog of the other sex. Observe the frog's reproductive structures. On the diagrams below, sketch the reproductive systems of a female and a male frog.

Female Reproductive System   **Male Reproductive System**

Analysis and Conclusions

1. What features and adaptations of the frog make it suited for life on land? List as many as you can.

   Suggested answer: lungs, nares, legs, nictitating membrane

2. What features and adaptations of the frog make it suited for life in water? List as many as you can.

   Suggested answer: nares that close, skin that absorbs oxygen, webbed feet, nictitating membrane

3. Some frogs live their entire lives in the water, but many frogs live most of their lives on land. For what purpose must all frogs return to a wet environment? Explain.

   Suggested answer: Frogs must return to the water for reproduction. Frog eggs do not have shells and therefore must be laid in a wet environment so that they do not dry out.

4. List three ways oxygen can be absorbed into a frog's blood.

   Suggested answer: through the skin, the lining of the mouth, and the lungs

5. Which aspect of the frog's anatomy did you find the most interesting? Explain.

   Students' responses will vary.

Extension

With your teacher's permission, continue the dissection to examine the frog's brain. Place the frog on its ventral side and use a scalpel to cut a triangular hole in the skull. Observe the narrow, lobed brain. On a separate sheet of paper, sketch the brain and describe your sketch. Your teacher may provide a diagram with the parts of the brain labeled. Add labels to your sketch.

Extension
Remind students to use caution with sharp instruments. Advise them not to cut with too much force or they will damage the brain, making it difficult to discern the different lobes. Much of the nervous tissue in the frog brain is devoted to vision and smell.

Suitcases for Life on Land

Discovering the Adaptations of a Bird Egg

Question What are the structures in a bird egg that support the growth and development of the embryo?

Lab Overview In this investigation you will take apart an unfertilized chicken egg. You will locate and observe the many structures that support the growth and development of the chick and examine certain structures with a microscope.

Introduction To start your investigation, you will examine a diagram of the inside of a chicken egg to become familiar with the structures that you will observe in your investigation. (Note that you will observe an unfertilized egg in this lab.) Then, you will explore the formation of an egg in the hen's reproductive system.

Prelab Activity Read the following descriptions of the major structures of a bird egg and study the cross-section diagram of an unfertilized chicken egg on the next page. Then, study the diagram showing how the egg forms inside the hen.

(**NOTE:** *The yolk sac, allantois, chorion, and amnion membranes discussed in Concept 26.1 only develop in fertilized eggs. You will not observe them in this investigation.*)

Shell: The hard shell, made of calcium carbonate, plays an important role in helping to prevent water loss from the embryo inside. (Note that in a fertilized egg, the amnion also protects the embryo from water loss.) The shell has small pores that allow for oxygen to enter the egg and carbon dioxide to escape. The shell is deposited onto the outer shell membrane during the egg's journey through the hen's reproductive system.

Yolk: The yolk is a highly concentrated source of sugars, fat, proteins, vitamins, and minerals. For the three weeks that a chicken embryo develops inside the egg, the yolk serves as the main supply of nutrition.

Attached to the yolk is the blastodisc, which in a fertilized egg would develop into the embryo. Surrounding the yolk is a membrane called the vitelline membrane. In a fertilized egg, this membrane, along with cells from the embryo, develops into the yolk sac.

Objective to study the structures of a chicken egg and learn about their functions

Inquiry Skills
• observing
• asking questions

Time
• 20–25 min for Prelab Activity
• 30 min for Part A
• 15 min for Part B
• 15 min for Analysis and Conclusions

Some chicken breeds produce white eggs, while other breeds produce brown or even pale green or blue eggs. The contents of the eggs are the same. Any pigments (colors) are added to the shell in the last stages of its production.

Egg White: The egg white (albumen) is a gel containing water and proteins called albumin. The egg white has two layers. The outer, thinner layer contains more liquid and less protein than the thicker layer closer to the yolk. In addition to providing nutrients for the embryo, the egg white contains enzymes that attack bacteria. The egg white also functions as a shock absorber.

Chalazae: Each egg contains two chalazae (singular, *chalaza*), one on each end of the yolk. The chalazae are twisted cords of albumin that hold the yolk centered in the middle of the egg and keep the developing embryo on top even if the egg is turned in the nest.

Membranes: There are two shell membranes just under the eggshell, an inner shell membrane and an outer shell membrane made of a web of protein fibers called keratin. This protein is similar to the one that makes up your hair and fingernails. The two membranes are semipermeable barriers that allow gas exchange and help prevent water loss from the egg interior. (In a fertilized egg, the amnion and chorion play the major role in enabling gas exchange and protecting the embryo.) They also help prevent bacteria that get through the shell from reaching the embryo.

When an egg is first laid, the shell membranes fill the interior of the shell completely. As the egg cools outside of the hen's body, the inner part of the egg contracts. The inner shell membrane separates at one end from the outer membrane, forming an air sac.

Structure of an Egg

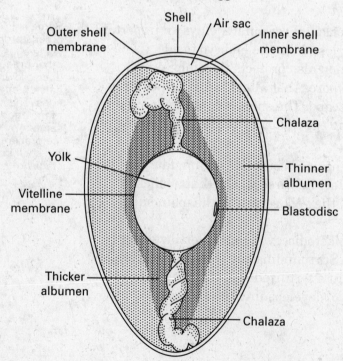

- Shell
- Air sac
- Outer shell membrane
- Inner shell membrane
- Chalaza
- Yolk
- Thinner albumen
- Vitelline membrane
- Blastodisc
- Thicker albumen
- Chalaza

Name _____ Class _____ Date _____

Structure of a Hen's Reproductive System

Female chickens hatch with two ovaries and oviducts, but only the left
ovary and oviduct develop and become functional. A hen's ovary produces one yolk about once a day. Yolks are produced whether or not
there are sperm present in the oviduct to fertilize them. Once the yolk
is released into the oviduct it takes about 23–24 hours for the entire
egg to form and be laid. Study the diagram below that shows the
development of an egg inside a hen's body. Afterward, answer the
Prelab Questions.

Egg Development in a Hen's Reproductive System

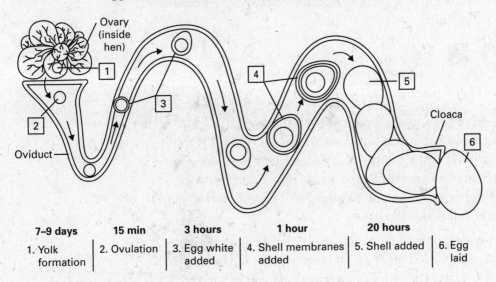

7–9 days	15 min	3 hours	1 hour	20 hours	
1. Yolk formation	2. Ovulation	3. Egg white added	4. Shell membranes added	5. Shell added	6. Egg laid

Prelab Questions

1. Which structures of an unfertilized egg help prevent water loss
from the egg interior?

Suggested answer: shell, outer and inner shell membranes

_____

2. What structures provide nutrition for the embryo?

Suggested answer: the yolk and egg white

_____

3. Summarize the formation of an egg.

Sample answer: Yolk is formed in the ovary and released into the oviduct. As the yolk travels through

the oviduct the egg white is added, then shell membranes, and then the shell. The egg is laid

23–24 hours after the yolk is released into the oviduct.

_____

Materials

- unfertilized chicken egg
- metal spoon
- plastic bowl or cup (disposable)
- microscope slides
- marker
- plastic dropper
- water
- microscope
- stereomicroscope (optional)

CAUTION: *If you are allergic to eggs, notify your teacher before taking part in this investigation.*

Procedure

Part A: Taking the Egg Apart

1. Tap the large end of the eggshell gently with the backside of a metal spoon until you see a cluster of small cracks. **CAUTION:** *Raw eggs may contain high numbers of* Salmonella *and other bacteria that could make you sick. Do not touch your mouth or face while handling the eggs. Wash your hands with antibacterial soap immediately after handling the eggs.*

2. Carefully peel away the shell from the shell membranes beneath it. Try to pull as much shell off from the top portion of the egg as you can without tearing the shell membranes. If you are using a stereomicroscope, save a piece of the shell without the membrane attached to observe under the stereomicroscope.

3. The membrane just beneath the shell is called the outer shell membrane. Take a piece of this membrane off and save it to view under the microscope later. Put it on a slide and label the slide.

4. Now you should be able to see the air sac located between the outer and inner shell membranes. When a chick starts to hatch, it first breaks the inner shell membrane. The air sac provides the chick with its first breaths of air.

5. While holding the egg with the open end up, carefully pull off a section of the inner shell membrane. Place the membrane sample on a second microscope slide and label it.

6. Observe the two layers of egg white inside the egg. One is liquid, while the other is denser. Slowly pour the egg white out of the shell into a bowl or cup. Leave the yolk inside the shell. The liquid layer will pour out first and the denser layer will pour out as a thick glob.

7. Now you will see a third membrane that surrounds the yolk. It is called the vitelline membrane. This membrane separates the yolk from the egg white.

8. Carefully turn the yolk around by tilting the egg or touching it carefully with your finger until you see a white spot. The white spot is called the blastodisc. If fertilized, this structure may grow into a chick.

9. You also should notice a white string-like structure. This structure is one of the two chalazae that hold the yolk centered in the middle of the egg. You cannot see the other chalaza because it is located on the other end of the yolk sac.

Part B: Observing Egg Structures With a Microscope

1. Look at the two shell membranes under the microscope. Place a drop of water on each membrane before viewing. Adjust the lighting on the microscope and find a part of the membrane where you can see the threads. Draw a sketch of the two membranes below. Be sure to label your sketches.

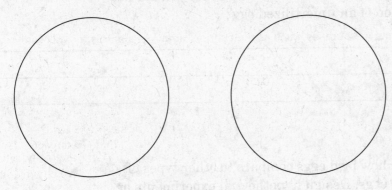

Student sketches will vary.

2. Look at the shell under the stereomicroscope if your lab has one. Be sure to turn the light on that shines down from above. Locate the pores on the shell. Draw a sketch of the shell below. Be sure to label your sketch.

Student sketches will vary.

Analysis and Conclusions

1. Describe several ways in which the structure of the bird egg fits its function.

   Sample answers: Pores in the shell allow for gas exchange. Shell membranes allow gas exchange and

   help protect the embryo from water loss. The egg white contains enzymes that kill bacteria that get

   through the pores of the shell and the shell membranes. The yolk and egg white provide enough

   nutrients to feed the embryo throughout its development.

2. If a hen were exposed to a pollutant that caused it to produce eggs with very thin shells, what would be the possible effects on the developing chicks?

   Suggested answer: The thin shells may not be able to keep water from escaping or bacteria from

   getting in. The embryo may dry out or become sick. The thin shells may break open before the chick

   is fully developed and able to survive.

3. What structures would you see in a fertilized egg that you did not see during this dissection of an unfertilized egg?

   Suggested answer: Additional membranes, such as the chorion, amnion, allantois, or yolk sac

Extension

Brainstorm questions about how bird eggs compare to other types of eggs such as turtle or snake eggs. Design hypothetical experiments or research plans to answer your questions.

Extension
Possible questions:
"Which type of egg is more water-proof?"

"Which type of egg shell is stronger?"

"Which type of egg contains the most nutrients?"

Review students' experimental designs.

Reference: Mississippi State University Cooperative Extension Service
www.msstate.edu/dept/poultry/avianemb.htm

Bones, Feathers, and Fur

Comparing Structures and Adaptations of Birds and Mammals

Question How do the structures of the bones and body coverings of birds and mammals relate to their functions?

Lab Overview In this investigation you will measure and compare the densities of bird and mammal bones and study the structures of feathers and fur. You will discover how the different structures of bird and mammal bones and body coverings reflect their diverse functions.

Introduction The structures of bird and mammal bones are quite different. Many bird bones have a honeycomb-like open internal structure. Mammal bones are typically solid and filled with fatty yellow bone marrow. The ends of some of the bones contain red marrow that produces blood cells. Birds have far fewer bones that contain marrow than mammals do.

Feathers, which are made of a protein called keratin, are used for flight and provide insulation. The long, stiff feathers you might find on the ground are primary flight feathers. On the bird, these feathers are attached to fingerlike structures of a bird's wing called phalanges. Secondary flight feathers are shorter and are attached to longer bones in the bird's wing. Tail feathers usually have a blunter end than flight feathers. They are used primarily to change direction or speed in flight.

The diagram below points out the different parts of a flight feather. The main branch running down the length of the feather is called the *rachis* (RAY kis). Barbs branch from the rachis. Hooked and straight barbules branch from each barb. The hooks on the hooked barbules snag the straight barbules of an adjacent barb. This holds the barbs together, creating a smooth surface while allowing for flexibility. The leading edge of the feather (the edge that cuts through the air in flight) has shorter barbs than the trailing edge. The barbs easily become unhooked during flight.

Objective to compare the densities of bird and mammal bones and to compare the structures of feathers and fur

Inquiry Skills
• predicting
• observing
• measuring
• calculating
• collecting data
• making inferences

Time
• 20 min for Prelab Activity
• 15 min for Part A
• 20–25 min for Part B
• 15 min for Analysis and Conclusions

Most bird bones are hollow, with networks of struts that maintain strength. Only a few of a bird's bones contain marrow. The wishbone (furcula) is a uniquely avian bone which enables the flight stroke. The breastbone (sternum) in birds is also unique in its keel shape, which allows for attachment of the flight muscles.

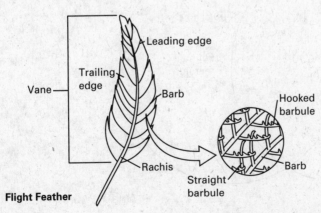

Flight Feather

Birds spend a lot of time grooming themselves, called "preening." During preening birds pull on their feathers, hooking the barbs back together. They also remove dirt and parasites from their flight feathers and contour feathers (the feathers that cover their body). Birds have an oil-producing preening gland at the base of their tail. As they preen, birds rub this gland with their beaks and then spread the oil throughout their feathers. Water birds have a particularly waxy, fatty oil that helps to make the contour feathers water-repellant.

Another type of feather, down feathers, provides insulation. They are not used in flight and are not linked by barbs. The first feathers of some baby birds are all down feathers. This keeps them warm, but leaves them flightless until they grow their flight and tail feathers.

The main function of fur is providing insulation. The fur of mammals that live in very cold environments tends to be very dense and consists of both short and long hairs. Grooming the fur by licking and rubbing removes dirt and parasites and keeps the fur smooth.

Prelab Activity Practice "preening" feathers to make them smooth for flight. Then answer the Prelab Questions.

1. Ruffle a feather by brushing it the "wrong way."

2. Hold your index finger and thumb to form a beak. Preen the feather by pinching it and pulling on the barbs from the base toward the tip of the feather.

3. Experiment with your preening technique until you can easily "rezip" the ruffled feather.

Prelab Questions

1. Based on what you have read, complete the Venn diagram below to compare and contrast the functions and structures of feathers and fur.

Polar bear fur closest to the body has a woolly texture. Longer hairs on top of the woolly hairs stick together when they are wet, keeping the woolly fur dry. Polar bear fur is so efficient at keeping a bear warm that even infrared cameras can detect a loss of heat only from a polar bear's mouth.

Sea otters have more than one million hairs in one square inch of their fur. One square centimeter of otter fur has more hairs than are found on the typical human head! Otters groom their fur continually to trap tiny air bubbles against their skin and to add a layer of oil on the outer fur to help keep it water-repellant.

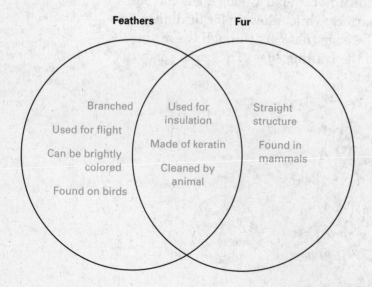

Feathers   **Fur**

Branched
Used for flight
Can be brightly colored
Found on birds

Used for insulation
Made of keratin
Cleaned by animal

Straight structure
Found in mammals

Name _____ Class _____ Date _____

2. Predict whether bird bones or mammal bones are less dense. Explain your prediction.

Sample answer: Bird bones should be less dense because lighter bones would be valuable for flight.

_____

3. Explain why mammals and birds spend a lot of time cleaning and grooming their body coverings.

Sample answer: Birds and mammals groom themselves to remove parasites and dirt from their

feathers and fur. Birds groom (preen) to smooth out their feathers, hooking the barbs together. Water

birds also spread oil on their feathers during preening, making them water-repellant. Grooming also

keeps fur smooth and water-repellant.

Materials
- bird bone
- mammal bone
- laboratory balance
- 100-mL graduated cylinder
- water
- flight feather
- down feather
- mammal fur
- 3 microscope slides and cover slips
- transfer pipette
- microscope
- scissors

Advance Preparation

One week before the lab
- Cook chicken legs and pork ribs. Remove the meat and save the bones. Place the bones in a large pot with enough water to cover them. Simmer bones for 15–30 min. Allow the bones to cool and pull off all remaining meat and cartilage.
- Let bones dry for 24 hr or more. Then cut them in half with a hacksaw blade.
- Collect feathers or purchase them from a craft store. Each group needs a barbed flight or tail feather and a down feather. Collect animal fur from a cat or dog brush.

Safety and Disposal
Students should wash their hands with antibacterial soap after handling the feathers and bones. Students allergic to feathers or fur should only observe. Place feathers and bones in two plastic bags and seal tightly. Then throw the bags in the trash.

Procedure

Part A: Comparing Bone Density

1. Measure the mass of each bone in grams using a laboratory balance. Record your measurements in the spaces provided.

Bird bone mass: ____5____ g
Mammal bone mass: ____9.1____ g

2. Measure the volume of each bone by using the displacement method. Fill a 100-mL graduated cylinder to the 75-mL mark with water. Immerse the bird bone in the water. Be careful not to put your finger below the water level, which would affect your measurement. Measure the volume with the bone immersed. The difference in the two measurements is the volume of the bone. (*Hint*: Remember that the volume of a solid object is expressed as cm^3 [1 mL = 1 cm^3].) Repeat with the mammal bone and record your results below.

Bird bone volume: ____6____ cm^3
Mammal bone volume: ____8____ cm^3

If the bone is the wrong shape to fit into a 100-mL graduated cylinder, any narrow, uniform, watertight container will work. Mark the water level before and after adding the bone (if the water level doesn't rise significantly, the container is too large). Then take out the bone and measure how many mL of water it takes to raise the water level from the first mark to the second mark.

3. Calculate the densities of the bones by dividing the mass of each bone by its volume.

Expected Results
The bird bone will be less dense than the mammal bone. The leg bone of a chicken is one of the densest in the bird because it contains marrow.

Bird bone density: ___0.83___ g/cm³

Mammal bone density: ___1.14___ g/cm³

Part B: Comparing Feathers and Fur

Expected Results
The flight feathers have barbules with hooks that fit around the straight barbules like Velcro™. Down feathers have fibers that are more like fur, but they do have tiny projections that resemble short barbules.

1. With scissors, cut off the base of the feather rachis. Inspect the interior of the rachis.

2. Identify the leading and trailing edges of the flight feather. Pull off a fragment of about 5 barbs from the middle section of the leading edge. Keep the barbs together as you pull them off.

3. To make a wet mount of the feather fragment, place the feather fragment on a microscope slide. Use a transfer pipette to drop one or two drops of water onto the fragment. Cover the fragment with a cover slip. Place the slide on the microscope stage and observe the barbules at medium and then high power (100× or 400×). Sketch the barbules. Describe them in the space provided.

Sketch:

Remind students to adjust the lighting on the microscope to see the detailed structure of the outside of the fur.

Description:

_____

_____

_____

4. Make a wet mount of the fluffy fibers from the base of a down feather. View the fibers under 100× power. Compare these fibers to the barbs of the upper part of the flight feather.

5. Make a wet mount of several hairs taken from the mammal fur. Observe the hairs under 100× and 400× power. Adjust the lighting as needed to observe the patterns on the hair shaft.

You may want to discuss with your students the uses of feathers for bedding and clothing. When do they think flight feathers would be preferable to down and vice versa?

Analysis and Conclusions

1. Compare the densities of the bird and mammal bones. How do you think their relative densities fit their function?

   Suggested answer: Bird bones are less dense which aids them in flight. Since mammals do not

   fly, their bones can be stronger and heavier.

2. How does the structure of the rachis fit its function?

   Suggested answer: It is hollow with a cross bar inside for strength, much like the bone of a bird.

3. Barbule hooks hold the barbules and the barbs together, maintaining a smooth surface for air to pass over. The hooks are looped around the barbules rather than fused to them. What do you think the benefit of barbules that can move might be?

   Suggested answer: The movement allows for flexibility of the wings.

4. Is the structure of a down feather more similar to the structure of a flight feather or the structure of fur? Explain.

   Sample answer: A down feather is similar to fur because it is loose and fibrous.

Extension

In this lab you read about three types of feathers. There are six main types of bird feathers in all. Study the table below, then go on a "scavenger hunt" to find as many types of feathers as you can. Good places to search are around an aviary at a zoo or park (with permission), or a shoreline. Discuss your plan with your teacher before completing this Extension. Before starting your scavenger hunt, research the benefits these feathers provide birds.

Extension
Review safety issues related to collecting feathers in the field, such as physical safety, handling animal material, and the importance of handwashing. Remind students not to take material from state or national parks, and not to collect material from private property without the owner's permission.

Table 1: Feather Types

Feather Type	Identifying Characteristics
Flight feather (primary, secondary, or tail)	Long and stiff feathers with a wider trailing edge than leading edge; the most common feathers to find on the ground.
Contour (body) feather	Feathers have almost equal-sized vanes
Semiplume feather	Fluffy with a rachis
Filoplume feather	Mostly rachis with a bit of fluff at the end
Down feather	Fluffy without a rachis
Bristle feather	Looks like stiff hair with a bit of fluff at the base. These feathers are found near the mouth and eye of a bird.

Every Flex Is Quite Complex

Structure and Function in a Chicken Wing

Question How do the tissues of a chicken wing work together during movement?

Lab Overview In this investigation you will carefully examine and dissect the tissues of a chicken wing to learn about its structure and to discover how bones, muscles, tendons, ligaments, and skin work together and function in movement.

Introduction In the Prelab Activity you will study the structure of the human arm and consider how the structure and function of the human arm may be similar to a chicken wing's structure and function. In the lab you will dissect the chicken wing and answer questions along the way about your observations.

During the lab, keep in mind that the surface of raw chicken may contain several different disease-causing species of *Salmonella* bacteria. To avoid infection, do not touch your eyes, nose, or mouth at any time while working with the chicken wing.

Prelab Activity Before beginning your dissection of a chicken wing examine the internal structure of a human arm, shown in the diagram below. Then answer the Prelab Questions on the next page.

Objective to dissect a chicken wing and relate it to structure and function of a human arm

Inquiry Skills
• observing
• predicting
• making inferences
• drawing conclusions

Time
• 10 min for Prelab Activity
• 10 min for Part A
• 15 min for Part B
• 15 min for Part C
• 10 min for Part D
• 15 min for Analysis and Conclusions

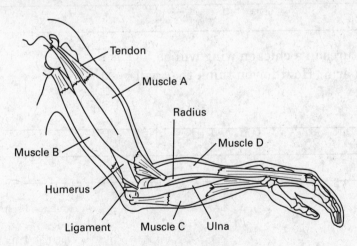

Internal Anatomy of a Human Arm

1. Which labeled bone(s) is (are) found in the upper arm? Which labeled bone(s) is (are) found in the lower arm?

   Suggested answer: The humerus is the bone in the upper arm. The radius and ulna are the

   bones in the lower arm.

2. You may remember from Concept 27.5 in your text that muscles can only pull—they cannot push. Therefore, muscles work in pairs. When one muscle contracts and causes a bone to move, a relaxed opposing muscle can contract and move the bone to its original position. Which lettered muscle shown in this diagram do you think causes the elbow to flex (bend)? Which lettered muscle do you think is the opposing muscle that causes the elbow to extend (lengthen)? Explain your answer.

   Suggested answer: Muscle A contracts and causes the elbow to flex. Muscle B is the opposing

   muscle that contracts and causes the elbow to extend.

3. Which lettered muscle shown in this diagram do you think causes the wrist to flex (bend upward)? Which lettered muscle do you think is the opposing muscle that causes the wrist to extend (bend downward)? Explain.

   Suggested answer: Muscle D contracts and causes the wrist to bend upwards. Muscle C is the

   opposing muscle that contracts and causes the wrist to bend downwards.

4. How do you think the structures in a chicken wing will be similar to those in a human arm? How do you think they will be different?

   Students' responses will vary.

Materials

- raw chicken wing
- scissors with pointed ends
- paper plate
- plastic gloves
- colored pencils or markers
- antibacterial soap

Advance Preparation

Day of the lab
Wash and dry the chicken wings just before the lab to remove as many bacteria as possible.

Procedure

Part A: Comparing External Structure and Function

1. Compare the external structure of your arm with the external structure of the chicken wing. To compare the function of a human arm and a chicken wing, flex (bend) and extend (lengthen) your elbow and then your wrist. Then flex and extend the joints of the chicken wing. Record your observations below.

_____

_____

_____

_____

2. Brainstorm at least one question about similarities and differences between the human arm and the chicken wing that you would like to explore further.

_____

_____

_____

_____

Part B: Examining the Skin

1. Use the scissors to cut under the skin of the upper wing down to the first joint. Repeat for both sides of the wing. **CAUTION:** *Handle sharp instruments with care to avoid injury.*

If students switch dissecting and note-taking roles during the investigation, remind students to remove and dispose of used gloves and wash their hands thoroughly before starting a new task.

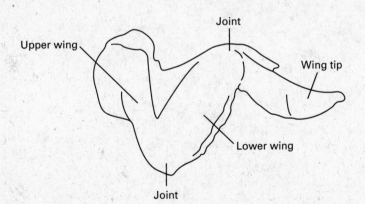

Safety and Disposal

Remind students to wear plastic gloves while doing the dissection to prevent infections and illnesses caused by microorganisms on raw chicken. Afterward have students use antibacterial soap to wash all working surfaces, dissection trays, scissors, pencils, and any other items they handled during the lab, and then to wash their hands thoroughly. Remind students to handle scissors carefully to prevent cuts.

After the lab activity, have students place their chicken wings and paper plates in a waste container with two plastic trash bags. Close both bags securely for disposal. Do not allow the trash to sit in the building overnight.

2. With your fingers, pull the skin of the upper wing away from the pinkish muscle. The now-visible film-like tissue that attaches the skin to the muscle is called the hypodermis. Just as in humans, the hypodermis is the connective tissue layer beneath the dermis of the skin. Compare the characteristics of the outer layer of skin (epidermis) to the hypodermis. Record your observations here.

_____

_____

_____

3. Completely remove the rest of the skin from the upper part of the chicken wing. In sections where the skin and muscles are strongly attached, use scissors to cut the skin away from the muscle. Be careful not to cut into the muscle, tendons, or ligaments as you remove the skin.

4. Repeat steps 1–3 to remove the skin from the lower wing.

5. Once you have removed the skin, observe the skin's elasticity by stretching it in different directions. Does the skin stretch in one direction more than another? Record your observations below.

Students should note that the skin does stretch in more than one direction.

_____

_____

Part C: Examining the Muscles

1. With your fingers, gently separate the muscles from each other. Notice the layers of loose connective tissue between the muscles. In the space below, sketch an outline of the chicken wing. Draw in the muscles you observe.

2. Pull on each muscle one at a time to observe if the muscle causes a part of the wing to flex (bend) or extend (lengthen). Observe what happens to the nearest joint. Try to locate each muscle's opposing muscle. Color-code the opposing muscle pairs on your sketch above.

Part D: Examining the Tendons, Bones, Ligaments, and Cartilage

1. Follow the muscles one at a time to the joint between the upper and lower wing. Cut the shiny white tendons that connect the muscles to the joint and remove the muscles.

2. Examine the bones of the upper part and lower part of the wing. Sketch the bones in the space below.

3. Observe the joint between the upper and lower wing. Do you think this joint is a pivot, ball and socket, hinge, or gliding joint? (See page 599 in your text to review the different joint types.) Explain your answer below.

   _____

   _____

   _____

4. Now look for shiny white ligaments holding bones together at the joint. Cut the ligaments so that the joint falls apart.

5. Observe the cartilage that covers the ends of the bones. Record your observations below.

   _____

   _____

   _____

Analysis and Conclusions

1. Review the questions you brainstormed in Part A. During the investigation, did you discover answers to any of your questions? If so, write your answers here. If you did not discover answers to any of your questions, describe an experiment that you could perform to find the answers.

   Students' responses will vary.

   _____

   _____

   _____

2. Describe the roles of bones, muscles, tendons, and ligaments in movement.

Suggested answer: When a muscle contracts, it moves a tendon attached to the muscle and a

bone, causing the bone to move also. Ligaments hold bones together at joints.

3. How does the structure of cartilage fit its function?

Suggested answer: Cartilage is connective tissue that is softer than bone. In a chicken wing, it provides

a cushion for bones at joints and keeps them from rubbing together.

4. How does the structure of skin help enable movement to occur?

Suggested answer: The flexibility of skin allows for a wide range of motion.

5. Match the structures that you observed in this lab with a type of tissue. Some letters may be used more than once or not at all.

c _____ ligaments   **a.** epithelial tissue

c _____ hypodermis   **b.** nervous tissue

c _____ bones   **c.** connective tissue

c _____ tendons   **d.** muscle tissue

c _____ cartilage

d _____ muscles

a _____ epidermis

Extension

Now that you have examined the tissues of a chicken at a macroscopic level, examine tissues at a microscopic level, by observing prepared slides of various tissue samples. As you observe the slides, consider how the structure of each tissue at this level relates to the function of the tissue.

Extension
Provide students with a microscope and prepared slides of tissues.

The Skin You're In

Observing Mammalian Skin Tissues and Structures

Question How do the structures of skin tissues relate to their functions?

Lab Overview In this investigation you will take a "guided tour" of a cross section of skin to learn more about the structures and functions of skin tissues. You will use a microscope to observe tissues and structures in mammalian skin and make sketches of your observations.

Introduction As you will discover in this lab, your skin contains each type of tissue discussed in Concept 27.2 of your textbook. The outermost layer of your skin, the epidermis, is composed of epithelial tissue. The layer of the epidermis that comes in contact with the external environment consists of dead epithelial cells containing high amounts of the protein keratin. Keratin helps give your skin its elastic and waterproof properties. Every day you lose millions of these cells, many of which contribute to the dust that builds up in your home.

The dermis is the layer of skin found underneath the epidermis. It is mostly composed of loose connective tissue. Hair follicles and sweat and oil glands are found in the dermis. Blood vessels and nerves also run through the dermis. Just below the dermis is a layer called the hypodermis, consisting of a type of connective tissue called adipose tissue, which contains fat-storing cells.

Your skin also contains muscle tissue attached to hair follicles. When you are cold or scared, these muscles contract and cause your body hair to "stand on end." Nerves attached to these follicles allow you to feel the movement of these hairs, alerting you to danger.

Two common and nearly unavoidable skin conditions are acne and wrinkles. Acne is caused by two main factors. In response to an excess level of hormones, an oil gland may produce so much oil that the gland's duct becomes blocked. Or, if the skin cells lining a duct are not shed as they should be, the dead skin may build up and block the duct. In either case, the result is a buildup of oil and inflammation, which makes a "friendly" environment for bacteria. The immune system's response to the invading bacteria leads to acne.

The elasticity of human skin is due to fibers woven throughout the dermis. These fibers allow skin to be pulled and stretched, but then recoil to their original length and shape. However, age, hormones, and sun damage reduce the ability of these fibers to recoil, which eventually leads to wrinkles and sagging of the skin. In the Prelab Activity, test the elasticity of your own skin and the skin of older adults. Then answer the Prelab Questions that follow.

Objective to examine structure and function of different tissues in skin

Inquiry Skills
- observing
- classifying
- making inferences

Time
- 15 min for the Prelab Activity (This works best as a weekend assignment.)
- 40 min for Procedure
- 15 min for Analysis and Conclusions

The fur of mammals such as some dogs and cats "puffs up" in response to cold or fear. Some scientists think that this response helps to conserve warmth. Some think that this response may scare away other animals. Because humans do not have enough body hair for this response to conserve warmth or appear frightening, some researchers think that these reactions are inherited from common mammalian ancestors.

Prelab Activity As people age, their skin becomes thinner and loses some of its elasticity. In some older people the skin becomes so thin that you can see the veins in their hands quite easily. To observe the thinning and loss of elasticity that occurs in skin with age, perform the skin elasticity test described below. You will need at least two adult volunteers. Choose a person at least twice your age and another person over 60 years old, if possible.

First perform the skin elasticity test on yourself. Gently pinch the skin on the back of your hand so you are grasping a fold of skin between your thumb and forefinger. Be sure to hold the skin gently and take care to avoid scratching it with your fingernails. Observe the thickness of the fold of skin. Hold the skin for 10 seconds and then release. As you release the skin, observe how quickly it returns to its normal shape, flat against your hand. Record your observations below.

_____

_____

_____

Repeat this test with the two adult volunteers. As you test each volunteer, notice how the thickness of the skin varies, along with the time needed for the fold of skin to return to normal (skin elasticity). Record your observations below.

_____

_____

_____

Prelab Questions

1. What four types of tissues can be observed in a cross section of mammalian skin? Describe an example of each tissue type.

Suggested answer: The four types of tissues that can be observed are epithelial tissue, connective tissue, nervous tissue, and muscle tissue. Epithelial tissue makes up the epidermis, or outermost layer of skin. Connective tissue is found in the dermis, the layer beneath the epidermis, and as adipose tissue in the hypodermis. Small nerves found in the dermis are composed of nervous tissue. Muscle tissue is found in the tiny muscles attached to hair follicles.

2. What differences did you observe in skin thickness during the Prelab Activity? Explain.

Suggested answer: My skin was thicker than the skin of either of the adults. The skin of the adult over age 60 was the thinnest of all. Over time, a person's skin becomes thinner.

3. What differences did you observe in skin elasticity during the Prelab Activity? Explain.

Suggested answer: My skin had greater elasticity than the skin of either of the adults. The skin of

the adult over age 60 had the least elasticity. Over time, a person's skin loses elasticity.

Materials

- prepared slide of cross section of mammalian skin
- microscope
- drawing paper
- colored pencils

Procedure

1. Place the slide on the microscope stage. Adjust the lighting as needed and focus on the slide with the low-power objective lens. As needed, switch to the medium-power objective lens and refocus to see greater detail.

2. Identify the epidermis, which is made of epithelial tissue. The epidermis is usually more darkly stained than the other layers. Look closely at the upper part of the epidermis. These are dead cells containing large amounts of the protein keratin. In the space below, sketch the epidermis.

3. Below the epidermis is the dermis, which consists of connective tissue and is embedded with hair follicles and glands. Look for differences in the cells that line the hair follicles and glands compared to other dermal cells. The cells that line the hair follicles and glands originate from cells in the epidermis. Record your observations in the space below.

Student observations will vary.

4. Focus on a hair follicle and look for oval-shaped oil (sebaceous) glands connected to the hair shaft near the top of the skin. These glands secrete the oily substance that helps to keep skin flexible and prevent it from drying out. The oil is released when secretory cells in the glands burst. The bursting cells are continually replaced from a layer of dividing cells.

Advance Preparation

A couple of weeks before the lab
If you have prepared slides of human, primate, or pig skin cross sections, check them to make sure the slides have not cracked or dried out. Scalp and unpigmented and pigmented skin sections work well for this lab. Scalp sections will have more hair follicles and oil glands. As needed, order prepared slides from a biological supply company. See the front of this Laboratory Manual Teacher's Edition for contact information.

Safety and Disposal
Caution students that the glass microscope slides break easily. Tell students to alert you immediately if a slide is broken, and not to touch the broken glass. If the microscopes have lamps, review electrical safety rules and make sure that all electrical cords are out of the way of foot traffic. Follow school guidelines for cleanup and disposal of broken glass.

Small groups of two students work well for this lab, ensuring that students are not sitting idle for long periods of time.

5. Look for a strip of long, thin overlapping cells emerging at an angle from a hair follicle. Their nuclei may be darkly stained. These are muscle cells that contract and cause hairs to stand on end. Look also for sweat glands—thin, darkly stained channels running from the top of the skin down into the dermis.

6. In the space below, sketch the dermis. Label any structures that you can identify.

7. Beneath the dermis lies the hypodermis (*hypo* means "under"), also called the subcutaneous layer. Look for large fat-storing cells. Sketch the hypodermis in the space below.

Analysis and Conclusions

1. In dry weather, your skin may become itchy and rough. Which structures of the skin play an important role in overcoming this condition?

   Suggested answer: the oil glands
   _____
   _____
   _____

2. Describe how the skin acts as a barrier to the external environment.

   Suggested answer: The epidermis has cells containing large amounts of the protein keratin, which
   _____
   provide a stretchable, watertight barrier. The dead cells on the surface form a protective coating.
   _____
   _____

3. Describe three structures you observed in the dermis and state their functions.

Sample answer: The dermis contains elastic fibers that help maintain the shape of the skin. The dermis

also contains oil glands that keep the skin moist and flexible. Also, the dermis contains hair

follicles with small muscles attached to them that cause the hairs to "stand on end."

4. Draw a combined sketch of the epidermis, dermis, and hypodermis. Label as many structures, tissues, and cell types as you can.

Student sketches will vary.

Extension

Look at cells in the skin with the high-power objective (400× or 1000×) and search for cells with visible chromosomes. These cells are undergoing mitosis. In which tissues do you think you most likely would find dividing cells? Explain your reasoning. Sketch and label your observations.

Extension
Chromosomes can often be observed in the cells that make up the basal layer of the epidermis. These cells are constantly dividing and producing new skin cells (keratinocytes).

What Gives Your Vision Precision?

Exploring Vision With a Model Eye

Questions How does the eye produce an image the brain can interpret? What physical differences exist in the eyes of people who are nearsighted or farsighted?

Lab Overview In this investigation, you will create a model eye using a glass lens and a shoe box. You will use your model eye to discover how the shape of the eye is related to common vision problems.

Introduction To start your investigation, you will read about eye structure and vision to prepare to construct and experiment with a model eye. Then you will do an activity that reveals the "blind spot" in your vision.

Background

The lens The eye contains a lens that focuses images on the retina at the back of the eye. The distance from the lens to the point where the image is focused is called the focal length. The image projected on the retina is upside down. Photoreceptors lining the retina detect light and send signals along the optic nerve to the brain. The brain integrates these signals and forms the right-side-up image you see.

Objective to construct a model eye, explore how the lens of the eye projects an image, and discover how eye shape affects vision

Inquiry Skills
- using models
- making inferences
- observing

Time
- 15 min for Prelab Activity
- 10 min for Part A
- 15 min for Part B
- 15 min for Part C
- 15 min for Analysis and Conclusions

The eye's lens bends light; light coming in the top of the lens is bent downward and light coming in at the bottom of the lens is bent upward. The result is an upside-down image projected at the focal length (the point at which the projected image is focused) of the lens.

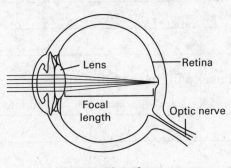

Cross section of eye

Blind spots The area of the retina where the optic nerve pokes through is not lined with photoreceptors. If an image hits this portion of your retina, no signals are sent to your brain. This "hole" in your vision is called the blind spot. Usually, you do not notice your blind spot because your brain uses information from the surrounding environment to fill in the missing information. In the Prelab Activity you will locate your blind spot.

Prelab Activity Close your left eye and stare at the + with your right eye. Focus only on the +. Now move your head slowly closer to the page and notice what happens to the spot on the right as you move your head forward. Write your observations below.

+   ●

Observations

Students should note that at one point the black circle could not be seen.

Prelab Questions

1. What causes the blind spot in the field of vision?

Suggested answer: The place where the optic nerve pokes through the retina is the blind spot. There

are no photoreceptors in this part of the retina.

2. What information does the brain use to fill in the blind spot?

Suggested answer: The brain uses information from the surrounding environment to fill in the

blind spot.

3. Each of your eyes has a blind spot in a slightly different area of the retina. How do you think this helps your brain "fill in" the missing parts of the visual field?

Suggested answer: The visual information missing by one eye's blind spot is filled in by information

obtained from the other eye.

Materials

- shoe box
- lens
- sheet of white cardboard or plastic foam block, cut to the width of the shoe box
- markers
- safety knife or scissors
- pencil
- 10-cm piece of yarn
- marker
- construction paper (various colors)
- black construction paper
- penlight or mini-flashlight
- red glitter glue or red marker
- black marker

Lens specifications:
- 50 mm or larger in diameter
- plano-convex (pre-ferred) or double convex
- focal length about 200 mm (about 5 cm shorter than the length of a typical shoe box)

It is easier to cut a circle in the shoe box with a box cutter or safety knife than with pointed scissors.

Advance Preparation

A week or two before the lab
- Obtain lenses. Ask a local optometrist to donate or sell to you unfinished lenses used to make glasses. The lenses can also be purchased at a bio-logical supply company such as Edmund Scientific. See the front of this Laboratory Manual Teacher's Edition for contact information.
- Make a model to show students. Test it in the lighting conditions of your classroom to see if the box lid is need-ed to reduce the light coming into the model eye. First make your classroom dim (but not dark) by turn-ing out lights, clos-ing drapes or blinds, or taping newspaper to the window. It is much easier for the stu-dents to see the image without lids on the boxes. If the lid is needed, cut a hole in the side of the box near the lens side. Look through the hole back toward the "retina."

Procedure
Part A: Constructing a Model Eye

1. With the safety knife or scissors, cut a hole in one end of the shoe box. The diameter of the hole should be about 1 cm smaller than the diameter of the lens. **CAUTION:** *Be careful when handling sharp instruments.*

2. Tape the edges of the lens to the inside of the box so that the lens covers the hole. The outward-curving side of the lens should face the outside of the box. **CAUTION:** *Handle glass carefully to avoid breakage.*

3. Move the box around and look for an image to form at the inside end of the box opposite the lens. If the image is blurry, place the cardboard or plastic foam in the box and slide it back and forth until the image is in focus. The distance between the lens and this "retina" is the focal length for your model eye. (**NOTE:** *If you are using your model eye outdoors, you will need to block out more light. Cover the shoe box and cut a second small hole in one side of the box near the lens. Look in the hole toward the "retina" to see the image of the outside world.*)

Shoe box eye model

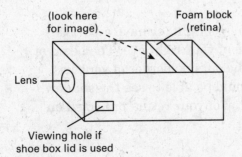

(look here for image)
Foam block (retina)
Lens
Viewing hole if shoe box lid is used

Part B: Modeling Vision Problems

1. To demonstrate how a nearsighted eye differs from an eye with normal vision, move the cardboard or plastic foam retina back from the focal length (away from the lens) or remove it. What happens to the image?

Student should note that the image becomes blurry.

The shape of a nearsighted eye is too long for the image to focus properly on the retina. The image is focused in the middle of the eye, which leads to the image being interpreted as blurred. People who are nearsighted can clearly see objects close to them because of the ability of the lens to change shape so that the image is focused on the retina. The shape of the lens cannot change enough to focus objects that are far away.

2. To demonstrate how a farsighted eye is different from an eye with normal vision, move the retina closer to the lens. What happens to the image?

Student should note that the image becomes blurry.

The shape of a farsighted eye is too short for the image to focus properly. People who are farsighted can clearly see objects far from them because the shape of the lens changes so that the image is focused on the retina. Images from nearby objects are focused so far behind the retina, however, that the lens cannot change shape enough to focus objects that are nearby.

Part C: Adding Features to the Model Eye

1. Follow the directions to observe the blood vessels crossing the lens side of your retina.

  a. With one hand, hold a sheet of black construction paper at arms length in front of your face.

  b. Close your left eye and shine the penlight (or have a partner do this for you) through the side of your right eye. The beam of the light should pass through the outside border of your iris.

  c. Jiggle the light slightly. You should be able to see the shadow of the blood vessels that lie on top of your retina projected on the black background.

Safety and Disposal
Students should wear safety goggles if handling sharp instruments, but will need to remove them to use the model eyes. Tell students to handle sharp and pointed instruments and lenses carefully and to notify you immediately if a lens breaks. Remind students not to touch broken glass. Follow school guidelines for glass disposal.

2. Using the materials listed below, add the following features to your model eye: blind spot, optic nerve, blood vessels crossing the retina, iris, and pupil.

   Materials: red marker or red glitter glue, colored construction paper, pencil, black construction paper, yarn

3. Use a black marker to label the lens, blind spot, optic nerve, retina, iris, pupil, and sclera.

Analysis and Conclusions

1. How is the model eye like a real eye? List as many similarities as you can.

   Sample answer: The lens is the same shape. The image is projected on the back of the box like the

   image in your eye is projected on the retina located at the back of the eye. The yarn creates a blind

   spot much like the optic nerve causes a blind spot. In both the model eye and a real eye, the iris

   is on the outside of the lens and light enters the eye through the pupil.

2. How is the model eye unlike a real eye? List as many differences in structure and function as you can.

   Sample answer: The shape is different. A real eye is filled with fluid. There is no cornea in our model.

   The lens in our model cannot change shape.

3. Nearsighted and farsighted people can wear glasses or contact lenses to correct their vision. How do you think these lenses help?

   Suggested answer: They change where the image is focused so the image will be projected in

   focus on the retina.

Extension

There are two types of photoreceptors in the retina—rods and cones. Rods allow you to see in dim light, although only in shades of gray. Cones, which require bright light to function, allow you to see colors. To test the action of cones, tape a bright piece of construction paper to a white or light-colored wall. Step back and stare directly at the paper for 30 seconds. Then, look at a blank space on the wall. What do you see? This image is called an *afterimage*. Research the function of cones and write a report describing the cause of the afterimage phenomenon.

Extension
When you stare at a bright color for a period of time, the affected cones in your eyes become fatigued. When your gaze turns to white paper, which reflects all colors of light, the fatigued photoreceptors will not respond. Without input from all of the cones, your brain will not interpret all the colors that are reflected by a white object. For example, if you stare at a piece of red paper, then look at a piece of white paper, only the blue and green cones will respond, and a bluish-green afterimage will appear.

Sensations Within Your Skin

Testing for Skin Mechanoreceptors

Question Are mechanoreceptors that respond to gentle pressure equally distributed in different areas of the skin?

Lab Overview In this investigation you will work with a partner to locate mechanoreceptors in the skin that respond to gentle pressure. You will use the ends of a paper clip to apply gentle pressure to points on your partner's fingertip, hand, and forearm. Based on each person's responses, you will be able to determine the approximate distance between mechanoreceptors in each location.

Introduction Mechanoreceptors are sensory receptors found in the skin that are stimulated by several forms of mechanical energy such as touch and pressure, stretch, and motion. The density of these receptors varies greatly in different areas of the skin. Some small areas do not contain any mechanoreceptors, while other areas contain so many mechanoreceptors that the slightest stimulus can be sensed.

Besides the density of mechanoreceptors, other factors may contribute to a person's sensitivity to pressure. For example, the soles of feet are known to contain a high density of mechanoreceptors. However, people who walk barefoot may develop thick skin on the soles of their feet. These individuals may not be as sensitive to touch or pressure as people with thinner skin.

In this lab, you will test the back of your partner's hand, fingertips, and forearm to determine which area contains the highest density of mechanoreceptors. You will do so by using the two ends of a bent paper clip. As shown in the diagram below, in areas of low mechanoreceptor concentration, you or your partner will not be able to distinguish the touch of the two paper clip ends. In areas where the mechanoreceptors are highly concentrated, both ends of the paper clip can be felt even when they are a very short distance apart. In the Prelab Activity you will practice this technique as you test the sensitivity of different parts of your hand.

Objective to explore the density of mechanoreceptors in skin

Inquiry Skills
- making measurements
- collecting data
- making inferences
- analyzing data

Time
- 15 min for Prelab Activity
- 30 min for Procedure
- 15 min for Analysis and Conclusions

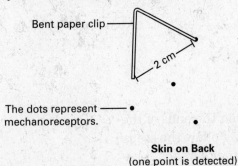

Bent paper clip

2 cm

The dots represent mechanoreceptors.

Skin on Back
(one point is detected)

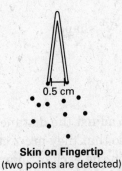

0.5 cm

Skin on Fingertip
(two points are detected)

Prelab Activity Follow the steps below to make a mechanoreceptor-testing tool and use it to test different parts of your hand. Then answer the Prelab Questions that follow.

1. Unfold a small paper clip and bend it into a "V" shape.

2. Gently touch the tips of the paper clip to the skin on your palm, the heel of your hand (the area of your palm just above your wrist), the back of your hand, the backs of your fingers, and your fingertips. Try to apply the same amount of pressure each time you touch your hand with the paper clip.

3. As you touch each part of your hand with the paper clip, notice how the sensation varies. For example, the end of the paper clip may feel sharp on one part of the hand, and dull on another part. Note on which parts of your hand you feel the touch more keenly and on which you feel the touch only dully. Rate the following parts of your hand 1–5. Use "5" to indicate the most sensitive areas and use "1" to indicate the least sensitive areas.

Palm: _____   Backs of fingers: _____

Heel of hand: _____   Fingertips: _____

Back of hand: _____

Prelab Questions

1. Which area of your hand was the most sensitive to touch and pressure?

   Sample answer: The heel of my hand was the most sensitive to touch and pressure.

2. Predict whether the variations in touch sensitivity found on different parts of the hand will vary from one person to another. Explain your prediction.

   Sample answer: I would predict that the sensitivity of parts of the hand would vary from person to person. For example, a person who works with their hands often, such as a construction worker or farmer, may have thicker skin on the heels of their hands, causing the heels of their hands to be less sensitive to touch than they might be for other people.

Materials

- paper clip bent into a "V" shape
- metric ruler

Procedure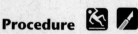

1. Use the metric ruler to adjust the distance between the ends of the "V-shaped" paper clip so that they are 2 cm apart. Follow the steps below to test the skin on the back of your lab partner's hand.

2. Your partner's eyes should be closed. Touch the skin on the back of the hand 5 times with both points of the paper clip and 5 times with just one point. Mix up the order so that your partner will not notice a pattern. **CAUTION:** *A gentle pressure is all that is needed. Be very careful not to pierce your partner's skin with the paper clip.* After each touch ask your partner if they felt one paper clip point or two. Record the number of times two points were detected and the number of times one point was detected in Data Table 1.

Data Table 1: Back of Hand

Touch	2 cm		1.5 cm		1 cm		0.5 cm		0.2 cm		0.1 cm	
	Points used	Points felt	Points used	Points felt	Points used	Points felt	Points used	Points felt	Points used	Points felt	Points used	Points felt
1												
2												
3												
4												
5												
6												
7												
8												
9												
10												

3. Decrease the distance between the ends of the paper clip so that they are 1.5 cm apart. Repeat Step 2.

4. Repeat Step 3 at the following distances apart: 1 cm, 0.5 cm, 0.2 cm, and 0.1 cm.

5. Test the skin on the tip of your lab partner's index finger using the same procedure described in steps 2–4. Record your data in Data Table 2 on the next page.

Data Table 2: Tip of Index Finger

Touch	2 cm Points used	2 cm Points felt	1.5 cm Points used	1.5 cm Points felt	1 cm Points used	1 cm Points felt	0.5 cm Points used	0.5 cm Points felt	0.2 cm Points used	0.2 cm Points felt	0.1 cm Points used	0.1 cm Points felt
1												
2												
3												
4												
5												
6												
7												
8												
9												
10												

6. Test the skin on top of your partner's forearm, using the same procedure. Record your data in Data Table 3.

Data Table 3: Forearm

Touch	2 cm Points used	2 cm Points felt	1.5 cm Points used	1.5 cm Points felt	1 cm Points used	1 cm Points felt	0.5 cm Points used	0.5 cm Points felt	0.2 cm Points used	0.2 cm Points felt	0.1 cm Points used	0.1 cm Points felt
1												
2												
3												
4												
5												
6												
7												
8												
9												
10												

7. From the data recorded in Data Tables 1–3, record the distance at which the two points of the paper clip could still be detected by your lab partner at least three times.

Back of hand: _____ cm

Fingertip: _____ cm

Forearm: _____ cm

8. Ask your lab partner about your results. For each area of the skin, record the distance at which you could still detect the two points of the paper clip at least three times.

Back of hand: _____ cm

Fingertip: _____ cm

Forearm: _____ cm

Analysis and Conclusions

1. From your data would you conclude that the density of mechano-receptors differs from person to person in the same area of the skin? Explain.

Students' responses will vary depending on their data.

_____

_____

2. What similarities did you find in the data you collected for both you and your lab partner? What differences did you find?

Students' responses will vary.

_____

_____

3. Develop a hypothesis to explain why humans have a higher con-centration of mechanoreceptors in some areas of the skin than other areas.

Students' hypotheses will vary, but may refer to the fact that the areas with the most mechano-

receptors are the areas that are most likely to be damaged. For example, fingertips are more likely

to be damaged during everyday activities than a forearm. A higher concentration of mechanoreceptors

in the fingertips ensures that contact with sharp or dangerous objects will be detected.

_____

Extension

The mechanoreceptors you tested in this lab are called tactile receptors. Proprioceptors are another type of mechanoreceptor that relay information to the central nervous system about the position of muscles and joints. To test the action of proprioceptors, stand up straight and close your eyes. Use your arms like the hands of a clock to model noon, 3 o'clock, and half past 8 o'clock. Repeat the exercise with your eyes open. Was this exercise any harder to do with your eyes closed?

Breaking Down Fat Digestion

How Bile and Pancreatic Juice Affect Fat Digestion

Question What are the roles of bile and pancreatic juice in fat digestion?

Lab Overview In this investigation you will determine the roles of bile and pancreatic juice in fat digestion. You will use whole milk as a source of fat, samples of bile and pancreatic juice, and the pH indicator phenol red.

Introduction In the Prelab Activity you will examine part of the experimental design and complete the plan. Then, you will answer questions about how the design of the experiment will help you determine the effects of bile and pancreatic juice on fat digestion.

Background From the stomach, food enters the small intestine. Several chemicals that are secreted into the small intestine continue the chemical digestion of food there. Two of these chemicals, bile (made in the liver and secreted by the gallbladder) and pancreatic juice (made and secreted by the pancreas), play roles in the digestion of fat.

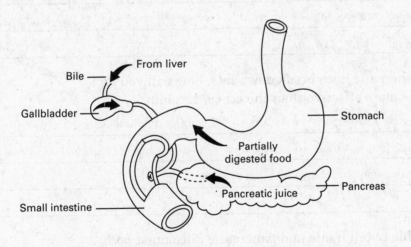

When fat molecules are digested, the result is molecules of glycerol and fatty acids. The presence of fatty acids can be detected with a pH indicator such as phenol red. In a basic solution, phenol red is hot pink, while in an acidic solution, it is orange. The faster a solution changes from basic to acidic, the faster the color change occurs. In this lab you'll use phenol red to determine when milk fat is broken down, and to compare how quickly it is broken down in different samples.

Objective to design and perform an experiment to determine the roles of bile and pancreatic juice in fat digestion

NOTE: You may wish to have the class do this lab before you cover Concept 29.2, which discusses the roles of bile and pancreatic juice in fat digestion.

Inquiry Skills
- designing experiments
- making measurements
- analyzing data
- drawing conclusions

Time
- 15–20 min for Prelab Activity
- 45 min for Lab Activity
- 20 min for Analysis and Conclusions

Pancreatic juice contains lipase, an enzyme that breaks the bonds between glycerol and fatty acids in fat molecules. Bile is an emulsifier that breaks up fats into smaller droplets. This increases the available surface area of the fats, enabling lipase to break down the molecules more efficiently.

Prelab Activity You will use four test tubes in the investigation. Examine the set-up of test tubes 1, 3, and 4 below.

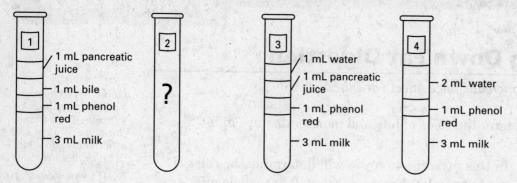

1 — 1 mL pancreatic juice
— 1 mL bile
— 1 mL phenol red
— 3 mL milk

2 — ?

3 — 1 mL water
— 1 mL pancreatic juice
— 1 mL phenol red
— 3 mL milk

4 — 2 mL water
— 1 mL phenol red
— 3 mL milk

Prelab Questions

1. **What should go in Tube 2? What is the purpose of this tube in the lab?**

   Suggested answer: Tube 2 should contain 3 mL milk, 1 mL phenol red, 1 mL bile, and 1 mL water.

   Tube 2 will show the effect of bile on fat.

2. **How will you be able to tell if either bile or pancreatic juice breaks down fats? Explain.**

   Suggested answer: The contents in Tubes 1, 2, and/or 3 will change from pink to orange because

   the breakdown of fats will produce fatty acids, which will cause the phenol red to turn orange.

3. **If both bile and pancreatic juice break down fats, how will you be able to tell if one is more effective than the other? Explain.**

   Suggested answer: By comparing the time it takes for the solutions in Tubes 2 and 3 to turn from

   pink to orange. If one chemical is more effective than the other, the color change will occur more

   quickly in the tube testing only that chemical.

4. **How will you be able to tell if bile and pancreatic juice must *both* be present for fat to be broken down?**

   Suggested answer: Only the tube with both bile and pancreatic juice (Tube 1) will change color.

5. Explain why Tube 3 contains 1 mL pancreatic juice and 1 mL water rather than 2 mL pancreatic juice.

Suggested answer: The concentration of pancreatic juice should be the same in both tubes.

_____

_____

6. Predict what you think will happen in this experiment.

Answers will vary, but the following would be a good response: Since both bile and pancreatic juice

are secreted at the same time into the small intestine, they probably interact as they break down fat.

I predict that the solution in Tube 1 will change color the fastest.

_____

Materials

- 4 test tubes
- labeling tape
- pen or marker
- 4 plastic film squares, stoppers, or caps
- test-tube rack
- graduated transfer pipettes
- 12 mL whole milk solution
- 2 mL bile solution
- 2 mL pancreatic juice solution
- 4 mL water
- 4 mL phenol red solution
- stopwatch or clock with second hand

See the end of this lab for **Advance Preparation**.

Safety and Disposal
Ask if any students are allergic to milk products. Remind students to wear goggles, aprons, and gloves during the investigation. Phenol red can stain skin and clothing. The bile and pancreatic juice (which contains protease) solutions are acidic. If any solution gets into a student's eye, flush the eye immediately with water and seek medical attention. Tell students to notify you immediately of broken glass. Remind them not to pick up any broken glass. Students should wash their hands after the lab. Follow school guidelines for glass disposal. Solutions can be flushed down the drain with excess water.

(**NOTE:** *In the Prelab Activity you determined the contents of Tube 2. Check your answer with your teacher before proceeding with the investigation.*)

Procedure

1. Label the test tubes 1–4. Fill the test tubes with the volumes of different liquids listed in the Prelab Activity. Place the test tubes in the test-tube rack.

2. Tightly cover each tube with a plastic film square, stopper, or cap. Thoroughly mix the sample in each tube by inverting the tube (turning it upside down). After mixing, place each tube back in the test-tube rack. Record the start time and the initial color of each sample in Data Table 1 on the next page.

Point out to students that the reaction time within the small intestine is faster than at room temperature due to its higher temperature. In fact, you can cut the reaction time in the lab by simulating internal conditions. Incubate the sealed test tubes in a warm water bath at 37°C (98.6°F).

Be sure that students know the proper way to use transfer pipettes. Bulbs should be squeezed slightly to pull the liquid up to the correct measurement line. The liquid is then dispensed by squeezing the bulb completely.

3. When you observe a color change in a tube invert the tube again. Then, record the time and a description of the observed color in Data Table 1 below.

See the end of the lab for **Expected Results**.

Data Table 1

Test Tube	Start time/ Initial color	Time/ Color	Time/ Color	Time/ Color	Time/ Color
1. Pancreatic juice and bile					
2. _____ _____					
3. Pancreatic juice and water					
4. Water only					

Analysis and Conclusions

1. From the results of your experiment, what conclusions can you draw about the effect of bile on fat digestion?

Bile alone does not break down fats. However, bile must have some role in fat digestion because the

test tube containing pancreatic juice and bile changed color faster than the test tube containing just

pancreatic juice.

_____

2. From the results of your experiment, what conclusions can you draw about the effect of pancreatic juice on fat digestion?

Pancreatic juice does break down fats into glycerol and fatty acids.

_____

_____

_____

3. What was the purpose of Tube 4 in the experimental design?

Tube 4 was the control. The control was needed to show that neither phenol red nor water had an

effect on the milk fat.

4. How might fat digestion be affected if the pancreas, liver, or gall-bladder were not functioning properly? Explain your answer.

Sample answer: If a person's pancreas is not functioning properly, his or her body may be incapable

of digesting fats. If a person has liver or gallbladder problems, his or her body may be not produce

or secrete bile in adequate amounts. Without bile, the rate of fat digestion is impaired.

Extension

The fat in butter is mostly saturated fat, while the fat in margarine is mostly monounsaturated or polyunsaturated fat. Design an experiment to determine if there is a difference in the rate of fat digestion between butter and margarine. **CAUTION:** *Always check with your teacher before carrying out any investigations.*

Extension
Review students' experimental designs. If students will be carrying out their experiments, assist them with the preparation of solutions.

Advance Preparation

A couple of weeks before the lab
Review the ingredients for the various solutions. See the front of this Laboratory Manual Teacher's Edition for supplier information.

One day before the lab
Make the solutions. The amounts below are enough for 15 lab groups.

Phenol red solution: Mix 0.4 g phenol red powder with 100 mL water.

Milk solution: Mix 400 mL whole milk with 100 mL 0.1M NaOH to raise the pH of the milk. Keep refrigerated until needed. 14 mL of household bleach could be used instead of NaOH.

CAUTION: *Wear safety goggles and plastic gloves. Concentrated NaOH can cause blindness. If NaOH pellets come in contact with your skin, immediately wash the area thoroughly with water.*

Test the pH of the solution before the lab by mixing 3 mL milk with 1 mL phenol red. If the solution is orange or salmon-colored, rather than hot pink, you need to add more base.

Pancreatic juice: Mix 3 g pancreatin with 100 mL distilled or bottled water. Keep refrigerated until needed. This solution will not keep for more than one day.

Bile: Mix 3 g bile salts with 100 mL distilled or bottled water.

Expected Results

At room temperature, Tube 1 will generally change color after about 10 min. Tube 3 will reach the same color as Tube 1 after about 30 min. However, the reaction times will vary depending on the conditions in the room and other factors. Perform the lab ahead of time in your lab room to determine how long the reaction will take. If you find there is a significant delay between the color change in different tubes, you may want to suggest that students check their samples at specific time intervals, such as every 5 min. You also may want to have planned activities for the students to do while they wait for the color changes.

Which Spread for Your Bread?

Comparing Taste, Nutritional Value, and Cost of Bread Spreads

Question How do different bread spreads differ in sensory appeal, nutritional value, and cost per serving?

Lab Overview In this investigation you will evaluate common bread spreads such as butter, margarine, and olive oil. You will assign a score from 1 to 10 to each spread based on its sensory appeal (appearance, smell, and flavor), nutritional value, and cost per serving. You will then calculate the average score for each spread to determine which is the best overall choice.

Introduction You will begin your investigation by examining the nutritional labels on the condiments and spreads you use at home. To rate the nutritional value of a product, you will compare the levels of saturated fat, cholesterol, *trans* fatty acids, and total fat in each product. Many researchers think that a diet high in saturated fats, cholesterol, and *trans* fatty acids can lead to high levels of blood cholesterol and triglycerides, which are associated with a high risk of cardiovascular disease.

Background A fat molecule consists of a glycerol molecule attached to three fatty acid chains. A saturated fat is solid at room temperature and contains the maximum possible number of hydrogen atoms. Single bonds link carbon atoms to hydrogen atoms and other carbon atoms. An unsaturated fat is liquid at room temperature. Some of the carbon atoms are double-bonded to each other. (See Figure 5-9 on page 98 in your textbook to review the molecular structure of fats.)

Butter, which is made from animal products, contains saturated fat and cholesterol. High levels of saturated fats and cholesterol in the diet have long been associated with an increased risk of cardiovascular disease. When health professionals speak of "bad fats," they are usually speaking of saturated fats. Margarine, which is made from plant products, does not contain cholesterol and contains little saturated fat. It is solidified by a process called *hydrogenation*. During hydrogenation, hydrogen is added to the unsaturated fat in vegetable oil, changing some of the double bonds of unsaturated fat molecules into single bonds. Flavoring and color are added to make margarine taste and look more like butter.

However, studies have found that hydrogenation creates unusual bonds in fats. Double bonds in natural unsaturated fats, called *cis* double bonds, have a C-shaped kink in the fatty acid chain. When *cis* double bonds are hydrogenized, some bonds become single bonds, but others

Objective to compare appeal, nutritional value, and cost of bread spreads

Inquiry Skills
• predicting
• observing
• calculating
• organizing data
• drawing conclusions

Time
• 15–20 min for Prelab Activity (recommended as a homework assignment)
• 10 min for Part A
• 10 min for Part B
• 10 min for Part C
• 10 min for Part D
• 15 min for Analysis and Conclusions

Using solid (saturated) fats in baking cookies, cakes, and crackers produces a more favorable texture than using liquid (unsaturated) fats. Many people also prefer to spread solid fats (butter, margarine, or cream cheese) on bread and toast, although it is becoming popular to dip bread in olive oil.

The first vegetable fats used in commercially prepared goods were palm and coconut oils, also known as tropical vegetable oils. These oils have some saturated fatty acids and are semisolid at room temperature. When studies found that saturated fat is associated with heart change shape and become *trans* double bonds. *Trans* double bonds have a Z-shaped kink in the fatty acid chain. Some researchers think that when these *trans* fatty acids are ingested, absorbed by the small intestine, and eventually incorporated into the plasma membranes of cells, they may affect how molecules flow in and out of the cells. *Trans* fatty acids are now thought to be associated with many forms of cardiovascular disease.

Some margarine products may be labeled "contains no *trans* fat." This means that the manufacturer has solidified the vegetable oil with a method other than hydrogenation. For example, starch and vegetable gum may be used to thicken the vegetable oil so that the margarine is solid at room temperature.

Prelab Activity Look in your refrigerator or pantry at home and locate one or more bread condiments or spreads. Before reading the labels, predict which condiment or spread is the highest in total fat. Then study the nutritional information on the label(s), read the ingredients, and fill in the table below.

disease, many commercial bakers stopped using palm and coconut oils and turned to hydrogenated vegetable oils. Studies comparing the use of animal fats and hydrogenated oils found that individuals who consume hydrogenated oils were at a greater risk for heart disease than individuals who consume equal amounts of animal fat. By 2006 all food labels in the United States are required to contain information about *trans* fats.

Condiment/ spread	Cholesterol (mg per serving)	Saturated fat (g per serving)	*Trans* fat (g per serving)	Total fat (g per serving)

(**NOTE:** *Some food labels may not list the amount of* trans *fat in the product. If there is not a listing for* trans *fat, look for hydrogenated oil in the ingredients list. If the product contains hydrogenated oil, place a check mark in the* trans *fat column.*)

Prelab Questions

1. What is a saturated fat? Give an example.

A saturated fat is a fat in which all three fatty acid chains contain the maximum number of hydrogen

atoms (all the carbon atoms in the fatty acid chains form single bonds with each other). Animal

fats, such as lard and butter, are examples of saturated fats.

2. How does the hydrogenation process change vegetable oils?

In the hydrogenation process, fatty acid molecules in vegetable oils are combined with hydrogen

atoms in a way that changes some of the double bonds in each fatty acid molecule to single bonds.

As a result, liquid vegetable oils are changed into hydrogenated fats that stay semisolid at

room temperature, as do saturated fats.

3. Of the condiments and spreads you examined in the Prelab Activity, which had the highest amount of saturated fat per serving? Which had the lowest amount of saturated fat per serving? Is this what you expected? Explain.

Students' responses will vary.

_____

_____

_____

Materials

- samples of various bread spreads
- plastic teaspoons
- paper towels
- bread or crackers
- drinking water in plastic cups
- nutrition and price information for each bread spread
- calculator

IMPORTANT: *Part A of this lab involves tasting food products and should take place in a classroom or cafeteria setting instead of a laboratory.*

Procedure

Part A: Rating the Spreads for Sensory Appeal

1. Spread about 1/2 teaspoon of a bread spread on a small piece of bread. Examine its appearance, smell it, and then taste it. Rate the overall sensory appeal of this spread on a scale of 1 (poor) to 10 (excellent). Record your rating in Data Table 1 below.

2. Repeat Step 1 to rate all of the spreads. Drink a little water between samples. Use a fresh spoon for each sample. Adjust each rating as needed. For example, you may rate one spread as a "10" and then try another spread that you like much better.

Advance Preparation

A couple of days before the lab
Go to a large grocery store and purchase a variety of condiments and spreads. Good examples of products for this lab are butter, whipped butter, cream cheese, fat-free cream cheese, margarine, low-fat margarine, fat-free margarine, and olive oil. Save your grocery store receipt so that students can calculate the cost per serving of each spread. If you are bringing in spreads from home, use a grocery store Web site to research prices.

Since some students may not normally eat slices of bread or butter-type spreads, you could ask students to bring in other foods such as pita and hummus if they wish.

Data Table 1

Name of Spread	Description of Appearance/Smell/Taste	Sensory Appeal Rating

Part B: Rating the Spreads for Nutritional Value

1. You will rate the nutritional value of each spread by comparing the amounts of cholesterol, saturated fat, *trans* fat and total fat found in one serving. Find the amounts of these substances listed on the nutrition information label for each spread. Record your findings in Data Table 2.

Safety and Disposal
Because students will be eating, do not do this activity in the laboratory. Do not allow the bread spreads, bread, or utensils to come in contact with any lab equipment. Do not store the bread spreads in the laboratory refrigerator. No special disposal required.

Data Table 2

Name of Spread	Cholesterol	Saturated Fat	*Trans* Fat	Total Fat	Overall Rating for Nutritional Value

2. Use the scoring guidelines below to help you calculate an overall rating of 1 to 10 for each of the spreads. Record the scores in Data Table 2.

Nutritional Scoring Guidelines

Category	Amount per 1 tablespoon serving (14 g)	Score
Cholesterol	0 mg	3
	1–10 mg	2
	11–20 mg	1
	Over 21 mg	0
Saturated fat	Less than 1 g	3
	1–3 g	2
	4–6 g	1
	More than 6 g	0
Trans fat*	0 g	4
	less than 1 g	2
	1–3 g	1
	4 grams or more	0
Total fat	Less than 1 g	4
	1–5 g	3
	5–10 g	1
	More than 10 g	0

*If the food label does not list the amount of *trans* fat, rate as follows: contains no hydrogenated oil = 4, contains both hydrogenated oil and vegetable oil = 2, and contains hydrogenated oil = 0.

Students may assume that low-fat spreads or margarines have fewer calories than butter. You could have students add a column to Data Table 2 where they can input the number of calories per serving for each spread.

The rating scale is based on the research findings that cholesterol, saturated fat, and hydrogenated oils are associated with cardiovascular disease. It is not meant to promote or proscribe any particular type of bread spread. Not all scientists agree on the health effects of hydrogenated oils and new studies may change the current view of others. You may wish to invent your own rating scale based on the latest dietary research.

Part C: Rating the Spreads by Cost per Serving

1. Calculate the cost per serving of each spread by dividing the cost per package by the number of servings each package contains. Record your data in Data Table 3 below.

Data Table 3

Name of Spread	Total Cost per Package	Cost per Serving	Cost Rating

2. Determine which spread has the lowest cost per serving and assign that one a rating of 10. Then, assign lower ratings to the other spreads based on how expensive they are per serving. Record the ratings in Data Table 3.

Part D: Calculating Overall Ratings

1. For each spread, add the three rating numbers (sensory appeal, nutritional value, and cost per serving) together. Record the sum in the appropriate column of Data Table 4 below.

Data Table 4

Name of Spread	Sum of Ratings	Average Overall Rating

2. Calculate the average overall rating for each spread by dividing the sum of the three ratings by 3. Record the results of your calculations in Data Table 4.

Analysis and Conclusions

1. Which of the spreads that you tested had the best overall rating? Explain.

Students' responses will vary based on the samples.

_____

_____

2. Do you think your results will affect what you put on your bread in the future? Explain.

Students' responses will vary.

3. When choosing a spread for your bread, what are some other factors you might consider besides taste, fat content, and cost?

Students' responses will vary, but could include salt content, calorie content, or if the ingredients in the product were produced organically.

4. What are some factors that could have affected the results of this lab? For example, if the products were unlabeled when you tasted them, do you think you would have rated them differently? Name at least two other factors that could have affected the results.

Students may respond that possibly they would have rated low-fat products differently if they had not known that they were low in fat ahead of time. Other factors that students may mention are level of hunger at the time of the tasting or differences in the labels. Some labels list the amount of *trans* fats in their products, while others do not.

Extension

Perform a similar test with several brands of the same type of fruit juice. Some juice products are much higher in vitamins, such as vitamins A and C, than others. Rate the juices based on taste, vitamins A and C content, and cost per serving. For taste, rate the juices based on a scale of 1 (poor) to 10 (excellent). For cost per serving, rate the least expensive juice as a 10. Then, assign lower ratings to the other juices based on how expensive they are per serving. Use the scoring guidelines below to rate vitamin content.

Vitamin Scoring Guidelines

Category	Amount per 8 oz. serving	Score
Vitamin A	100%	5
	51–100%	3
	10–50%	2
	Less than 10%	0
Vitamin C	100%	5
	51–100%	3
	10–50%	2
	Less than 10%	0

Extension
Remind students not to perform the test in a laboratory setting. This exercise will help students realize that not all fruit juices are necessarily "healthy."

Additional Resources
Enig, Mary. *Know Your Fats*. Bethesda Press, 2000.

Aro, A, et al. "Stearic Acid, *Trans* Fatty Acids and Dietary Fat: Effects On Serum and Lipoprotein Lipids, Apolipoproteins, Lipoprotein(a), and Lipid Transfer Proteins in Healthy Subjects." *American Journal of Clinical Nutrition*, v65 n5, May 1997.

Food and Drug Administration Web site www.fda.gov

Sensing Circulation

Exploring the Effects of Exercise on Heart Rate

Questions How do the sounds you hear through a stethoscope relate to the stages of a heartbeat? How does your heart rate change with exercise?

Lab Overview In this investigation you will use a stethoscope to listen to your heart beating. You will learn to take your pulse, determine your target heart rate, and perform a cardiac efficiency test to explore how your heart rate changes during and after exercise.

Introduction To start your investigation, you will learn about the parts of a stethoscope and the relationship between heart rate, pulse, and physical fitness. Then, you will determine the best place on your body to take your pulse.

Background When the ventricles in your heart contract, your atrioventricular valves (the valves located between the atria and ventricles), pulmonary valve, and aortic valve open and allow blood to flow through them. The valves then close, stopping blood from flowing backward. As the valves close, they make sounds that can be heard using a stethoscope. When the atrioventricular valves close, a "lub" sound is produced. When the pulmonary and aortic valves close, a "dupp" sound is produced.

To learn more about the parts of a stethoscope, study the diagram below.

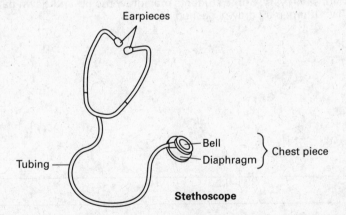

Earpieces

Tubing

Bell

Diaphragm

Chest piece

Stethoscope

Health professionals use the cup-shaped bell side of the stethoscope to listen to low-pitched sounds. They use the flat diaphragm side to listen to high-pitched sounds. For this lab, you should use the diaphragm.

When listening for heart murmurs, doctors use the stethoscope bell to detect diastolic murmurs (which occur when the heart is relaxed). They use the diaphragm to detect systolic murmurs (which occur as the heart is pumping).

Objective to listen to heart sounds with a stethoscope, to take a pulse to measure heart rate, to determine target heart rate, and to test changes in heart rate during and after exercise

Inquiry Skills
• observing
• making measurements
• calculating
• making inferences

Time
• 15 min for the Prelab Activity
• 15–20 min for Part A
• 10 min for Part B
• 15–20 min for Part C
• 15 min for Analysis and Conclusions

Health professionals use stethoscopes to listen for abnormal sounds produced when the heart valves open and close. The most common problem detected is mitral valve prolapse. The mitral valve is the atrioventricular valve located between the left atrium and left ventricle. In people with mitral valve prolapse, the valve tissue is loose. When the heart contracts, the valve may not close all the way. A clicking sound or a "murmur" sound may be produced as a small amount of blood leaks through.

Heart rate is the number of times each minute that the ventricles in your heart contract and pump blood. Each time blood is pumped, artery walls expand and then relax. This causes a surge of blood that can be felt at certain points in your body—your pulse. Heart rate can be measured without a stethoscope, by measuring pulse rate.

When you exercise, your heart rate increases, enabling oxygen and nutrients to be delivered to your cells faster. The heart of a person in top physical condition usually pumps a larger volume of blood with each contraction than the heart of a person in poor physical condition. After exercise, the heart rate of a person in top physical condition returns to normal faster than the heart rate of a person in poor condition. The length of time it takes for heart rate to return to normal after exercise is a measure of the efficiency of the heart.

Prelab Activity In this lab you will measure your pulse rate at different levels of physical activity. First, you should determine which artery is the best one to use for measuring your pulse. Two possible places you can detect a pulse are the left side of your neck or the inside of your wrist at the base of your thumb. Use your first two fingers to detect your pulse. Do not use your thumb because it has a pulse of its own.

A pulse typically has an even, steady beat, with an equal amount of time between each beat. (If you feel that your pulse does not have an even, steady beat, it is probably not a cause for concern, but you should tell a family member, school nurse, or doctor about what you observed.)

Prelab Questions

1. In the space below draw a pattern representing your pulse as you felt it. Explain in words how the diagram represents your pulse.

   Students' drawings and explanations will vary. Some students may draw the up-and-down pattern of an EKG as they may have seen on TV. Others may draw a dashed line.

2. Explain the connection between heart rate and pulse.

   Suggested answer: When the ventricles contract with each heartbeat, the arteries expand from

   the pressure. You can feel a pulse when you place your fingers near a major artery.

Materials

- stethoscope
- rubbing alcohol
- cotton balls
- stopwatch (or clock with second hand)
- calculator (optional)

Advance Preparation
Obtain stethoscopes and stopwatches as needed. Stethoscopes can be purchased from most biological supply companies for less than $10 each.

Alternate Methods
If you don't have enough stethoscopes you could have half the class do parts B and C first. Or, you can have students make simple stethoscopes. A funnel or the top half of a cut-off 1-liter bottle can be used as the chest piece. A piece of rubber tubing can be attached to the small end of the funnel or bottle to serve as an earpiece.
  If you have students in wheelchairs, you could have them participate in Part C by doing just the arm motions of jumping jacks as quickly as they can for 30 sec.

Procedure
Part A: Listening to Heart Sounds

1. Use a cotton ball and rubbing alcohol to clean the earpieces of the stethoscope.

2. Insert the earpieces into your ears, angling the earpieces slightly forward. Place the diaphragm (flat side of the stethoscope) over your heart (just to the left of the center of your chest).

3. Listen to your heart. If you're having trouble locating your heart sounds, first try adjusting the stethoscope earpieces. If you are wearing several layers of heavy clothing, try removing an outer sweater or jacket if you can. Describe what you hear.

If the room is fairly quiet, students should be able to distinguish the "lub" sound from the "dupp." It is

unlikely that they will hear the common heart murmurs that, statistically, some of your students

probably have. If they do hear something they think is unusual, advise them to tell a family member,

school nurse, or doctor about what they observed.

4. When you have finished listening to your heart and have recorded your observations, clean the stethoscope earpieces again. Dispose of used cotton balls as directed by your teacher.

Part B: Determining Target Heart Rate

You can use your heart rate as a tool to find out if your heart is getting the maximum benefit from exercise. The benefit of exercise for your heart is to increase the efficiency of your heart muscle so that it pumps a greater volume of blood with each beat. To get the maximum benefit while exercising without causing injury, you should adjust your level of activity so that your heart rate is in a certain range called the *target heart rate zone*. Calculate your target heart rate zone as follows.

1. Use the equation below to calculate your maximum heart rate (beats per min).

   220 − your age in years = maximum heart rate per min (MHR)

   MHR = __205__ beats per min

   (**NOTE:** *Maximum heart rate decreases with age, regardless of your physical condition.*)

Safety and Disposal
Since Part C of this lab requires students to run in place for 30 sec, students with asthma or certain other health problems should not participate. You may wish to consult the school nurse for information about students who should not be allowed to participate. Remind students to take care not to injure themselves or others while exercising. Advise students to sit down if they feel dizzy or faint at any time during exercise and to notify you immediately. Remind students to wipe stethoscope earpieces with alcohol prior to inserting them into their ears. You may wish to have students place used cotton balls in a covered, plastic-lined trash container.

2. Use the equation below to calculate the lower end of your target heart rate zone, which is 70% of your maximum heart rate.

maximum heart rate × 0.7 = lower end of target heart rate zone

Lower end of your target heart rate zone = ___144___

3. Use the equation below to calculate the upper end of your target heart rate zone, which is 80% of your maximum heart rate.

maximum heart rate × 0.8 = upper end of target heart rate zone

Upper end of target heart rate zone = ___164___

(**NOTE:** *Allowing your heart rate to climb over 80% of your maximum heart rate during exercise may be a sign of overexertion and could lead to injury.*)

Part C: Determining Your Cardiac Efficiency

Follow the steps below to see how your heart rate changes with exercise. **CAUTION:** *If you have a health problem that restricts your ability to exercise, talk to your teacher and do not participate in this part of the lab.*

1. While sitting, take your pulse for 15 sec. Record the result below.

Sitting pulse (per 15 sec): _____

2. Run in place with your knees held high for 30 sec. (**CAUTION:** *If at any time you do not feel well, stop exercising and tell your teacher.*) Immediately afterward, take your pulse for 15 sec.

Peak pulse (per 15 sec): _____

3. After an additional 45 sec (to allow a total recovery time of 1 min after exercising) take your pulse again for 15 sec.

Recovery pulse (per 15 sec) _____

4. Make a line graph to represent how your heart responds to exercise. Plot time on the *x*-axis and pulse rate on the *y*-axis.

Most students expect that their heart rate will increase with exercise. However, they may be surprised at how quickly their heart rate returns to normal after exercise. Recovery time is a good indicator of cardiovascular fitness.

See Analysis and Conclusions Question 5 for sample data.

Name _____ Class _____ Date_____

Analysis and Conclusions

1. While listening to someone's heart, a doctor discovers that the "lub" sound is weaker than the "dupp" sound. What might this clue suggest about the functioning of the heart valves?

Sample answer: The weaker "lub" sound suggests that one or both of the atrioventricular valves may

not be functioning completely.

2. While listening to your heart, did you find that there was more time between the "lub" and the "dupp" sounds, or between one "lub dupp" and the next? Suggest a possible explanation.

Sample answer: There is more time between one "lub dupp" and the next "lub dupp" than there is

between the "lub" sound and the "dupp" sound. A possible explanation is that the heart rests a

moment between beats.

3. How is it useful to know your target heart rate zone? What forms of exercise do you think might increase your heart rate so that it is in your target heart rate zone?

Suggested answer: It is useful to know your target heart rate zone so that you make sure that your

heart is receiving the maximum benefit from exercise. Running or jogging, walking fast, or a

sport such as basketball are forms of exercise that might increase heart rate.

4. Explain why athletes often have lower resting pulse rates than nonathletes.

Suggested answer: An athlete's heart may pump blood more efficiently so that fewer beats are needed

to deliver adequate oxygen and nutrients.

5. Study the graph below. From the data, which student's cardiovascular system would you conclude is probably more efficient? Explain your response on the lines below the graph.

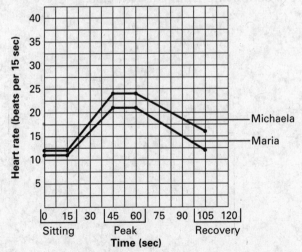

Suggested answer: Maria's cardiovascular system is most likely more efficient. Her sitting heart

rate was lower than Michaela's. Also, her heart rate returned to normal faster than Michaela's.

Extension

There are several methods for determining target heart rates. Another example besides the one described in this lab is the Karvonen method, which takes basal heart rate (resting heart rate) into consideration. Basal heart rate measurements are most accurate if they are taken in the morning when you first wake up and are still lying down. Follow the equation below to calculate your target heart rate using the Karvonen method. Compare your results to those from Part B of the Procedure. Suggest possible reasons for any significant differences.

Karvonen Method

Target heart rate = (220 − age − basal heart rate) × (0.75) + basal heart rate

Extension
Students will comment that the Karvonen method does not give a target heart rate zone, but rather a specific number. If the student's basal heart rate is higher than average, the Karvonen method may produce a target rate that is higher than the upper end of the zone provided by the method in Part B.

_____

_____

_____

During physical education class, or after school, exercise for 15 min and measure your heart rate for 6 sec. Multiply this number by 10 to get your heart rate in beats/min. If the number is in your target heart rate zone, the exercise is helping your heart and lungs stay fit. If it is too high or too low, adjust your level of exertion and continue exercising for another 10 min. Then take your heart rate again to see if you are in the target zone. With practice, you will learn how it feels to exercise in your target heart rate zone, and you won't need to take your pulse to ensure your heart is benefiting from the exercise.

You Are a Cardiac Surgeon

Observing Chambers, Vessels, and Valves in a Mammalian Heart

Questions What do the chambers, vessels, and valves look like in a mammalian heart? How can the aortic valve be replaced in a heart?

Lab Overview In this investigation you will dissect a pig's heart. In Part A you will cut the heart open and observe the chambers, vessels, and valves. In Part B you will surgically remove the aortic valve.

Introduction In the Prelab Activity you will examine the external structure of the pig heart and compare it to the diagrams you have studied of the human heart. Because the pig heart is very similar to the human heart, it is an excellent model for learning about the structure and function of the human heart. In fact, pig hearts are so similar to human hearts that malfunctioning aortic valves in humans often can be replaced with aortic valves from pigs.

Background The aortic valve is located between the heart's left ventricle and the aorta. Aortic valve disease is a condition in which the valve does not function properly. Aortic valve disease can be congenital (existing at birth), or it can occur as the valve wears out with age. The most common congenital defect of the aortic valve in infants is the presence of only two flaps (cusps) of tissue instead of three. This can lead to a narrowing of the valve opening, or to blood leaking back into the left ventricle from the aorta. A child may be several years old before this condition is detected.

As the aortic valve ages, calcium deposits may form on the valve, causing it to harden. This condition can lead to aortic valve disease. As with congenital aortic valve disease, the valve opening may narrow or blood may leak back into the left ventricle from the aorta. In either case, the heart has to work much harder to deliver adequate amounts of blood. Eventually symptoms such as shortness of breath, dizziness, and chest pain may develop.

Currently, a failing aortic valve cannot be repaired. The failing valve must be completely replaced, either with a mechanical (artificial) valve or a biological valve from another organism. While a mechanical valve can last a lifetime, there is a tendency for blood clots to form around it. If the clots dislodge, the patient can suffer a stroke or heart attack. Patients who receive a mechanical valve must take blood-thinning medication for the rest of their lives to reduce the risk of clots.

Some biological valves are made from pig aortic valves. The risk of life-threatening blood clots is not nearly as high as it is for mechanical

Objective to identify chambers, vessels, and valves in a mammalian heart and to model the surgical removal of the aortic valve

Inquiry Skills
• observing
• using models
• making inferences

Time
• 15–20 min for Prelab Activity
• 30–40 min for Part A
• 20 min for Part B
• 15 min for Analysis and Conclusions

Tell students a few days ahead of time that they have the right to opt out of the dissection. Have an alternative activity available for students who do not wish to participate.

valves, but these biological valves typically need to be replaced every 10–20 years. A medical team takes many factors into consideration to decide which type of replacement valve is best for a patient.

Prelab Activity Before starting the lab, you will study the external anatomy of the pig heart. First identify the front (ventral) and back (dorsal) sides of the heart. The ventral side of the heart is the side that faces up when the pig is placed on its back. Below is a drawing of the ventral side of the heart. Use clues from the drawing to orient your pig heart to match the one in the diagram.

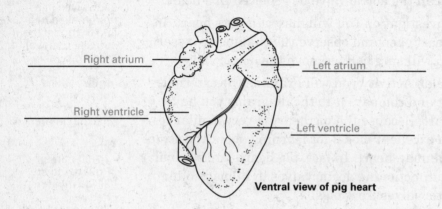

Ventral view of pig heart

Note that the preserved pig heart you receive may differ slightly in appearance from the examples depicted in this lab. In addition to the coronary arteries, another way to identify the dorsal and ventral sides of the heart is to look at the major vessels at the top of the heart. Most of the openings of the veins and arteries (with the exception of the aorta) can be seen most easily from the dorsal side of the heart.

Look for the coronary artery. The coronary artery runs diagonally along the front of the heart and then branches into many smaller arteries. The coronary artery extends from the aorta and leads to the heart muscle. It delivers blood carrying the fuel and oxygen the heart itself requires to function.

The ventricles make up the lower section of the heart. The walls of the left ventricle are about four times thicker and more muscular than the walls of the right ventricle. The atria make up the upper section of the heart. They are very small and have thin walls compared to the ventricles. The atria can be identified as the flaps on top of the heart that look like a dog's ears. Label the left and right ventricles and the left and right atria on the diagram above. (**NOTE:** *Remember that the terms "left" and "right" refer to the pig's left and right sides when the heart is in place, not left and right as you are looking at the heart.*)

Prelab Questions

1. Describe the most common causes of aortic valve failure in children and in older adults.

   Suggested answer: The most common cause of aortic valve failure in children is the presence of

   two flaps of tissue instead of three. In older adults the most common cause of aortic valve failure is that

   the valve becomes diseased and calcium deposits form, which cause it to harden. In both cases the

   result is that either the opening of the valve narrows or blood flows back into the left ventricle, which

   requires the heart to work harder to pump the same amount of blood throughout the body.

2. Describe the two types of valves that may be used in an aortic valve replacement surgery.

Suggested answer: Mechanical or biological valves may be used in an aortic valve replacement

surgery. Mechanical valves are synthetic and will last a lifetime, although blood clots may form. Biologi-

cal valves can be made from pig aortic valves. They need to be replaced every 10–20 years.

3. Make a rough sketch of what you predict the interior of the pig heart looks like. Label the four chambers and draw arrows to indicate the direction blood travels through the chambers. If needed, refer to Figure 30-5 on page 658 in your textbook for guidance.

Materials

- pig heart
- scalpel
- dissection tray
- 10 wooden craft sticks
- marker
- masking tape for labels
- small paper plate

Advance Preparation
Order one pig heart for each lab group from a biological supply company. See the front of this Laboratory Manual Teacher's Edition for supplier information.

Procedure

Part A: Examining the Chambers and Vessels

1. Examine the diagram on the next page. Note the label "First incision." This incision (cut) will reveal the inside of the right ventricle. Using the diagram on the next page as a guide, make the first incision to the heart with your scalpel. **CAUTION:** *Handle sharp instruments with care to avoid injury.*

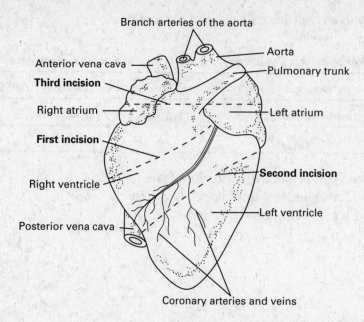

Branch arteries of the aorta

Anterior vena cava

Third incision

Right atrium

First incision

Right ventricle

Posterior vena cava

Aorta

Pulmonary trunk

Left atrium

Second incision

Left ventricle

Coronary arteries and veins

2. Push the right ventricle open with your gloved fingers and look up into the heart toward the right atrium. You should see cords of connective tissue attached to the atrioventricular valve. This tissue ensures the valve only opens in one direction.

3. Use your index finger to locate the opening where blood would exit the right ventricle and enter a structure called the pulmonary trunk. The pulmonary trunk starts at the top left of the heart (your right) and winds around the top of the heart. Then the pulmonary trunk branches into the left and right pulmonary arteries. The pulmonary arteries carry deoxygenated blood to the lungs. (**NOTE:** *Recall that arteries carry blood away from the heart. Veins carry blood to the heart.*)

4. Use the diagram as a guide to help you make the second incision. Since the left ventricle wall is very thick, it will probably take several cuts along the same incision line to cut through to the chamber. Once you have cut through the wall, open the incision to reveal the inside of the left ventricle.

5. Locate and observe the cords of connective tissue attached to the left atrioventricular valve.

6. Use your finger to locate the opening where the blood would enter the left ventricle from the left atrium through the atrioventricular valve. Also locate the opening where blood would enter the aorta and flow to the rest of the body.

7. Observe the wall of the left ventricle and compare its thickness to that of the right ventricle. Compare the sizes of the chambers of the left and right ventricles. How do the functions of the right and left ventricles relate to the relative thicknesses of the walls and sizes of the chambers?

Suggested answer: While the right ventricle pumps blood only to the lungs, the left ventricle pumps

blood throughout the body. Because of their different roles, the left ventricle has a greater muscle mass

than the right ventricle.

8. Label one wooden craft stick "Aorta." Label two wooden craft sticks "Pulmonary artery." Locate the aorta where it exits the left ventricle and insert the craft stick. Since the pulmonary trunk exits the right ventricle and then winds around the heart, you will have to feel along the outside of the artery to observe when it branches into the right and left pulmonary arteries. Insert a labeled craft stick inside the cut end of each artery.

9. Use the diagram above Step 2 as a guide to make the third incision, which will allow you to see into the atria. Cut into the atria. Do not remove the atria from the heart, but instead cut just enough to open a hole so that you can see into them.

10. Now you should be able to identify the veins leading to the heart. Label two wooden craft sticks "Pulmonary vein." The pulmonary veins lead from the lungs to the left atrium. (If you only see one vein, it may be because the other vein was cut off.) To identify the pulmonary veins, place your finger inside the left atrium and push upward to find the vessels it leads to. Place a labeled wooden craft stick inside the pulmonary veins.

11. Repeat Step 10 in the right atrium to locate the anterior vena cava and the posterior vena cava (the veins that return deoxygenated blood from the rest of the body to the heart). Label two wooden craft sticks "Vena cava." Place a labeled craft stick inside each vena cava.

12. Feel the thickness of the walls of the arteries and veins. Does one type of vessel have thicker walls than another? Why do you think this is so?

Suggested answer: The walls of the arteries are thicker because they need to withstand more pressure

as the heart pumps blood through them.

Part B: Removing the Aortic Valve

1. Now you will model one of the first steps of a surgical valve replacement, removing the aortic valve from the pig. Place your fingers on the aorta and feel where it leads to the top of the left ventricle. Cut through the base of the aorta so that the aortic valve remains attached to the heart.

2. Note the ring of stiff cartilage that surrounds the aortic valve. This cartilage supports the aortic valve against the tremendous force of blood pushed from the left ventricle. Remove the valve by using your scalpel to cut around the outside ring of cartilage.

3. Place the valve on a small paper plate and bring it to the sink. Hold the valve under the running water. Observe the difference when you try to pour water through the valve in the wrong direction. Describe the action of the valve below.

Sample answer: The valve flaps stop most of the water from going through the opening.

The next steps for processing this valve for placement in a human would be to remove the muscle and treat it with chemicals that would prevent the patient's immune system from attacking it. Afterward, the valve would be frozen and sold to a hospital.

Analysis and Conclusions

1. Explain the general roles of valves in the heart and the specific role of the aortic valve.

Suggested answer: Properly functioning valves allow blood to flow in only one direction through the heart. The aortic valve opens, allowing blood to flow from the left ventricle to the aorta. Then the valve closes, preventing blood from flowing back into the ventricle.

2. What was the hardest vessel to identify? Explain.

Students' responses will vary.

3. What techniques did you learn during the dissection that you would share with someone who has not dissected a pig heart?

Students' responses will vary.

4. Identify ways that the pig heart is similar to or different from the human heart.

Students may not be able to identify any differences based on their knowledge of the human heart and the pig heart. As for similarities, they may note that both have four chambers that connect to the same types of vessels and that they both have the same number of valves.

Extension

Remove the other three valves from the heart. Describe their similarities and differences. Describe how their form fits their function.

Extension
Students should note that the other valves are not nearly as easy to remove as the aortic valve. The other valves are not supported by the same rigid cartilage.

Additional Resource
A good resource to demonstrate how to cut into a pig heart can be found at the Web site for the University of Western Ontario, John P. Robarts Research Institute, http://www.heartlab.robarts.ca/heartlab.html.

Detecting Disease

Performing a Lyme Disease Assay

Question How can you tell if a person is infected with the bacteria that cause Lyme disease?

Lab Overview You will take on the role of a medical laboratory technician in a diagnostic lab and test simulated blood serum samples using a test called an Enzyme-Linked Immunosorbent Assay (ELISA).

Introduction Students from Ms. Garcia's biology class went on a field trip to study plant communities in the hills near their school. After the trip was over, one student noticed a tick on her leg. The tick was identified as a black-legged (deer) tick. This tick species is often host to *Borrelia burgdorferi*, the bacteria that cause Lyme disease. Other students developed possible Lyme disease symptoms. For example, one student developed an unusual skin rash with a large red spot that grew bigger each day. Another student developed fever and muscle aches.

You will take on the role of a medical laboratory technician in a diagnostic lab. You will test three samples of simulated blood serum (plasma without blood-clotting proteins) from students in Ms. Garcia's class using a procedure called an ELISA test. This test is similar to those used in real medical diagnostic labs.

Background The ELISA test is based on the specific fit of an antibody to only one type of disease antigen. For example, antibodies that "match" the Lyme disease antigen will bind tightly to that type of antigen only. Antibodies that "match" other antigens will not bind at all to Lyme disease antigens.

In the model ELISA test you will first add simulated Lyme disease antigen, which consists of proteins, to a set of wells on a plastic plate. The protein molecules will bind to the plastic wells. Next, you will add to the wells simulated blood serum samples from patients who are being tested for Lyme disease. If a patient has been exposed to *B. burgdorferi*, the patient's blood serum should contain the antibody to the Lyme disease antigen (this antibody is referred to as the primary antibody). If present, the primary antibody will bind to the Lyme disease antigen molecules that are stuck to the plastic wells.

To some other wells, you will add a positive control solution known to contain the antibody to the Lyme disease antigen. To the last set of wells, you will add a negative control solution known *not* to contain the antibody to the Lyme disease antigen. The control solutions will help you confirm the results of your patient sample tests.

Objective to learn how antibody-antigen interactions are used in the diagnosis of Lyme disease by screening simulated blood serum samples with an ELISA test

Inquiry Skills
- observing
- collecting data
- analyzing data
- controlling variables
- drawing conclusions

Time
- 15–20 min for Prelab Activity
- 10 min for Part A
- Part B: See your kit manual for specifics.
- 15–20 min for Analysis and Conclusions

The antigens and antibodies used in the kits are not actually the Lyme disease antigens or human antibodies, but are common proteins and antibodies produced in animals against these proteins.

All cases of Lyme disease in the United States to date have been caused by *B. burgdorferi*. This bacterium lives in the gut of two species of black-legged (deer) ticks (*Ixodes pacificus* and *Ixodes scapularis*). If an infected tick remains attached to a person for a day or more, it is likely that the person will develop Lyme disease.

After adding the patient samples, positive control solution, and negative control solution, you will rinse the wells. Any antibodies or other proteins not bound to the Lyme disease antigen will wash away. Next, you will add a solution containing another antibody bound to an enzyme. This other antibody (called the secondary antibody) will bind to the primary antibody if it is present. Then you will rinse the wells again. In the final step you will add a solution containing a color-producing chemical (called the substrate). If the secondary antibody with the enzyme is still in the wells, then the enzyme will act on the substrate. A colored product will form, giving the liquid in the well a purple-pink color. If the secondary antibody and enzyme are not present, no color change will occur.

Prelab Activity Use the symbols in the key below to draw a sketch showing the contents of a positive and negative well after all the steps of an ELISA test have been completed. Your sketch should indicate the reactions that occur among the substances. Afterward, answer the Prelab Questions.

A bull's-eye-shaped rash at the site of the tick bite is a hallmark of infection, although not all infected individuals develop or notice the rash. Lyme disease is often misdiagnosed since many of its symptoms, such as fatigue and aching joints, are common to other illnesses. Lyme disease can be cured with antibiotics if diagnosed early. If the disease goes untreated, it can cause severe arthritis, nervous system problems, and memory loss.

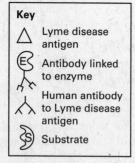

Key

△ Lyme disease antigen

Ⓔ Antibody linked to enzyme

⋀ Human antibody to Lyme disease antigen

Ⓢ Substrate

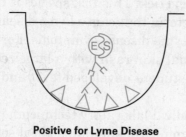

Positive for Lyme Disease

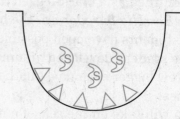

Negative for Lyme Disease

Prelab Questions

1. Describe the contents of each well in your sketches. What do the two wells have in common?

Sample answer: The sketch in the positive well shows Lyme disease antigens stuck to the walls of the well. Antibodies are attached to the antigen. An antibody linked to an enzyme is attached to the first antibody. A substrate is reacting with the enzyme, producing a purple-pink product. In the negative well, Lyme disease antigen is stuck to the walls of the well. Substrate is present, but since there is no enzyme for it to react with, a color change does not occur.

2. If antibodies bind to the Lyme disease antigen in the ELISA plate well, how do you know that the antibodies were released in response to a *B. burgdorferi* infection?

Suggested answer: Antibodies are specific. Only antibodies that were produced in response to *B. burgdorferi* would bind to the antigen.

3. Would either the negative or positive control solution, or both, contain the primary antibody? Explain.

Suggested answer: The positive control would contain primary antibody. The sample is known to contain antibodies to the Lyme disease antigen.

4. Suppose an ELISA test of a patient who had been exposed to *B. burgdorferi* several weeks before produced a negative result. Which of the following could be a possible explanation? Explain your response.

a. There was no primary antibody in the serum.

b. You did not change pipettes between samples.

c. You didn't allow enough time for the antigen to bind to the well.

Suggested answer: c. If not enough time were allowed for the antigen to bind to the well, it would have been washed away.

5. When performing ELISA tests in a medical diagnostic lab, it is important to change pipettes between patient samples. Why?

Suggested answer: A new pipette should be used because there can be trace amounts of a previous sample left in the pipette that can contaminate another sample.

Materials

- ELISA multi-welled plate
- marker
- 3 simulated blood serum samples
- positive control solution
- negative control solution
- disposable transfer pipettes or micropipettor and tips
- Standard Lyme Disease Antigen solution
- antibody-linked enzyme solution
- color-producing substrate solution
- wash buffer in wash bottle
- paper towels
- clock or watch

Advance Preparation

A few weeks before the lab
Order an ELISA kit from Bio-Rad or Edvotek. Follow the advance preparation procedures the manual recommends. If you do not wish to purchase this kit, see below for an alternate method to simulate an ELISA test.

Safety and Disposal
Remind students to wear safety goggles while in the laboratory. Have students wash their hands with soap after completing the lab. For disposal information, see specific kit instructions.

Procedure

Part A: Setting up a Sample Key

1. To ensure that patients receive proper care, it is vital to keep accurate records. In the space below record the identification numbers marked on your three simulated blood serum samples.

Identification numbers:

Alternate Method
A cheaper alternative is to simulate an ELISA test using a phenolphthalein solution. Phenolphthalein is a pH indicator that binds to plastic. It can be used in place of the positive serum samples. You can substitute bottled water for all other solutions required in the procedure (except for the color-producing substrate). For the color-producing substrate, use dilute NaOH (0.5% solution). If the phenolphthalein is present in the patient sample (representing the presence of the antibody to the *B. burgdorferi* antigens), then the phenolphthalein will turn pink in the presence of the NaOH. You will still need to purchase multi-welled strips.

2. You will test each patient sample and control solution three times, so you will need three wells for each sample. As shown in the sample ELISA plate below, each set of three wells is called a "lane." The lanes are numbered from left to right. Prepare a key to record the lane you will use for each sample.

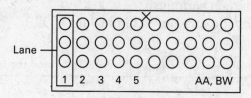

Lane

1 2 3 4 5   AA, BW

Sample ELISA plate

Key for Investigation

Sample	Lane
Patient 1	1
Patient 2	2
Patient 3	3
Positive control	4
Negative control	5

3. Use a marker to write an X on the ELISA plate showing where your lanes end (see the sample above). You may also want to label the plate with your group's initials.

Part B: Performing the ELISA Test

1. Load the Lyme disease antigen solution into all 15 wells. Let the antigen sit at room temperature for the amount of time specified by your teacher. This will give the antigen adequate time to bind to the wells.

2. Use wash solution to rinse the wells, removing any antigen that has not bound to the wells.

3. Using a new transfer pipette for each sample, load the simulated blood serum samples, positive control solution, and negative control solution into the appropriate wells. Let the plate sit for the amount of time specified by your teacher.

4. Rinse the wells again with wash solution to remove any unbound antibodies and other proteins.

5. Load the secondary antibody-enzyme solution into all 15 wells. Let the plate sit for the amount of time specified by your teacher. Rinse the wells to remove any unbound antibody-enzyme solution.

Infections with certain bacteria that have similar structures to *B. burgdorferi* can cause false positive results for Lyme disease with an ELISA test. For example, the bacteria that cause syphilis and some forms of gum disease can cause someone to produce antibodies that will bind to some *B. burgdorferi* antigens.

There are many different tests for Lyme disease. If more than 6 weeks have passed since exposure, the patient will have sufficient antibodies to detect using ELISA or other antibody tests. If 6 weeks have not yet passed, then an antigen test can be used to look for bacterial antigens or DNA in the patient's blood serum. You can find extensive information about antibody and antigen tests in the Lab 31 Online Companion Teaching Guide.

6. Add the color-producing substrate to all 15 wells. Watch for the liquid in any of the wells to turn purple-pink. This color change indicates a positive result, meaning antibodies to the Lyme disease antigen are present in the sample. Record your results in Data Table 1 by placing a check mark in the appropriate column.

Data Table 1 (Results will vary depending on which samples you designated as positive and negative.)

Sample		Positive for Antibody	Negative for Antibody
Patient 1	Sample 1		
	Sample 2		
	Sample 3		
Patient 2	Sample 1		
	Sample 2		
	Sample 3		
Patient 3	Sample 1		
	Sample 2		
	Sample 3		
Positive control	Sample 1		
	Sample 2		
	Sample 3		
Negative control	Sample 1		
	Sample 2		
	Sample 3		

Analysis and Conclusions

1. Did any of your patient samples test positive for antibodies to the bacteria that cause Lyme disease? Explain.

Answers will vary depending on which samples should be positive. Students should explain that the

positive results were indicated by a purple-pink color.

2. Summarize the reactions that lead to a positive ELISA test for Lyme disease.

Suggested answer: Lyme disease antigens stick to the walls of the well. The wells are washed. Primary

antibodies are added to the well and attach to the antigen. The wells are washed. Then, a secondary

antibody linked to an enzyme is added to the well and attaches to the primary antibody. A substrate is

added that reacts with the enzyme, producing a purple-pink product.

3. Sometimes medical labs have different technicians test samples from the same patient to reduce the possibility of technician error. Compare data with your classmates to determine whether they observed the same results as you did for patients 1, 2, and 3. Summarize your findings and suggest possible reasons for any differences you note.

Answers will vary based on students' results.

4. Explain the purpose of making a key for the samples on the ELISA plate.

Suggested answer: It was important to make a key to ensure that the patient samples were not confused. Otherwise, patients could be misdiagnosed.

5. Explain the purpose of having three of each sample on the plate.

Suggested answer: Testing a sample more than once will help ensure that the results are accurate.

6. What might have happened if you didn't wash the plate after adding the secondary antibody?

Suggested answer: All of the results would be positive.

Extension

Research how Lyme disease is treated and how it can be prevented. Then create a public awareness poster or public service announcement for radio or television that describes your findings. Consider ways to make your poster or announcement capture people's attention and deliver useful information.

Extension
Check students' posters for creativity and clarity of their message. Remind students to choose reliable sources.

Additional Resources
Murray, P. *The Widening Circle: A Lyme Disease Pioneer Tells Her Story*. New York: St. Martin's Press, 1996.

Centers for Disease Control and Prevention. Lyme Disease Home Page: http://www.cdc.gov/ncidod/dvbid/lyme/index.htm

The University of Arizona Biology Project: www.biology.arizona.edu/immunology/activities/elisa/main.html

Compatible Types

Testing Simulated Blood Samples for Blood Type

Question How does the human immune system respond to "foreign" red blood cells?

Lab Overview In this investigation you will explore how antibodies produced by the immune system bind with specific antigens found on the plasma membranes of red blood cells. You will test a simulated blood sample from an emergency room patient and discover how blood cell antigens are used to identify a person's blood type. Based on your findings, you will determine which blood type or types would be compatible for the patient.

Introduction A person may have one of four blood types—A, B, AB, or O. The letters refer to two carbohydrates, designated A and B, which are antigens found on the surface of red blood cells. A person's red blood cells may be coated with the A carbohydrate (blood type A), the B carbohydrate (blood type B), both A and B carbohydrates (blood type AB), or neither (blood type O).

The presence of one, both, or neither of these antigens on a person's red blood cells determines whether the person produces antibodies for the antigens. For example, people with blood type A do not produce anti-A antibodies, but they do produce anti-B antibodies. People with blood type B do not produce anti-B antibodies, but they do produce anti-A antibodies. People with blood type AB do not produce either antibody. People with blood type O produce both anti-A and anti-B antibodies.

These antibodies determine blood-type compatibility. For example, if a person with type B blood receives type A blood in a transfusion after an accident or surgery, the patient's anti-A antibodies attach to the type A red blood cells and cause them to clump together (a process called *agglutination*). Massive blood clotting results, and without quick treatment the patient may die.

People with type O blood are often called "universal donors." Because there are no A or B antigens on the red blood cells of type O blood, anyone can receive this blood. People with type AB blood are sometimes called "universal recipients." People who have AB blood do not make either anti-A or anti-B antibodies, so they can receive any type of blood.

In the Prelab Activity on the next page, model how anti-A antibodies interact with red blood cells bearing the A antigen. Then answer the Prelab Questions that follow.

Objective to test simulated blood samples to determine the blood type of a "patient".

Inquiry Skills
- observing
- classifying
- making inferences
- analyzing data

Time
- 15 min for Prelab Activity
- 20 min for Procedure
- 15 min for Analysis and Conclusions

Approximate prevalence of blood types in the United States:
Type O = 46%
Type A = 38%
Type B = 11%
Type AB = 4%

Prelab Activity ⬛ ⬛

Follow the steps below to model agglutination. Then answer the Prelab Questions that follow.

1. You will use 6 plastic forks to represent anti-A antibodies and 18 grapes to represent type A red blood cells. To make the anti-A antibodies, carefully remove the two middle tines (prongs) from each fork. Handle all the broken edges with care, as the ends of the plastic will be sharp.

2. Use the antibodies (forks) and red blood cells (grapes) to create a model of how anti-A antibodies and red blood cells bearing the A antigen interact and form a clump (agglutinate). Read the information below to help you.

- In the body, an antibody can bind to two red blood cells at the same time. On your antibody model, one blood cell can be attached to each of the two tines.

- In the body, antibodies can attach from above and below the red blood cell. Also, more than one antibody can attach to a particular red blood cell.

Remind students never to eat anything in a laboratory setting.

Prelab Questions

1. In the Prelab Activity, was it possible to get all 18 of the red blood cells together in one clump using just 6 antibodies? If this group of red blood cells and antibodies went through a small artery on its way to a capillary, what might happen?

Suggested answer: Yes, because antibodies can attach to more than one red blood cell.

The clump of red blood cells and antibodies might form a clot, blocking the capillary.

2. Fill in the chart below based on the information you read in the Introduction.

Blood Type	Antigen on the red blood cells	Antibody produced
A	A	anti-B
B	B	anti-A
AB	A and B	no antibody produced
O	no antigen	anti-A and anti-B

3. Explain why it is critical that the right type of blood be given to a patient that needs a transfusion.

Suggested answer: If incompatible blood is given, the foreign blood and the patient's antibodies will

clump together, leading to the formation of blood clots in the veins and arteries. The blockage of

blood flow can lead to tissue damage or death.

4. Which blood type is often called the "universal donor"? Explain.

Suggested answer: Type O blood is called the universal donor because there are no A or B antigens on

red blood cells of type O. Therefore, type O blood is compatible with all blood types, and anyone can

safely receive it.

5. Which blood type is often called the "universal recipient"? Explain.

Suggested answer: People who have type AB blood do not produce either anti-A or anti-B antibodies.

Therefore, they can receive blood transfusions of any type.

Materials

- agglutination plate
- paper towel
- simulated blood sample
- 3 transfer pipettes
- simulated anti-A serum
- simulated anti-B serum
- 2 toothpicks

Procedure

1. Read the following scenario. When you are finished, obtain a simulated blood sample, agglutination plate, and other materials and continue to Step 2.

The day has been quiet, and doctors and nurses working in the emergency room of South Hills Hospital find a free minute to enjoy a cup of coffee. Suddenly a rush of activity bursts through the emergency room door. A bus has slid across an icy highway and crashed into the oncoming traffic. Many passengers have been severely injured. Dozens of gurneys pour into the emergency room and the staff spring to work, immediately assessing who is most critically injured. Many of the passengers need blood. Because of a shortage of blood units at the hospital, the recipients' blood must be typed quickly to determine what is needed. At the lab, you receive a blood sample. You need to accurately identify the blood type of this patient.

Advance Preparation

A couple of weeks before the lab Order simulated blood-typing kits from a biological supply company such as Ward's Natural Science or Carolina Biological. See the front of this Laboratory Manual Teacher's Edition for contact information. Be sure to order a simulated blood-typing kit containing anti-A and anti-B "sera" and the four types of simulated blood. If students are doing the Extension, also order the anti-Rh sera. Although you can mix the simulated blood with the anti sera in a petri dish or any other clear plastic surface, the agglutination plates work especially well because they have wells of just the right size and they are labeled.

2. Place the agglutination plate on a paper towel. Use a transfer pipette to place 4 drops of the simulated blood sample into each of the A and B wells on the plate.

3. Using another transfer pipette, place 4 drops of the anti-A serum into the A well on the plate. It is important to use a transfer pipette that has only been in contact with the anti-A serum.

4. Using another transfer pipette, place 4 drops of the anti-B serum into the B well on the plate. It is important to use a transfer pipette that has only been in contact with the anti-B serum.

5. With a clean toothpick, stir the sample in the A well. Use a second clean toothpick to stir the sample in the B well.

6. Wait 5 min. Observe any changes in the blood samples and record your observations in the data table below. If the blood has agglutinated, it will appear gelled and clumpy. If you are in doubt as to whether agglutination has occurred, slide a printed page underneath the agglutination plate. If the sample has agglutinated, you will not be able to see the letters clearly.

Data Table

Before the lab, you may want to show students what an agglutination reaction looks like.

Patient ID	Agglutination in anti-serum A?	Agglutination in anti-serum B?	Simulated blood type

7. Based on the test result, determine the patient's blood type. Record it in the data table above. As directed by your teacher, write your results on the board.

Analysis and Conclusions

1. What type of blood does your patient have? If this patient needs a blood transfusion, what type(s) of blood can he or she receive? Explain.

Students' responses will vary depending on the "patient" they were assigned.

_____

_____

_____

2. The blood types of 42 patients needing blood transfusions and the units of blood available are listed below. Describe a plan for distributing the blood to patients so that they all receive safe transfusions.

Blood types of patients needing a transfusion (each patient needs one unit):

Type O	20 patients
Type A	12 patients
Type B	8 patients
Type AB	2 patients

Blood types of the units of blood available for transfusion:

Type O	30 units
Type A	10 units
Type B	2 units
Type AB	0 units

Suggested answer: Type O blood should go to all type O patients. Give the 10 units of type A blood to

10 of the 12 type A patients. Give type O to the remaining two type A patients. Give the 2 units of type B

to type B patients. Give 6 units of type O to the remaining six type B patients. Give the AB patients the

remaining units of type O blood.

_____

_____

3. If there were only 10 units of O blood available, could you give the type A or B blood to the type O patients? Explain.

Suggested answer: No, because type O people produce antibodies against antigen A and B.

_____

Extension

There is another type of antigen on red blood cells, called the Rh antigen. People with this antigen on their red blood cells are said to have Rh⁺ blood, and those without it are said to have Rh⁻ blood. If a pregnant woman has Rh⁻ blood, but her fetus has Rh⁺ blood, this can pose a serious health threat for the fetus because the mother's body may produce antibodies that will attack the fetus's blood cells. In this situation, a doctor may prescribe medication to suppress the mother's immune system.

Your task as a medical technician is to determine the "Rh status" of a mother and fetus. The Rh antigen is hereditary, and Rh⁺ is the dominant allele. Therefore, if the father has Rh⁺ blood and the mother has Rh⁻ blood, their children will most likely have Rh⁺ blood. Follow the instructions on the next page to model this test.

Extension
Explain that testing for Rh incompatibility is important for women with Rh⁻ blood. Babies born to Rh⁻ mothers and Rh⁺ fathers are at risk for hemolytic anemia, which occurs when antibodies produced by the mother's immune system destroy Rh⁺ red blood cells in the fetus. Treatment of the mother during pregnancy can prevent the development of these antibodies, as well as prevent Rh problems in future pregnancies.

Obtain two agglutination plates, transfer pipettes, simulated blood samples representing both of the baby's parents, and other materials. Place 4 drops of the simulated blood sample representing the baby's father in the Rh well of agglutination plate 1. With a second transfer pipette, place 4 drops of the simulated blood sample representing the baby's mother in the Rh well of agglutination plate 2. With a third transfer pipette, place 4 drops of the anti-Rh antibody in each well. Stir the contents of each well with a separate toothpick. If the anti-Rh antibody agglutinates the blood sample, then the sample is Rh^+.

You Are a Medical Technologist

Testing Simulated Urine for Protein and Sugar

Question How does the detection of sugar or protein in the urine aid in the diagnosis of certain conditions?

Lab Overview In this investigation you will take on the role of a medical technologist as you test simulated urine samples from three "patients" to detect the presence of sugar and protein. You will compare test results from the samples with results from solutions containing known amounts of sugar or protein.

Introduction To start your investigation, you will create a model of a nephron tubule. Then you will use your model to simulate how filtration and reabsorption normally occur and how these processes could be affected by diabetes, high blood pressure, or kidney damage.

Background Sugars such as glucose are not normally present in urine. Recall that during filtration in the kidneys, blood pressure forces water, dissolved sugars, and other substances through the walls of the capillaries in the glomerulus. The fluid, called filtrate, collects in the nephron tubule. During reabsorption, the dissolved sugars (along with other substances) are normally reabsorbed from the tubule into the blood. However, if a person's blood sugar concentration is abnormally high, as occurs in the disease diabetes mellitus, some of the glucose is not reabsorbed. Instead, the excess glucose remains in the nephron tubule and eventually exits the body in urine. (People with diabetes mellitus have elevated blood glucose levels because they do not have enough insulin in their blood, or because their body cells do not respond to insulin. Insulin is a hormone secreted by the pancreas that increases the amount of glucose that enters body cells.)

Similarly, when the kidneys are functioning well, little protein is present in urine. Most proteins are too large to leave the blood by passing through the walls of the glomerulus, and so they never enter the nephron tubule. However, when a person has kidney damage or high blood pressure, proteins sometimes are forced from the blood into the tubule. These proteins are not reabsorbed and eventually exit the body in the urine. High blood pressure and abnormally high amounts of protein in the urine occur in a condition called preeclampsia (pree ih KLAMP see uh), which affects about 5% of women during middle to late pregnancy. When not treated promptly, preeclampsia can lead to seizures and other serious complications.

Objective to test simulated urine samples for the presence of sugar or protein and relate the test results to changes in kidney function caused by diabetes or preeclampsia

Inquiry Skills
- observing
- controlling variables
- analyzing data
- drawing conclusions

Time
- 20–25 min for Prelab Activity
- 20 min for Part A
- 15 min for Part B
- 20 min for Analysis and Conclusions

Normally, more than 99% of glucose in the filtrate is reabsorbed from the tubules to the blood. To detect medical problems characterized by problems reabsorbing glucose, health professionals often use test strips to detect glucose in the urine. The test strips contain an enzyme called glucose oxidase that only reacts with glucose. Another testing method, Clinitest® tablets, contain the same ingredients as Benedict's solution. With this method, the presence of monosaccharides other than glucose will also result in a positive test. Infant urine is often tested with these tablets to detect the presence of galactose (from milk digestion).

Medical technologists routinely analyze urine samples from patients to help doctors diagnose certain diseases. In this procedure, called urinalysis, a urine sample is usually tested for the presence of sugar, protein, and other substances. In this investigation you will take on the role of a medical technologist. First you will use Benedict's solution to test for glucose. Benedict's solution contains a copper compound that reacts with glucose. In the presence of glucose, Benedict's solution changes color from blue to dark red or orange. This reaction occurs best in hot water. Next you will use Biuret reagent to test for protein. Biuret reagent contains molecules that react with the bonds between amino acids in proteins. When proteins are present, Biuret reagent changes color from light blue to deep blue or purple.

Prelab Activity Use the materials listed below to build a model of a nephron. Study the diagram for guidance. The black arrows represent the direction that the filtrate moves through the nephron. Remember that glucose and proteins are present in the blood that enters the nephron. The glomerulus you design will need holes for molecules to pass out of the blood into the nephron tubule. Devise a way to model filtration, as well as reabsorption in tubules of healthy individuals, as well as reabsorption in individuals with diabetes or high blood pressure. Afterward, answer the Prelab Questions.

- 1 leg from brownish nylon stocking (nephron tubule)
- 1 leg from black or white nylon stocking (glomerulus and capillary)
- clear plastic cup (Bowman's capsule)
- scissors
- small candies or beans (sugar)
- large candies or beans (proteins)

Protein is normally found in the urine in small amounts because the lining of the urinary tract secretes mucus that contains protein. Sloughed-off cells also contain proteins. The most common causes of high protein levels in the urine are high blood pressure and kidney damage caused by diabetes. Alkaline urine from urinary tract infections, vaginal secretion contamination, and certain antibiotics can cause false positive results.

See the online Teaching Guide for Lab 32 for a description of one way that students could build their models.

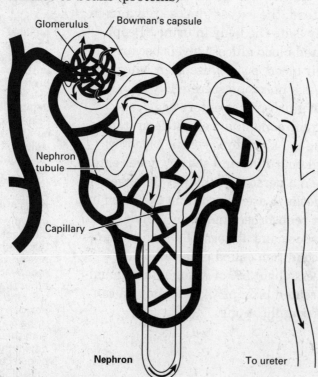

Glomerulus   Bowman's capsule

Nephron tubule

Capillary

Nephron   To ureter

Prelab Questions

1. How does high blood pressure result in the presence of protein in urine? How did your model represent this effect?

Suggested answer: High blood pressure can cause proteins to be pushed out of the capillaries of the

glomerulus and into the nephron tubule. Some proteins are too large to be reabsorbed into the blood

from the nephron tubules. Students' responses will vary regarding how they reflected this in their

models.

2. How do high blood glucose levels result in the presence of glucose in the urine? How did your model represent this effect?

Suggested answer: If blood glucose levels are very high, then not all of the glucose will be reabsorbed

from the nephron tubule into the blood. Some of the glucose will be excreted in the urine. Students'

responses will vary regarding how they reflected this in their models.

3. Preeclampsia is a disorder that affects some pregnant women and is characterized by high blood pressure and protein in the urine. During prenatal examinations, a doctor checks a pregnant woman's blood pressure, and also tests her urine for proteins. Why might both tests be necessary to diagnose preeclampsia?

Suggested answer: There are other reasons why protein may be in the urine besides high blood

pressure (kidney damage). High blood pressure does not necessarily lead to protein in the urine.

Together, the two symptoms can indicate preeclampsia.

Materials

- 8 microcentrifuge tubes
- marker
- 10 transfer pipettes
- simulated urine samples from Patient 1, Patient 2, and Patient 3
- positive control solution for sugar
- Benedict's solution
- hot water
- plastic foam cup
- foam rack (optional)
- positive control solution for protein
- Biuret reagent
- tongs (or spoon)

Alternate Materials
Glucose test tape and Clinitest® tablets are other methods for detecting glucose. You could ask a local pharmacist to keep expired test tape for you. Do not use honey as the sugar source with test tape. You must use glucose (dextrose).

Bradford's reagent can be substituted for Biuret reagent. Protein detection dipsticks are available at most pharmacies, though note that they may be expensive.

Advance Preparation

A couple of weeks before the lab
Obtain Benedict's solution and Biuret reagent from a biological supply company. See the front of this Laboratory Manual Teacher's Edition for supplier information.

Day of the lab
Make urine samples using the instructions provided at the end of this lab.

Procedure ⬛ 🧍 ✋ 🗑 🔥

Part A: Testing for Glucose

1. Label three microcentrifuge tubes 1S, 2S, and 3S for the three patients. Label the fourth tube SC for the positive sugar control.

2. Use separate transfer pipettes to transfer 0.5 mL of each simulated urine sample to the appropriate microcentrifuge tube, and 0.5 mL of the positive sugar control to the tube labeled SC.

3. With a new transfer pipette, add 0.5 mL Benedict's solution to each tube. Do not allow the pipette to touch the samples. Tightly close the lid of each tube. **CAUTION:** *Benedict's solution is corrosive. Use extreme care when handling Benedict's solution to avoid getting it on your skin or clothing.*

4. Carefully add hot water to your plastic foam cup until it is half full. **CAUTION:** *Use extreme care when working with hot water. Do not let the water splash on your skin or clothes.*

5. Check each tube to make sure that it is tightly closed. Place the four tubes in the cup with the hot water. (If available, use a floating plastic foam rack. Push the tubes through the rack enough so that part of them is submerged in the water.)

6. Observe each tube after the time indicated by your teacher. In Data Table 1, record the color of each sample. If you need to take the tubes out of the water to see the results clearly, use tongs or a spoon to lift the tubes (or rack) out of the water.

Data Table 1: Glucose Testing

Sample	Results	
	Color	**Positive or Negative?**
1S (Patient 1)		
2S (Patient 2)		
3S (Patient 3)		
SC (control)		

Part B: Testing for Protein

1. Label three microcentrifuge tubes 1P, 2P, and 3P for the three patient samples. Label the fourth tube PC for the positive protein control.

2. With separate transfer pipettes, transfer 1 mL of each simulated urine sample into the appropriate microcentrifuge tube, and 1 mL of the positive protein control to the tube labeled PC.

Safety and Disposal
Remind students to wear safety goggles, aprons, and plastic gloves, as the Benedict's solution and Biuret reagent are caustic. Tell students to use extreme care when working with hot water. Have students wash their hands with soap after the lab. Samples containing Benedict's solution and Biuret reagent can be flushed down the drain with excess water.

The hotter the water is, the faster the reaction will occur. Do a trial run with hot tap water to see how long the reaction will take. You may need to heat the water if the reaction is too slow.

3. With a new transfer pipette add 3 drops of Biuret reagent to each tube and close the caps tightly. **CAUTION:** *Biuret reagent is corrosive. Use extreme care when handling Biuret reagent to avoid getting it on your skin or clothing.*

4. Mix each tube by tilting it upside down. Observe the tubes after 1 min. Record the results in Data Table 2.

Data Table 2: Results of Protein Testing

Sample	Results	
	Color	Positive or Negative?
1P (Patient 1)		
2P (Patient 2)		
3P (Patient 3)		
PC (control)		

Analysis and Conclusions

1. Summarize each patient's results.

Sample answer: The samples from Patient 1 did not react with either Benedict's solution or Biruet reagent. Neither glucose nor proteins are present in the patient's urine. The sample from Patient 2 that was tested for sugar did react with Benedict's solution. The sample turned dark red, as did the positive control solution for sugar. The sample from Patient 2 that was tested for protein did not react with Biruet reagent. The sample from Patient 3 that was tested for sugar did not react with Benedict's solution. The sample that was tested for protein in the urine did react with Biruet reagent. The sample turned purple, as did the control solution for protein.

2. What diagnoses do your findings support? What other tests would you perform or questions would you ask to confirm your diagnosis?

Sample answer: The findings indicate that Patient 1 does not have diabetes or preeclampsia. Patient 2 may have diabetes and should have blood glucose levels checked. If Patient 3 is pregnant, then her blood pressure should also be checked. If her blood pressure is high this could indicate she has preeclampsia.

Extension

Although the pH values of urine vary from morning to night, the average pH of urine is 6.5 to 8. Acidic or alkaline urine may be an indication of various health problems. For example, the cells of a person with uncontrolled diabetes will break down fats for energy. This results in the release of acidic molecules, which are removed from the body in the urine. A diet too high in proteins could also lead to acidic urine because the waste products resulting from the breakdown of proteins are acidic. A bacterial infection in the bladder or ureters can lead to alkaline urine. Use pH test paper or a pH meter to determine the pH of several simulated urine samples provided by your teacher. What diagnoses might your findings support? What other tests or information would you want to have based on your findings?

How to make the simulated urine samples and control solutions:

Patient 1 (normal)
• 500 mL water
• 1 drop yellow food coloring
• 5 mL diet cola (Use diet cola to make the appearance of the urine more realistic. Do not use regular cola, since the sugar will react with the Benedict's solution.)

Patient 2 (diabetic)
• 500 mL water
• 1 tsp (5 mL) honey or 5–10 g glucose (dextrose)
• 1 drop yellow food coloring
• 5 mL diet cola

Patient 3 (high blood pressure)
• 500 mL water
• 1 egg white, beaten
• 1 drop yellow food coloring
• 5 mL diet cola

Positive control for sugar
• 500 mL water
• 1 tsp (5 mL) honey or 5–10 g glucose (dextrose)

Positive control for protein
• 500 mL water
• 1 egg white, beaten

Extension
To make simulated urine samples that students can test for pH, add very small amounts of vinegar or ammonia to the same solutions you prepared for the investigation.

Think Like an Endocrinologist

Modeling an Endocrine Disorder

Questions What clues do endocrinologists use to diagnose endocrine disorders? How can you model the cause of an endocrine disorder?

Lab Overview In this investigation you will learn how an endocrinologist gathers clues from a patient's symptoms, medical history, physical examination, and clinical test results to diagnose endocrine system disorders. You will then work with your lab group to model how endocrine function is disrupted in a specific endocrine disorder.

Introduction An endocrinologist is a physician who specializes in the diagnosis and treatment of endocrine disorders. Like all physicians the endocrinologist begins by gathering information about the patient's symptoms, including how long the symptoms have been present and if there have been changes over time. Next, the endocrinologist asks about the patient's medical history and performs a physical examination. After examining the patient, the endocrinologist determines if clinical tests can provide further clues to a diagnosis. For example, the endocrinologist may order blood tests to measure the levels of glucose or specific hormones. After receiving the results and examining all of the data, the endocrinologist either makes a diagnosis or asks more questions.

Background Tables 1 and 2 below contain background information that will help you in this lab. After reviewing the tables, complete the Prelab Activity that follows.

Objective to identify hormonal disorders in various case studies and make models representing the causes of specific hormonal disorders

Inquiry Skills
- classifying
- making inferences
- using models

Time
- 20 min for Prelab Activity
- 15 min for Part A
- 2 class periods for Part B (one for group planning and one for presentation of models)
- 15–20 min for Analysis and Conclusions

Table 1: Terms and Definitions

Terms	Definitions
Fasting blood sugar	The amount of glucose in the blood after 12 hours without food or drink (except water). Fasting blood sugar levels should be less than 100 mg/dL (dL=deciliter).
Glycosuria	The presence of glucose in the urine. There should be zero or only trace amounts of glucose in urine.
Islet cell antibodies in serum	The islet cells are the insulin-producing cells of the pancreas. Many forms of type I diabetes mellitus are caused by the immune system producing antibodies that attack islet cells.
T_3 and T_4 (thyroid hormones)	These hormones control metabolism by influencing the rate of cellular respiration. Thyroxine (T_4) helps maintain heart rate and reproductive functions.
Thyroid-stimulating hormone (TSH)	A pituitary hormone that stimulates the thyroid gland to produce thyroxine.

Table 2: Endocrine Disorders

Endocrine Disorder	Common Signs and Symptoms	Typical Laboratory Findings
Type I diabetes mellitus	• Frequent urination, excessive hunger and thirst, rapid weight loss associated with high blood glucose levels • Involuntary urination at night	• Fasting blood sugar greater than 140 mg/dL, documented on more than one occasion • Positive test for islet cell or insulin antibodies
Type II diabetes mellitus	• Frequent urination and excessive thirst • Patient more than 40 years old and overweight • No weight loss reported at time of diagnosis	• Plasma glucose of 140 mg/dL or higher after fast, documented on more than one occasion • Negative test for islet cells antibodies
Hyperthyroidism	• Increased sweating, increased appetite, weight loss, nervousness, heat intolerance, irritability, fatigue, weakness, irregular menstrual periods • Rapid heart rate; thin, moist skin; shakiness and tremor • Goiter (lump in the thyroid) may be present; eyes may be red and bulging	TSH less than 0.4 µU/mL (µU = microunits)
Adult hypothyroidism (primary)	• Weakness, fatigue, cold intolerance, constipation, weight gain, depression, hoarseness, muscle cramps, headaches, excessive menstrual bleeding • Slow heart rate; dry, cold skin with yellow, puffy appearance; thick tongue; thinning of nails; slow tendon reflexes • Anemia (low red blood cell count), low blood sodium levels • Thyroid may be enlarged, or a goiter may be present	• T_4 under 5µg/dL (thyroid gland unable to produce adequate amounts of thyroxine) • TSH over 5 µU/mL (excess thyroid-stimulating hormone needed to stimulate thyroid gland)
Hypothyroidism (secondary)	• Weakness, fatigue, cold intolerance, constipation, weight change, depression, excessive menstrual bleeding, hoarseness, muscle cramps, headaches • Slow heart rate; dry, cold skin with yellow, puffy appearance; thick tongue; thinning of nails; slow tendon reflexes • Anemia, low blood sodium levels	• TSH less than 0.4 µU/mL (pituitary gland cannot produce enough TSH to stimulate the thyroid to produce thyroxine)

Name _____ Class _____ Date_____

Prelab Activity Study the negative feedback loop below showing how two hormones secreted by the pancreas regulate blood glucose level. Then review the information in Concept 32.4 in your textbook about TSH and thyroxine. Draw your own feedback loop showing how the amount of thyroxine in the blood is regulated by thyroid-stimulating hormone. Then answer the Prelab Questions on the next page.

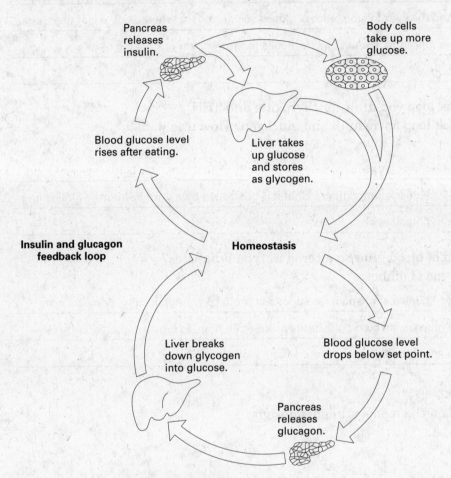

Pancreas releases insulin.

Body cells take up more glucose.

Blood glucose level rises after eating.

Liver takes up glucose and stores as glycogen.

Insulin and glucagon feedback loop

Homeostasis

Liver breaks down glycogen into glucose.

Blood glucose level drops below set point.

Pancreas releases glucagon.

TSH and Thyroxine Feedback Loop:

Prelab Questions

1. How does negative feedback regulate the amount of glucose in the blood?

   Suggested answer: Negative feedback regulates blood glucose by counteracting changes in blood glucose levels. When blood glucose levels are high, the pancreas secretes insulin, stimulating body cells to take up glucose and the liver to store excess glucose as glycogen. When blood sugar levels are low, the pancreas secretes glucagon, stimulating liver cells to break down glycogen into glucose and release it into the blood.

2. How was the feedback loop you drew for thyroxine and TSH similar to the feedback loop for insulin and glucagon? How was it different?

   Suggested answer: Both feedback loops involve negative feedback that regulates blood levels of a substance. The thyroxine/TSH feedback loop differs in that it is controlled by a third hormone—a releasing hormone secreted by the hypothalamus.

3. How is the regulation of blood glucose altered in type I diabetes? How is it altered in type II diabetes?

   Suggested answer: In type I diabetes, the pancreas does not produce enough insulin. Body cells are not stimulated to take up glucose, so blood glucose levels remain high. In type II diabetes, body cells do not respond to insulin, and blood glucose levels remain high.

Materials

Materials will vary based on the model students design.

Procedure

Part A: Evaluating Case Studies

1. With your lab group, read and discuss the following case studies of two patients with endocrine disorders. Use the information in the Background section of this lab to identify the specific endocrine disorder involved in each case.

Case 1

Identification and Chief Complaint (ID/CC) Patient is a 10-year-old boy, brought to his pediatrician because of a rapid weight loss of 3 kg over a period of two months.

History of Present Illness (HPI): The boy's mother says that he has been excessively hungry and thirsty despite his weight loss and he urinates often both during the day and at night.

Physical Exam (PE): The boy looks very thin, but no other symptoms are visible.

Lab Results: Elevated fasting blood sugar (180 mg/dL); urinalysis shows that glucose is present in the urine. Islet cell antibodies are present in blood serum.

Endocrine disorder of patient in Case 1:

Suggested answer: The patient most likely has type I diabetes mellitus.

Describe how you would explain the diagnosis to the patient.

_____

_____

_____

Case 2

ID/CC: Patient is a 48-year-old female with symptoms of progressive weakness and excessive tiredness. Patient also states that she feels cold all the time.

HPI: Patient reports weight gain, constipation, and hair loss. She states that her menstrual periods have become irregular and heavy. She reports feeling depressed and forgetful.

You can go online or to a library to purchase or borrow medical case study textbooks for resources or to provide students with more challenging case studies.

PE: Patient's heart rate is slower than normal. She has puffy skin around her eyes. The reflex on the back of her ankle is slow. It is clear she is losing hair from her eyebrows as well.

Lab Results: T_4 level = 3 µg/dL (below normal range); TSH = 7.5 µU/mL (above normal range)

Endocrine disorder of patient in Case 2:

Suggested answer: The patient most likely has adult hypothyroidism (primary).

Describe how you would explain the diagnosis to the patient.

_____

_____

_____

Part B: Modeling the Mechanism of an Endocrine Disorder

1. With your lab group, select one of the endocrine disorders you learned about in the Prelab Activity. Discuss how endocrine function changes in the disorder you have selected.

2. Devise a role-play, make a model, or develop a multimedia presentation that demonstrates how endocrine function is altered in the disorder your group has selected. Describe your model in the space below.

If students plan to do a role-play, you could provide them with materials to make signs and props, such as cardboard, paper, colored markers, and string. Wrapped hard candies could be used to represent blood glucose, other objects such as game tokens (or cut-out shapes) could represent hormones.

Part B and the Extension are good opportunities to have students work in small groups outside of school, allowing them to express creativity and learn about cooperation.

Analysis and Conclusions

1. How did the lab results help you identify the endocrine disorder in Case 1? Which of the other clues were most useful?

Suggested answer: The lab results in Case 1 showed that the boy's blood glucose levels were unusually high, providing evidence of diabetes. The presence of islet cell antibodies shows that islet cells are being attacked and the pancreas probably cannot produce adequate insulin. This is consistent with type I diabetes. Other useful clues include extreme weight loss, excess hunger and thirst, and frequent urination.

2. How did the lab results help you identify the endocrine disorder in Case 2? Which of the other clues were most useful? Explain.

Suggested answer: The lab results in Case 2 showed that the thyroid gland did not produce enough T_4 (thyroxine), even in the presence of high levels of TSH. These results provide evidence of primary hypothyroidism. Other useful clues include weakness, tiredness, feeling cold all the time, unusual hair loss, slow heart rate, slow tendon reflexes, and dry, puffy skin.

3. Describe the lab group's model that you think most effectively represented an endocrine disorder.

Students' responses will vary.

Extension

Revise the model your group created to show how homeostasis is restored when the endocrine disorder is properly treated. For example, you could model how blood sugar levels return to normal in diabetics treated with dietary changes and insulin, or model how thyroxine can be used to help those with hypothyroidism.

Extension
Provide students with additional resources they may need to understand treatments for type I diabetes or hypothyroidism.

Name That Tube

Form and Function in Tubules of the Reproductive System

Questions How are the structural features of tubules (very thin tubes) involved in sperm and egg transport related to their functions? How can structural features help you identify these tubules under a microscope?

Lab Overview In this investigation you will use a microscope to view slides with cross sections of unidentified mammalian reproductive tubules, then use your observations of structural features to identify the male and female tubules.

Introduction To start your investigation, you will find out more about the functions of reproductive tubules in male and female humans and other mammals. In the male reproductive system, sperm cells are formed, stored, and transported within tubules. Fertilization occurs when a sperm penetrates an egg (oocyte) in a tubule within the female reproductive system. Each tubule has structural features that relate to its function in reproduction. In the lab, you will use a microscope to observe these structural features and identify different reproductive tubules.

Prelab Activity Study the diagram below and read the descriptions on the next page of tubules found in the male and female reproductive systems. Then answer the Prelab Questions.

Objective to view prepared microscope slides and identify tissues from the mammalian oviduct, testes, vas deferens, and epididymis by relating structural features to function

Inquiry Skills
• observing
• classifying
• making inferences

Time
• 20–30 min for Prelab Activity
• 45–50 min for the lab
• 15–20 min for Analysis and Conclusions

Male Reproductive System

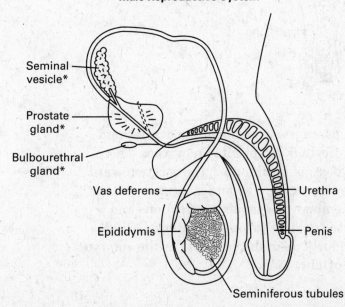

Seminal vesicle*

Prostate gland*

Bulbourethral gland*

Vas deferens

Epididymis

Urethra

Penis

Seminiferous tubules

*The seminal vesicles, prostate gland, and bulbourethral glands secrete fluids that function in the transport and survival of sperm.

Seminiferous tubules Sperm are produced in the walls of the seminiferous tubules within the testes. Interstitial cells surrounding the tubules release testosterone, which stimulates sperm production. Cells in the walls of the tubules secrete fluids rich in nutrients and hormones (testicular fluid). Millions of cells go through mitosis and meiosis each day, producing millions of sperm. Sperm are released tail-first into the seminiferous tubules along with testicular fluid.

Epididymis When newly-formed sperm cells enter the tightly coiled epididymis tubules from the seminiferous tubules, the sperm are not yet fully mobile or capable of fertilization. Tiny hair-like projections called microvilli lining the epididymis gently circulate fluid containing nutrients and hormones that influence sperm development in the tubule. Muscular contractions slowly push the sperm along the tube toward the vas deferens.

Vas deferens This tubule has thick muscles that contract rhythmically during ejaculation. The muscle contractions rapidly propel semen (the substance containing sperm and fluids secreted by several glands) toward the urethra.

Female Reproductive System

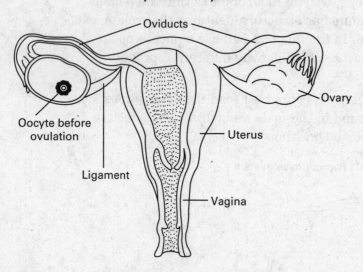

Oviducts These tubules are a passageway between the ovaries and the uterus. After ovulation, an oocyte is swept into an oviduct. There, muscular contractions and the beating of cilia push the oocyte toward the uterus. If a sperm fertilizes the oocyte, a zygote is formed. As the zygote divides and becomes an embryo, muscular contractions and cilia push the embryo through the oviduct toward the uterus. Fluids secreted by microvilli in the oviducts nourish the oocyte or the embryo during its journey through the oviduct.

Prelab Questions

1. Based on the descriptions you have just read of the functions of the various reproductive system tubules, match each tubule listed below with the structural features you would expect it to have. There may be more than one type of structural feature per tubule. Match all that apply.

<u>C, D, E</u>   Seminiferous tubules   A. thick muscular lining

<u>A</u>   Vas deferens   B. cells with hair-like projections

<u>B, D</u>   Epididymis   C. many dividing cells

<u>A, B, D</u>   Oviduct   D. cells that secrete fluid

   E. surrounding cells that produce testosterone

2. Which of the tubules found in the male reproductive system do you think is the most similar in function and structure to the oviducts? Explain.

Suggested answer: The epididymis. Both types of tubules are lined with hair-like projections.

They also contain fluids that sustain the egg or sperm cells and influence their

development.

3. Describe the role of hair-like projections in the male and female reproductive systems.

Suggested answer: The beating of cilia make currents in the oviducts that push an oocyte toward the

uterus. Microvilli in the oviducts and epididymis secrete nourishing fluids.

Materials

- coded prepared cross-section slides:
  mammalian oviduct
  mammalian testis (seminiferous tubules and surrounding tissue)
  epididymis
  vas deferens
- microscope
- colored pencils

Advance Preparation

Several weeks before the lab
Order the prepared slides from a biological supply company, such as Carolina Biological or Ward's Natural Science. See the front of this Laboratory Manual Teacher's Edition for supplier contact information.

A couple of days before the lab
Use colored tape or stickers to code and conceal the labels of the prepared slides. Place a piece of paper over the label before applying a sticker or tape to avoid damaging the label. Make a key to identify the slides (for example, yellow = epididymis) for your reference during the lab.

Procedure 🔒 🧤

1. Record the color code of the first slide in Data Table 1 on the next page. Position the slide on the microscope stage so that the stained section is just over the light.

2. Focus on low power. Then, select a higher power so that you can easily see the layers of the tubule. Focus again. Use the diaphragm to adjust the lighting so that all the structures can be observed.

3. Make a detailed sketch of the tissue in Data Table 1. Label any structural features you can identify. Use the information in the Background and your observations to infer the identity of the tubule. Record the inferred identity in Data Table 1.

4. Repeat steps 1–3 with the other three slides. When you have finished, compare your tubule identifications with the actual ones provided by your teacher. Record the actual identifications in Data Table 1.

Data Table 1

Color Code	Sketch of Tubule	Inferred Identity and Reasoning	Actual Tubule Identity
	Expected Results The slide of the vas deferens is generally the easiest for students to identify because of the thick wall of muscle tissue surrounding the tubule. The seminiferous tubules are usually also easy to identify because they clearly contain many cells with dividing nuclei. Advise students to look for the dark purple (stained) chromosomes of the dividing cells. The epididymis can be identified by the sperm inside of the tubule and the lining of cells bordered with microvilli. The oviduct has a thick wall of muscle tissue surrounding it, and a lining of cells bordered with cilia and microvilli.		

Analysis and Conclusions

1. If you correctly identified one or more of the four slides, which structural features helped you with the identification? If you did not correctly identify the tubules on each slide, which structural features made identification difficult?

Suggested answer: Answers will vary, but students generally find the muscular walls in the vas deferens

and oviduct the easiest structural features to identify. Sometimes students find it difficult to distinguish

between the tails of the sperm found in the seminiferous tubules and the microvilli that line the epididymis.

_____

_____

2. How are the structural features of the tubules you observed important to their functions? Give two examples.

Examples will vary but may include the following: Muscles of the vas deferens are used to propel the

semen. Microvilli of the epididymis circulate the fluids that are required for the sperm to mature.

_____

_____

3. The cilia in the oviduct help the oocyte move from the ovary end of the oviduct to the uterus. How might this make it difficult for sperm to reach the oocyte?

Suggested answer: The cilia gently move fluids from the ovary end of the oviduct to the uterus.

As sperm travel toward an egg in the oviduct, they are moving "against the current."

_____

_____

Extension

Study a prepared slide of a cross section of a mammalian ovary. Look for follicles at various stages of development. Look for the developing egg inside the follicle. Make a detailed sketch of what you observe. Label as many structural features as you can. See Figure 33-1 (p. 720) and Figure 33-5 (p. 725) in your text for reference.

Extension
Prepared slides of rodent ovaries are an ideal choice for this activity because they are small enough so that students can see a cross section of the entire ovary on a slide. Explain to your students that rodents release several eggs within a short period of time (unlike humans who generally only release one) so there may be several visible follicles at varying stages of development.

Mammal Morphology

Dissection of a Fetal Pig

Questions What organs make up a mammal's body systems? How do the organs' locations and structures relate to their functions?

Lab Overview This investigation reviews what you have learned in Unit 8. The tissues, organs, and organ systems of a fetal pig are similar in structure and function to those found in humans. You will observe structures of the integumentary, muscular, digestive, endocrine, excretory, reproductive, circulatory, lymphatic, and respiratory systems.

Introduction In the Prelab Activity you will examine the pig's external anatomy and determine its sex. During the lab investigation each group member will become a "specialist" on at least one organ system. You will perform the steps of the dissection that relate to your assigned system. While dissecting, dictate your notes to a group member so that later you can discuss your observations with others who were assigned the same system. Pay close attention to the entire dissection and note how your system interacts with other body systems.

Wear goggles and an apron at all times during this investigation. Also, wear gloves when handling the pig. Remove the gloves and wash your hands each time your part of the dissection is over so that you can assist other members of your group with note-taking. If you need to return to the dissection, put on fresh gloves.

Prelab Activity

Study the table of terms below that describes regions of the pig's body throughout the lab. Then follow the directions to study the external anatomy of the fetal pig. Finally, answer the Prelab Questions.

Regions of the Body

ventral = abdominal (belly) side
dorsal = back side
anterior = toward the head
posterior = toward the tail

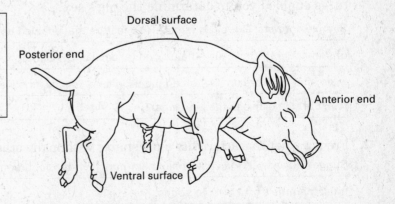

Studying the External Anatomy

1. Rinse the pig to remove some of the preservative. Then place the pig on its back (dorsal side) in the dissection tray.

2. Observe external features, such as the skin, eyes, ears, umbilical cord, and feet. Also look at the nares (nostrils). Then open the mouth and take a closer look at the tongue and taste buds.

3. Observe the nipples on the ventral surface. Both male and female pigs have nipples (though only the female's produce milk). To determine whether your pig is male or female, first look for a tiny, fleshy projection under the tail. This structure, called the urogenital papilla, is found only in female pigs. It is the point where the female urinary and genital systems open to the outside. If you think your pig is male, go to Step 4. If you think your pig is female, go on to Step 5.

4. To confirm that your pig is male, look for the urinary opening, located posterior to the umbilical cord. This structure eventually would have developed into the penis. Look for a thin patch of skin between the hind legs. This area would have developed into the scrotum. Testes may or may not have descended into the scrotum.

5. Sketch the pig. Predict where the heart, stomach, intestines, liver, and lungs will be found and add them to your sketch.

Prelab Questions

1. Is your fetal pig male or female? What anatomical feature or features enabled you to determine the pig's sex?

Sample answers: Our pig is female. The feature that enabled us to determine the sex is a tiny projection

of skin under the tail called the urogenital papilla. OR Our pig is male. We determined that the pig is a

male after we were unable to find the urogenital papilla, and we noticed the urinary opening and a thin

patch of skin between the hind legs.

2. Predict what characteristics a pig shares with many other mammals.

Suggested answer: Pigs have hair, mammary glands, diaphragms, a four-chambered heart, and like

most mammals give birth to young.

3. List three body systems you have already observed, at least in part, through the examination of the pig's external anatomy.

Examples are the integumentary system, muscular system, reproductive system, and excretory system.

_____

Materials

- fetal pig
- dissection tray
- 1 meter of string
- scissors
- dissecting probe
- scalpel
- paper towels
- transfer pipette
- plastic freezer bag

Circle the body system(s) assigned to you in Table 1 below. When an organ of one of your systems has been identified by you or another group member, place a check mark next to it in the table.

Table 1

Body System	Organs and Tissues to Study	✓	Lab Part
Integumentary	Skin layers		Part A
	Underlying connective tissue		Part A
Muscular	Skeletal muscles		Part A
	Diaphragm		Part A
	Cardiac muscle		Part E
Digestive	Esophagus		Part B
	Stomach		Part B
	Liver		Part B
	Gallbladder		Part B
	Pancreas		Part B
	Small intestine		Part B
	Large intestine		Part B
Endocrine	Pancreas		Part B
	Adrenal glands		Part C
	Ovaries		Part D
	Testes		Part D
	Thymus		Part E
	Thyroid		Part E
Excretory	Kidneys		Part C
	Ureters		Part C
	Bladder		Part C
Reproductive	Uterus		Part D
	Vagina		Part D
	Ovaries		Part D
	Oviducts		Part D
	Testes		Part D
Lymphatic	Spleen		Part B
Circulatory	Heart		Part E
	Posterior vena cava		Part E
	Aorta		Part E
Respiratory	Lungs		Part E
	Trachea		Part E
	Bronchi		Part E
	Larynx		Part E

Advance Preparation

A couple of weeks before the lab
Order the fetal pigs from a biological supply company. See the front of this Laboratory Manual Teacher's Edition for contact information.

Day of the lab
Soak pigs in a 5-gallon bucket of water before the lab. Change the water at least once.

You may wish to have students create a grid on a separate sheet of paper to record information about how their organ system interacts with other systems. Encourage them to be specific and to refer to their textbook or other references for information.

Procedure

Part A: Examining the Skin and Muscles

1. To make the dissection easier, use string to hold the legs apart. Cut the string in half. Tie one end around one front foot of the pig. Pull the string under the dissection tray and tie it around the other front foot, pulling tightly to hold the front legs apart. Repeat with the other piece of string for the back legs.

2. Use the diagram below as a guide to cut through the skin and body wall of the pig. Make the incisions (cuts) in the order they are numbered. **CAUTION:** *Handle sharp instruments with care to avoid injury.* Be careful not to cut into the organs that lie beneath the muscle layer.

3. Compare the underside and outside of the skin. Notice how the skin is attached to the muscle layers. Record your observations in the space below.

_____

_____

_____

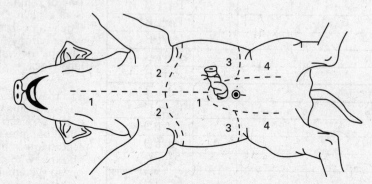

Order of incisions

4. Remove a section of the abdominal muscle. Study the structure. This is an example of skeletal muscle. You will also observe smooth muscles within the digestive system, diaphragm, and blood vessels, as well as the cardiac muscle of the heart.

5. Pull the skin and muscles back from the rest of the body. Cut the connective tissue connecting the body wall to the diaphragm, a dome-shaped muscle below the lungs. Point out the diaphragm.

6. Some brown fluid from the liver may have seeped into the body cavity. Pour some water into the body cavity to wash it out. Then pour this liquid out of the tray into a sink or container.

Safety and Disposal
Remind students to wear plastic gloves, goggles, and aprons during the dissection to prevent infections and illnesses caused by microorganisms. Afterward have students use antibacterial soap to wash all working surfaces, dissection trays, scissors, pencils, and any other items they handled during the lab, then wash their hands thoroughly. To prevent cuts remind students to handle sharp objects carefully. Good ventilation is critical for the health and comfort of students. Open windows and doors and use a powerful fan. Although present preservation methods do not use as much formaldehyde as in the past, the specimens will still have an unpleasant smell. For disposal, all parts of the animal should be double wrapped in paper and tightly sealed in a plastic bag. Do not allow the trash to remain in the building overnight.

7. Your group will dissect several more body systems. Your task is to identify glands of the endocrine system including the pancreas, adrenal glands, thymus, thyroid, and ovaries or testes.

Part B: Examining the Digestive System

1. You will remove the digestive tract in one piece, including the esophagus, stomach, liver, gallbladder, pancreas, small intestine, and large intestine. Use the diagram below as a guide. First, cut the esophagus at the upper part of the stomach where it emerges from the chest cavity. **CAUTION:** *Handle sharp instruments with care to avoid injury.* Then, cut through the thin connective tissue that holds the digestive system in place. Once the organs are free, pull the whole tract out and place it on a paper towel or in the dissection tray. Why is it difficult to trace the esophagus? What organs have to be pushed aside or left behind in order to remove the digestive tract?

_____

_____

_____

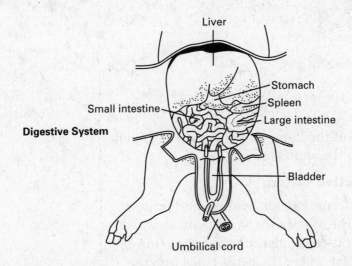

Digestive System

Labels: Liver, Stomach, Spleen, Large intestine, Small intestine, Bladder, Umbilical cord

2. Carefully disconnect the liver (large reddish-brown organ) and the pancreas (light-colored and globular) from the rest of the digestive system. Turn the liver over and look for the greenish, sac-like gallbladder. Note the thin duct that connects the gallbladder to the small intestine. The pancreas releases hormones as well as digestive enzymes. Give the pancreas to the student assigned to the endocrine system to study further.

3. The tongue-shaped organ on top of the stomach is the spleen. The spleen recycles materials from old red blood cells. Remove the spleen and give it to the student assigned to the circulatory, lymphatic, and respiratory systems to study further.

If you'd like students to do the Extension for this lab, have students wrap the appropriate organs in plastic wrap after they have studied them. Tell them to be sure that the organ they wish to examine is not surrounded by other organs or they won't be able to access it without thawing it.

Remind students that their fetal pig specimens may differ in appearance from the examples depicted here.

Extension: Digestive System Cut through the small intestine. Make a very thin cross section of the midsection of the small intestine. The liquid you may find in the small intestine is called *meconium* and consists of bile and ingested amniotic fluid. Make a wet mount and observe the cross-section under the microscope. Look for villi. Slice the stomach open to observe the folds that allow it to expand.

4. Gently pull apart the connective tissue so that you can uncoil the small and large intestines. If the intestines break, continue anyway. Measure the combined length of the intestines and record it below.

Combined length of small and large intestines: _____ cm

Part C: Examining the Excretory System

1. The kidneys are dark brown organs at the back of the pig's abdomen. As you remove the kidneys, note how the ureters connect them to the bladder, which is connected to the umbilical cord. Two large blood vessels, the posterior vena cava and the aorta, lie between the kidneys.

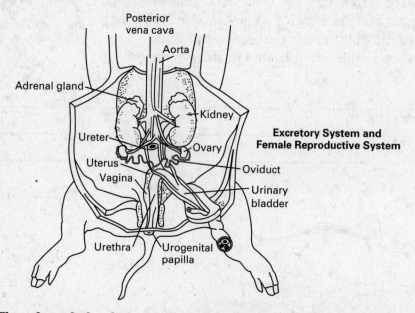

Excretory System and Female Reproductive System

2. The adrenal glands are on top of the kidneys. Point out the glands to the student who is studying the endocrine system.

Part D: Examining the Reproductive System

If your pig is female, identify the uterus, vagina, ovaries, and oviducts (see the diagram in Part C). Show the ovaries to the student assigned to the endocrine system. If your pig is male, identify the testes (inside the body if your pig is small). Look for where the penis leads into the body from the urethral opening (see the diagram on the next page). Show the testes to the student assigned to the endocrine system. Describe how the urinary and reproductive systems are connected in the space below.

_____

_____

_____

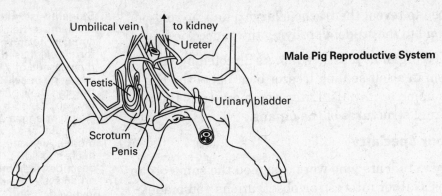

Male Pig Reproductive System

Umbilical vein to kidney
Ureter
Testis
Urinary bladder
Scrotum
Penis

Part E: Examining the Lungs and Heart

1. Notice how the lungs are attached to the diaphragm (see the diagram below). Record your observations below.

_____

_____

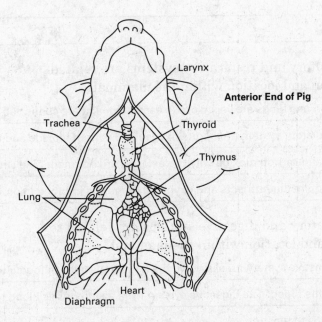

Anterior End of Pig

Larynx
Trachea
Thyroid
Thymus
Lung
Heart
Diaphragm

2. The trachea passes between the lungs. You may need to lift the heart from where it attaches to the lungs, but do not cut into the heart, lungs, or the vessels that connect them. The globular organ at the anterior end of the heart is the thymus. Point out the thymus to the student studying the endocrine system.

3. Observe where the trachea splits into the bronchi. Place the tip of a pipette into the trachea and fill the lungs with air. The lungs won't inflate very much, but you may be able to observe how the air "fizzles" through the tiny alveoli.

4. Remove the heart and lungs. Try to keep the arteries and veins that connect them attached.

5. Observe the structures of the heart. The large vessel on top is the posterior vena cava. The vessel beneath that is the aorta.

Extension: Circulatory System
Cut through the ventricles as shown in Investigative Lab 30A. Notice the difference in thickness of the muscle in the left and right ventricles. Notice the two earflap-shaped atria on top of the heart. Cut a thin slice from a vein and an artery attached to the heart. Make wet mounts of these and observe them under the microscope. Notice the difference in thickness of the walls.

Extension: Respiratory System
Cut a thin slice through the lung. Practice several times until the slice is paper-thin. Make a wet mount of this and study it under the microscope. You should be able to see tiny air sacs—the alveoli.

Explain that the lungs do not inflate much because the preservative has stiffened their tissue.

6. Pull the throat open to reveal the trachea, larynx, and thyroid. Point out the thyroid to the student studying the endocrine system.

7. Wrap each removed organ in plastic wrap. As directed by your teacher, place them in a self-sealing freezer bag. Label the bag with your group's name or initials. Later, you may study the tissues and the internal structures of the organs.

Part F: Discussing Your Specialty

Form a group with other students who were assigned the same organ system. Compare notes. Gather interesting observations you made about how this system looks inside a mammal. What surprised you? What did you learn that you didn't know before? You may be asked to present your system to the class.

Analysis and Conclusions

1. How well did you predict the placement of the pig's organs?

Students' responses will vary.

_____

_____

2. Explain how the circulatory and respiratory systems are related to each other in function and location within the mammal.

Suggested answer: The heart and lungs are very close to each other and are connected by the pulmonary

arteries and veins. The circulatory system transports oxygen and carbon dioxide and the respiratory

system exchanges oxygen and carbon dioxide with the external environment. The circulatory and

respiratory systems also require the nutrients and oxygen transported in blood in order to function.

3. Explain how the circulatory and digestive systems are related to each other in function and location within the mammal.

Suggested answer: The digestive system breaks down the large molecules in food into small

molecules that diffuse into the blood. The digestive system itself also requires blood to bring it the

nutrients and oxygen it needs to function.

4. What role do you think a pig's umbilical cord serves?

Suggested answer: Carrying oxygenated and nutrient-rich blood from the placenta to the fetus and

carries deoxygenated blood containing carbon dioxide and nitrogenous wastes from the fetus to

the placenta.

Extension

With a microscope, examine the tissues of frozen organs from your dissection of the fetal pig. Obtaining a thin slice of the tissue to place on a slide is easier to do when the tissues are frozen. Your teacher will provide directions on viewing tissues of several body systems.

Students assigned to the same system could write and perform a skit based on the passage of a key molecule or cell through their system (a drop of blood, a sperm or egg, a urea molecule, or a hormone). Also, students should describe when other organ systems are involved.

Students could present a poster depicting relationships between their system and other systems. Or, students could do a multimedia presentation.

Extension
Organs should be removed from the freezer about 15 min before the dissection so that they are soft enough for the scalpel to penetrate. See specific instructions in annotations in parts B, C, and E.

Life as a Pond Organism

Changes and Interactions in a Pond Environment

Question How do changes in abiotic factors affect organisms living in a pond ecosystem?

Lab Overview In this investigation you will use a microscope to observe various organisms living in a pond water sample and choose one type of pond organism to observe more closely. Then you will change the water temperature or light conditions. You will make observations over time to discover how the life of "your" pond organism changes in response to different environmental conditions.

Introduction In the lab, you will use a microscope to make careful observations of a miniature "pond ecosystem" inside a plastic tube. The plastic tube, called a demo slide culture tube, has a flattened section that allows you to view a small amount of liquid (about 0.2 mL) through a microscope.

Each day, you will tour the ecosystem by scanning slowly back and forth over this flattened section with your microscope. You will observe and draw sketches of the organisms you see. To help you understand how environmental change can affect pond organisms, you will keep a journal of the life of one type of pond organism and describe how its life changes in various conditions of light or temperature.

Background When abiotic factors change, organisms in an ecosystem may be affected. As you change the temperature or light affecting your miniature ecosystem, you will see changes in the population of pond organisms. For example, as the temperature increases, the level of dissolved oxygen in the water decreases. Some organisms may thrive in lowered oxygen levels, but many will die. Changes in the amount of light will cause the numbers of producers (autotrophs) to either increase or decrease, changing the foundation of the ecosystem's food chain.

Prelab Activity Read and consider the experiment described on the next page. Then answer the Prelab Questions that follow.

Objective to observe a pond microorganism, study its interactions with other organisms, and observe how a change in abiotic conditions can affect a community

Inquiry Skills
- observing
- making inferences
- predicting
- controlling variables
- drawing conclusions
- communicating conclusions

Time
- 15 min for Prelab Activity
- 15–20 min for setup and first observations
- 10–15 min for observations, 2–3 times per week for 2–3 weeks
- 15–20 min for Analysis and Conclusions

On a warm summer day (27°C/80°F), students collected a water sample near the surface of a local pond. After taking the water back to the lab, the students placed equal amounts of water in four different containers, and stored one container in each set of environmental conditions below.

Sample	Light Conditions	Temperature
A	bright light	room temp 21°C (70°F)
B	dark	room temp 21°C (70°F)
C	dark	warm temp 35°C (90°F)
D	bright light	warm temp 35°C (90°F)

Prelab Questions

1. In which of the above-mentioned conditions do you predict most of the organisms in the sample would thrive? Explain your reasoning.

Student answers will vary.

2. Predict how the amount of *light* might affect the autotrophic pond organisms in each container.

Sample prediction: Autotrophic organisms need light for photosynthesis. Without light, they cannot make food for energy.

3. Predict how the amount of *light* might affect the heterotrophic pond organisms in each container.

Sample prediction: If autotrophic organisms cannot perform photosynthesis, then heterotrophic organisms will lose their food supply and their source of oxygen.

4. When the temperature of water increases, the level of dissolved oxygen decreases. With this in mind, answer the following questions.

a. Predict how the *temperature* might affect the autotrophic pond organisms in each container.

Sample prediction: Autotrophic organisms would not be affected by warmer temperatures.

b. Predict how the *temperature* might affect the heterotrophic pond organisms in each container.

Sample prediction: Many heterotrophic organisms cannot survive if the level of dissolved oxygen

becomes too low.

Materials

- pond water sample
- 4 demo slide culture tubes
- transfer pipette
- stirring rod
- demo slide culture tube stage
- fluorescent light
- heating pad
- lidded opaque container
  (large enough to hold culture tube)
- microscope
- references for identifying organisms
  (books; Web sites)

If there are no ponds or marshes nearby, you can also make your own pond water. See **Advance Preparation**.

Advance Preparation
- Collect 1 L of water from a local pond or marsh. Be sure to also collect bottom sludge and scrapings from pond rocks for a larger sample of organisms. As an alternative, you could collect water from an established freshwater aquarium.
- To make your own "pond water," inoculate bottled water with cultures from a biological supply company. Good organisms to use are ciliate protozoa, such as *Blerasphema*, *Paramecium multinucleatum*, and *Paramecium busaria*; algae, such as *Spirogyra*; and microcrustaceans, such as ostracods. Pour all of the organisms together. Then, add 300–350 mL of bottled water.

Procedure

Part A: Observing and Selecting Your Pond Organism

1. With a stirring rod, thoroughly mix your sample of pond culture.

2. Using a transfer pipette, fill four demo slide culture tubes, leaving about 1 cm of space at the top of each tube. Flick the flattened section of the tube with your fingers to release the air bubbles.

3. Put the lids on the tubes.

4. Put one of the culture tubes into the demo slide stage and examine the culture under the microscope at low power.

5. Focus the microscope and observe the organisms at low power, medium power, and then high power.

6. Take notes on the organisms you observe. Then choose an organism that is particularly interesting to you, and observe it closely. The organism that you choose should be present in all four culture tubes.

Safety and Disposal
Remind students to wash their hands thoroughly with soap after handling pond water and slides. Tell students to handle fluorescent lights carefully, and caution students about electrical shock hazards. Place used culture tubes in a container of soapy water with bleach. Wash and rinse each tube (squeezing the flat section) for reuse.

Part B: Writing About Your Pond Organism

1. As you are observing the organism, consider the questions below.

   a. What is your organism doing? Observe it for at least 1 min.

   Sample answer: It is swimming with hairlike legs and eating nonstop. It often bumps into things. Sometimes it just creeps along, but most of the time, it scurries about.

   b. How is it interacting with other organisms?

   Sample answer: It does not seem to interact with other organisms. It eats "scummy" debris and cleans up the ecosystem.

   c. Is the organism moving? If so, do its movements seem to be for moving from place to place, obtaining food, or both?

   Sample answer: Some of the hairlike legs seem to move the organism. Others seem to move food toward it.

   d. How does it obtain food? Describe its food.

   Sample answer: The hairlike legs push food into the organism's mouth.

   e. How big is your organism? Use the approximate diameters of the different fields of view to estimate its size.
   Low power (40×) = 5 mm or 5000 μm (micrometers)
   Medium power (100×) = 2 mm or 2000 μm
   High power (400×) = 0.5 mm or 500 μm

   Sample answer: It is the largest organism in the community—about 1 mm long.

   f. Is it the most common organism in the culture?

   Sample answer: No, algae and paramecia are more common.

   g. Draw a sketch based on your observations.

   Illustrations will vary.

2. Your teacher will provide resources to learn more about the organism. Include this information in your further writing. Include answers to the following questions.

a. Classify your organism. What is its name? What kingdom, phylum, and class is it in? What are some examples of other organisms that are "class" mates?

Sample answer: Name: Ostracod. Kingdom: Animalia. Phylum: Arthropoda. Class: Crustacea.

Other members of class Crustacea include crabs, pillbugs, shrimp, and lobsters.

b. How does it obtain food? Does it make its own food through photosynthesis, or does it need to absorb or ingest food? Be aware that some microorganisms can do both.

Sample answer: The ostracod eats constantly. It eats lots of algae and sometimes turns green.

c. How does it obtain oxygen?

Sample answer: Ostracods have gills.

d. How does it get rid of wastes?

Sample answer: Ostracods have a complete digestive tract with an anus.

e. What other features or interesting facts did you learn about the organism?

Sample answer: If conditions are unfavorable, an ostracod can shut its shell and hibernate. In this state, it can survive being eaten, being frozen, or drying out.

f. Use a photo or drawing in a reference book to draw another, more detailed sketch of the organism in the space below.

Illustrations will vary.

If you have already covered the microbiology and animal diversity units you could also ask students:
• At 400× can you identify organelles in unicellular organisms or organs in multicellular organisms?
• How does the organism move or propel itself?
• How does the organism reproduce?

Part C: Changing Abiotic Factors in Your Miniature Pond Ecosystem

See end of lab for Expected Results.

1. Your teacher will assign you one set of environmental conditions described in the Prelab Activity. Place two of your tubes in this new environment.

2. Place the other two tubes where they will receive normal room temperature and classroom light conditions. These tubes will be your experimental controls.

3. Twice a week, for 3 full minutes, observe your organism in its new environmental conditions.

4. Move the tube around to observe as much of the flattened part of the culture tube as possible.

5. Observe how your organism is doing in the tubes under new environmental conditions and in the experimental controls. Be sure to take notice of how the other organisms are faring as well.

6. Keep a "diary," making entries regularly for two weeks describing how the life of your pond organism has changed due to changes in its ecosystem.

Analysis and Conclusions

1. Compare the overall types and abundance of organisms in the pond water cultures placed in changed environmental conditions to the control tubes.

   Answers will vary but should be supported by student observations.

   _____

   _____

   _____

   _____

2. How have the changed environmental conditions affected the well-being of your pond organism? Are there more of the type of organisms you selected, or fewer? How energetic do individuals appear? If all the individuals are dead, continue your observations, describing what is happening in the environment your organism once inhabited.

   Answers will vary but should be supported by student observations.

   _____

   _____

   _____

   _____

3. How do the results of your experiment compare with the predictions you made in the Prelab Activity?

Answers will vary but should clearly describe how experimental results supported or differed

from predictions.

4. Did you notice any dramatic change in the organisms' numbers or activity? How could the changes you observe affect the survival of other organisms in the ecosystem?

Answers will vary but should be supported by student observations.

Extension

Design an experiment to test how organisms in a miniature pond ecosystem respond to cold temperatures, or a change in a different abiotic factor. Show your procedure to your teacher and, with permission, perform the experiment. Compare data from your new experiment to the data you collected previously. What conclusions can you draw from your data?

Extension
Students should describe how to set up a controlled experiment, similar to the one in the procedure, to test the response of the miniature pond ecosystem to cold temperatures or a change in another abiotic factor. Have students make arrangements with you to use the microscopes for their observations. Afterward, ask students to present their results to the class.

Expected Results
Classroom light and temperature The pond water cultures are amazingly stable in the demo slide culture tubes and will thrive, even with the lids on, for several weeks. If the temperature is cool enough (about 13–18°C, or 55–65°F), the cultures can live for months.
Bright light and classroom temperature Microcrustaceans and large ciliates do not do well in bright light conditions. Algae will turn bright green but do not overgrow the culture.
Darkness and classroom temperature Ciliates thrive. Algae can stay healthy and green for many days in the dark.
Classroom light and cold temperature (7–10°C or 45–50°F) The best conditions for most cultures.
Classroom light and warm temperature (about 32°C, or 90°F) Most of the heterotrophs will die under these conditions, possibly owing to the decrease in dissolved oxygen levels. Algae live but are not healthy. After a couple weeks of these conditions, organisms such as sarcodines and *Vorticella* increase in number because they are no longer prey of ostracods and no longer have to compete for food.

Name _____ Class _____ Date _____

Diversity Discovery

Identifying Organisms in a Leaf Litter Community

Question What types of organisms can be found in a leaf litter community?

Lab Overview In this investigation you will collect invertebrate animals that live in leaf litter. You will also construct a Berlese funnel, which you will use to separate invertebrates from the leaf litter. Then you will identify the different types of invertebrates you collected.

Introduction A Berlese funnel is a device that contains a circular screen to hold and filter samples of leaf litter and soil. When a light source is placed at the open end of the Berlese funnel, invertebrate animals living in the leaf litter sample move away from the light and heat produced by the light source. Eventually, the animals fall into a collecting container placed at the opposite end of the funnel. The collecting container is padded on the bottom with a moistened paper towel to help the animals survive.

Background Leaf litter is made up of the decaying plant material that accumulates on the ground surface. The spaces between decaying fallen leaves and other decomposing plant materials provide homes for a rich diversity of invertebrate organisms. Hundreds of mites, spiders, pseudoscorpions, centipedes, millipedes, small insects, and other invertebrates can live in a few handfuls of leaf litter. Moisture trapped between fallen leaves and other organic material is vital to these organisms' survival.

   Complex interactions exist within leaf litter communities. Bacteria, protists, and fungi feed on the decaying material in leaf litter. These organisms and the decomposing plant material serve as food sources for some of the invertebrates in the leaf litter community. In turn, other animals living in the same environment consume these invertebrates.

Prelab Activity Some typical invertebrates found in leaf litter communities and their food sources are listed in Table 1 on the next page. Analyze Table 1 and then answer the Prelab Questions.

Objective to observe the variety of organisms found in a leaf litter community

Inquiry Skills
• predicting
• observing
• classifying

Time
• 15 min for Prelab Activity
• 15 min for Part A
• 30 min for Part B (collection could be done outside of class time)
• 20 min for Part C
• 25 min for Part D (1–3 days after Part C)
• 20 min for Analysis and Conclusions

Table 1: Typical Inhabitants of Leaf Litter Communities

Invertebrates in Leaf Litter	Food Sources	Sample Sketches
Earthworms	plants, fungi, and decomposing material	
Snails and slugs (Slugs look similar to snails without shells.)	plants, fungi, decomposing material	
Spiders	insects and other leaf litter animals	
Mites	some types eat leaves and organic debris; some eat fungi; some eat insect larvae, other mites, and springtails	
Pseudoscorpions	mites, larvae, earthworms	
Pillbugs (sowbugs or woodlice) (Pillbugs sometimes curl into small balls.)	decomposing plants	
Millipedes	plants, fungi, decomposing material	
Centipedes	beetles, millipedes, spiders, flies	
Springtails	plants, fungi, decomposing material	
Ants	plants, fungi, other leaf litter animals	
Beetles/ beetle larvae	some types eat fungi; others eat insects, snails, and other leaf litter animals	

Name _____ Class _____ Date_____

Prelab Questions

1. What abiotic factors will change when the funnel is placed near the light source?

light and temperature
_____

_____

_____

2. Which of the animals in Table 1 do you predict will be most common in your sample? Which do you predict would be least common? Explain.

Sample predictions: Mites will be most common because they are so small. Centipedes will be

least common because they are large.
_____

_____

3. Animals that eat other animals (predators) tend to require a larger range than animals that eat only plants. Does this change your prediction in Question 2? Why or why not?

Sample answer: Centipedes are predators, so there may be fewer of them. I had thought that mites

might be most common because they are very small, but perhaps there might be more pillbugs or

other animals that just eat plants.

Materials

- hardware cloth or rain gutter screen (1/8 inch)
- filter pattern
- permanent marker
- metal shears
- cloth gloves
- duct tape
- ruler
- clean 2-L plastic soda bottle
- scissors
- 8-oz opaque paper coffee cup
- masking tape
- desk lamp with a 40–60 watt bulb
- gallon-size self-sealing plastic bag
- trowel or large spoon
- thermometer
- clock or watch
- half of a petri dish (optional)
- hand lens or stereomicroscope
- forceps

For more information, see the **Materials** section at the end of this lab.

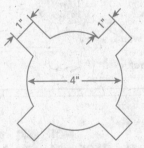

Filter pattern

Advance Preparation

A week before the lab
- Purchase screening material from hardware store
- Have students bring in 2-L plastic bottles

A couple days before the lab
- Identify possible areas for students to collect samples.
- Use light cardboard or construction paper to make filter patterns.

Procedure

Part A: Making the Berlese Funnel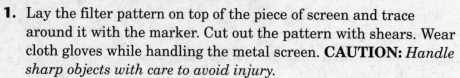

1. Lay the filter pattern on top of the piece of screen and trace around it with the marker. Cut out the pattern with shears. Wear cloth gloves while handling the metal screen. **CAUTION:** *Handle sharp objects with care to avoid injury.*

2. Wrap duct tape around the flaps of the cut screen to cover the sharp edges.

3. Using scissors, cut a 2-L soda bottle about 18 cm from the mouth to form a funnel. **CAUTION:** *Bottle edges will be sharp. Handle with care.*

4. Bend the flaps of your screen up and fit it inside the funnel. Use masking tape to adhere the flaps of the screen to the inside walls of the funnel. (See the diagram of the Berlese funnel below.)

5. Cut out a circle of paper towel that will fit in the bottom of the cup. Moisten the paper towel circle with water and place it in the bottom of the cup.

6. Place the funnel with the screen inside the cup. Tape the funnel to the cup.

7. With masking tape, secure the paper cup to the place where you will leave it overnight.

8. Place a lamp with a 40–60 watt bulb about 15 cm from the top of the funnel. At this point, do not turn the lamp on.

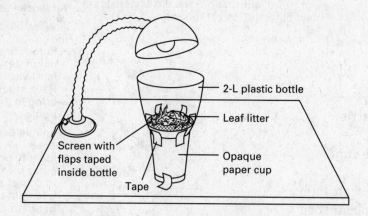

- 2-L plastic bottle
- Leaf litter
- Screen with flaps taped inside bottle
- Opaque paper cup
- Tape

Part B: Gathering Leaf Litter

1. Find an area of dirt under trees where there are lots of decaying leaves in a forest, park, your backyard, or on your school's grounds. (**NOTE:** *Do not carry out your investigation on private property unless you have specific permission from the owner.*)

The greatest diversity of invertebrates will be found in areas where the leaf litter is moist and fairly decomposed. The ground should be warm so that the animals are not dormant. Some good spots are compost piles, ground beneath a large deciduous tree (especially if the leaves haven't been removed), and moist pine needles beneath evergreen trees.

2. Measure and mark off an area that is 20 cm². With a trowel or large spoon, scoop up the leaves and the top 1 cm of soil into a large self-sealing bag. **CAUTION:** *Be aware of any poisonous or prickly plants and biting or stinging insects. Alert your teacher in advance to any allergies you may have.*

3. While you are spooning the leaves and soil into the bag, watch for animals in the layers of the leaves. Don't attempt to capture animals that scamper away, but try to take note of the types that get away. **CAUTION:** *Wash your hands with soap when you are finished collecting the sample.*

Part C: Collecting Organisms with a Berlese Funnel

1. Place the contents of your bag into your Berlese funnel.

2. Turn the light on. Place a thermometer on the surface of the leaf litter. Observe the surface and look for movement. You will probably see some invertebrates moving as the soil warms up. Try to identify them using Table 1 and add their names to Data Table 1. If necessary, continue the table on a separate piece of paper.

3. After 15 min, read the temperature at the surface of the leaves. It should be at least 29°C and no warmer than 35°C. Adjust the lamp distance to the top of the leaf litter until the temperature is right, but do not place the light any closer than 10 cm from the top of the leaf litter. **CAUTION:** *Work with care around the light source to avoid coming in contact with the hot light bulb or breaking it.*

4. Leave the light on overnight.

Many animals will be found in the cup after only an hour or so. Several more will be found the next day. Some could take up to 4 days to move down. Some animals, such as fly larvae, will stay in the soil even when it is fully dry.

Data Table 1

Name and Description	Approximate Size (mm)	Observed in Funnel, Cup, or Both?	Sketch

Part D: Observing Invertebrates

1. Disassemble the Berlese funnel and look inside the cup. Do not handle centipedes or spiders because they may sting you. If you collect arthropods that may sting, cover the cup with its lid or a half of a petri dish. Take the cup outside and allow them to crawl out. Observe them from a safe distance so that you can identify them later.

2. Use a hand lens to observe the invertebrates in the cup. If you are using a stereomicroscope, place the cup on the stage and turn on the light.

3. Focus on the wet paper towel. Look for movement. You may wish to use scissors to trim down the sides of the cup a few centimeters so that you can hold the hand lens closer to the animals. Add the names, descriptions and sketches of any additional organisms you see to Data Table 1. Use Table 1 in the Prelab Activity to help identify animals.

4. Using forceps, turn the paper towel over and look at its underside. Add any more animals you find to Data Table 1. If necessary, continue the table on a separate piece of paper.

If students do not find many animals in the cups after one day, instruct them to gently remove the dried leaves from the top of the funnel and continue to expose the leaf litter to the light for another day or two.

Analysis and Conclusions

1. What abiotic factors characterize the leaf litter community in its natural environment?

low light, cool temperatures, high moisture

2. How quickly did the organisms respond when you changed those factors by turning on the lamp?

Sample answer: Right away. As soon as the light was turned on, I saw a mite and a worm moving down through the soil, away from the heat and light.

3. Using the information given in the Background section and Table 1, describe possible interactions between the organisms you listed in Data Table 1. Which animals do you predict would eat which other animals?

Student responses will vary based on the animals they observed, but answers should follow the food source information they studied in Table 1.

4. Manuel described the movements, behavior, and interactions among the mites, centipedes, slugs, and worms he observed in his Berlese funnel. Did he describe an ecosystem or a community? Explain.

Suggested answer: Manuel's description did not include abiotic factors, so it is a description of a

community.

5. If you collected leaf litter after several weeks of hot, dry weather, would you expect to see more or fewer animals than after a rainy day? Explain.

Suggested answer: I would expect fewer animals in the leaf litter during periods of warm, dry weather

because the animals cannot tolerate dry conditions.

Extension

Identify another location to study with abiotic factors that are different than your original location. Make predictions about how this community will differ from the first one you studied. Test your predictions by repeating this experiment with leaf litter gathered from the new location. (**NOTE:** *Do not carry out any investigations without checking with your teacher.*)

Adapted from: Drewes, C. (2002) "Leaf Mold Community," 7 pp. See: www.eeob.iastate.edu/faculty/DrewesC/htdocs/

Extension
Examples of different environments that students could collect samples from are sandy soil, a forest floor, or a lawn.

Additional Resources
Lavies, B. *Compost Critters.* New York: E.P. Dutton, 1993.

Ruppert, E. and R. Barnes. *Invertebrate Zoology*, 6th ed. New York: Saunders College Publishing, 1994.

Wheater, C. and H. Read. *Animals Under Logs and Stones.* Slough, England: Richmond Publishing, 1996.

Materials
So that fewer shears are needed, you may wish to have half the class prepare the funnels while the other half cuts the screening. Or, you could prepare the screening to avoid the risk of students getting cut.

Inexpensive clip lamps with metal shades can be found at hardware stores. You could put two setups under one lamp.

Use light bulbs that are brand new or close to new to make sure they do not blow out overnight.

Collecting cups need to be short enough to fit on the stereomicroscope stage. It is important to use an opaque cup because the animals may not travel down into the cup if light is coming through its sides.

Dynamic Populations

Determining the Size of a Moving Population

Question How can you determine the size of a population of organisms when the organisms move around or are hard to locate?

Lab Overview In this field investigation you will discover how to use the mark-recapture method to estimate the size of a population of moving organisms. You will then use the mark-recapture method to do your own population study of local garden invertebrates.

Introduction In the Prelab Activity you will read about one study in which a fisheries biologist used the mark-recapture method to estimate the size of a trout population. Then you will estimate the trout population of a stream two years after a severe flood. In your own field investigation you will locate a population of garden invertebrates, such as snails, and do your own mark-recapture study.

Prelab Activity In June 1995, storm clouds brewed over Shenandoah National Park in Virginia. Torrential rains fell, and in just three days, as much as 61 cm of rain soaked the area. Streams overflowed, and trees were uprooted. Huge amounts of debris washed downstream, scouring the streambeds and killing many trout. In many stream areas, the trout were eliminated. When it was all over, fisheries biologists assessed the damage. They asked, "Will the trout population be able to recover on its own, or will we need to intervene by introducing new trout to the area?"

The notebook pages below show the data of a fisheries biologist who has just returned from the damaged stream site. Using the formula in the notebook, calculate the estimated population of trout found in 100 m^2 of the stream in October 1998. Insert your answer in the data table on the right-hand side of the notebook.

Objective
to gain first-hand experience with the mark-recapture method of estimating population size

Inquiry Skills
- calculating
- collecting data
- analyzing data
- drawing conclusions

Time
- 15–20 min for Prelab Activity
- 30–45 min for first capture
- 30–45 min on a different day for second capture
- 20 min for Analysis and Conclusions

The mathematical theory behind the mark-recapture method is based on the following ratio:
If
A = number in first capture
B = number in second capture
C = number of marked animals in second capture
D = total population
then
$$\frac{C}{B} = \frac{A}{D}$$
$(C)(D) = (A)(B)$
$D = \frac{(A)(B)}{C}$

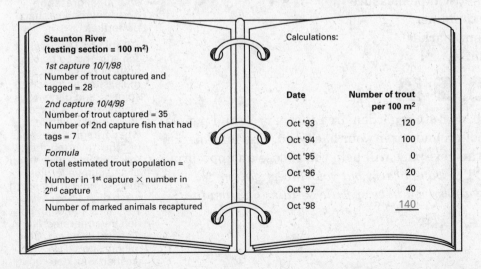

Staunton River
(testing section = 100 m²)

1st capture 10/1/98
Number of trout captured and tagged = 28

2nd capture 10/4/98
Number of trout captured = 35
Number of 2nd capture fish that had tags = 7

Formula
Total estimated trout population =

$\dfrac{\text{Number in 1st capture} \times \text{number in 2nd capture}}{\text{Number of marked animals recaptured}}$

Calculations:

Date	Number of trout per 100 m²
Oct '93	120
Oct '94	100
Oct '95	0
Oct '96	20
Oct '97	40
Oct '98	140

Prelab Questions

1. What question were you and the fisheries biologists trying to answer by measuring the trout population over time?

Suggested answer: Will the trout population recover from the flood on its own?

2. Based on the data in the notebook, how long did it take for the trout population to recover from the flood?

2–3 years

3. Do you think the number of organisms captured in a mark-recapture study is important?

Sample answer: Yes, the number is important. The more organisms are collected, the more accurate the estimate will be.

4. Consider the trout population size just after the flood. Hypothesize possible sources for the trout that re-established the population.

Sample answers: Trout could have traveled from upstream. Eggs may have survived the flood and hatched.

Materials

- area where snails or other garden invertebrates live (ivy or other ground cover, flowerbed)
- meter stick or metric tape measure
- bucket or other container
- felt-tip permanent marker (for marking snails)

Procedure

1. Locate a flowerbed or other garden area that has a snail population on the school grounds or in your backyard. The information in the table on the next page will help you choose an appropriate study area. (**NOTE:** *Do not carry out your investigation on private property unless you have specific permission from the property owner.*)

Advance Preparation

A week before the lab
Locate areas to recommend for collecting snails or other garden invertebrates such as sowbugs, grasshoppers, or white cabbage butterflies.

Safety and Disposal
Tell students to be cautious of poisonous animals, such as insects or spiders, and dangerous plants, such as poison ivy or plants with thorns, when foraging for snails or other invertebrates. Ask students to alert you of any plant allergies. Also, remind students to wash their hands with soap after handling garden invertebrates. No disposal required. Containers should be washed with detergent.

Good Snail Habitats	Places to Avoid
• *Plants that grow from bulbs* Snails are attracted to plants that grow from bulbs, such as irises and calla lilies. Look under the leaves and at the base of the leaves.	• *Grassy areas* Since snails tend to hide from predators and sunlight, they are unlikely to be found in open grassy areas during the day.
• *Ground cover such as ivy, African daisy, or other plants* These plants provide good hiding places for snails. Look on the ground under the plants and under the leaves.	• *Cacti, roses, or other thorny plants* There may be some snails on these plants, but the plants have many sharp spines and thorns that can hurt you.
• *Lemon trees* Snails eat the leaves of lemon trees and other citrus trees. You can use a dwarf citrus tree as your entire study area. Look underneath the leaves.	• *Junipers, woody shrubs* These tall shrubs are prickly and woody, making it hard to move the branches away to look for snails.
	• *Fragile gardens* Avoid areas with fragile flowers that may be trampled and destroyed.

2. Measure your study area with a meter stick or metric tape measure. For best results, the study area should be about 4 m². Record measurements and make a sketch of your study area below.
    CAUTION: *Be aware of physical hazards in the study area to avoid injuring yourself or others.*

Alternate Methods
Students can also experience the mark-recapture method using inanimate objects such as dried beans or macaroni. Give each student a plastic sandwich bag full of objects. They should remove roughly 20% of the objects, mark them, place them back in the bag, and shake the bag. Students then capture about 20% of the objects again and record how many are marked. After students calculate the estimated population they can check their estimates by counting the objects or weighing them.

3. Work with your team to search the entire study area for snails, and collect the snails in a bucket or other container. You may find snails under plants, on walls behind plants, or on the underside of leaves. Take care not to harm the snails and the surrounding plants. **CAUTION:** *Be aware of any poisonous or prickly plants and avoid insects that bite or sting. Alert your teacher in advance to any allergies you may have.*

4. Use a felt-tip marker to mark each snail you have captured with a *small* "X" on its shell.

5. Record the number of snails you have captured and marked below. Then gently release the marked snails back into your study area. **CAUTION:** *Wash your hands with soap when you are finished working with the animals.*

Number of snails captured and marked: _____32_____

6. Wait at least one day for the snails to redistribute themselves, but not longer than one week.

7. Return to your study area and capture snails again as you did in Step 2. When you have finished collecting, record the total number of snails and the total number of marked snails below.

Number of snails captured: ___28___

Number of marked snails recaptured: ___18___

Analysis and Conclusions

1. Write a brief description of your study area in the space below. What environmental factors can you identify that might make it possible for a population of snails to live there? Explain.

Students should describe their study area and identify environmental factors such as moisture, shade, places to hide, and food supply.

2. Use the mark-recapture formula to determine the size of the snail population in your team's study area.

$$\text{Total population} = \frac{\text{Number captured first time} \times \text{number captured second time}}{\text{Number of marked animals recaptured}}$$

Size of snail population in the study area: ___50___

3. Compare your data with your classmates. What was the largest snail population estimate? Describe the environment where this population is found.

Student responses will vary.

_____

_____

4. In general, biologists using the mark-recapture method to estimate population size assume that the mark or tag needs to be inconspicuous. Why might a more obvious mark affect your population estimate?

Sample answer: If the mark is conspicuous, predators may be more apt to spot the marked snails.

_____

_____

5. What factors could affect your estimates?

Sample answers: We did not collect enough snails. It was sunny and hot on the first day we did

the capture, and cloudy and rainy the second day.

_____

6. Why is mark-recapture a good method to use for this population?

Suggested answer: Snails move around a lot and are often hiding from predators.

_____

_____

Extension

A snail population living and feeding in a home garden can weaken or destroy many plants. Fortunately, there are many nontoxic methods for controlling the population of snails in a garden. Nontoxic methods do not introduce toxic chemicals into the food chain. Cornmeal, crushed eggshells, diatomaceous earth, wood shavings, and cocoa bean shells are nontoxic materials often used to repel snails. Try spreading one of these materials in the area you studied and do another mark-recapture study several days afterwards to see if the population of snails has diminished. **CAUTION:** *Check with your teacher before carrying out any investigations.*

Extension
Review students' plans for safety issues. Remind them not to mistreat organisms. Students should notice a population drop several days after adding the materials to the area.

Population Patterns

Analysis of a Human Population

Question How can birth and death data be used to analyze human populations?

Lab Overview In this investigation, you will collect data on birth-dates and ages of death of members of a population during a specific time period. Using the data, you will construct and analyze two types of graphs—a survivorship curve and an age-structure graph. Then, you will compare data with other groups and make inferences about the patterns that you observe.

Background The data you will examine are from the Hanover Green Cemetery near Scranton, Pennsylvania. The birthdates on the head-stones span three centuries. Your study of this Pennsylvania population will reveal information about its age-structure and death-rate patterns during certain time periods. In the process you will explore how data can be used to make various inferences about a population. As with any scientific study, the number of data points affects how likely it is that the data accurately reflect reality. The more data you analyze, the more confident you can be in making inferences based on those data.

Prelab Activity Age-structure graphs can help scientists analyze historical trends in populations or predict future birth and death rates for a population. To prepare you for the lab, review the discussion of age-structure graphs and their significance on page 775 in your textbook.

Survivorship curves indicate the average number or proportion of individuals in a population who survive past a certain age. Typical survivorship curves for populations of different species can look vastly different. Some organisms produce thousands or even millions of off-spring at once. These organisms typically do not provide care for their young, and many of the offspring die before reaching adulthood. Other organisms (particularly larger mammals) only produce a few, or even just one, offspring at a time. These parents often provide care for their young, many of which live to adulthood. Study the survivorship curves on the next page. Then answer the Prelab Questions.

Objective to construct survivorship curves and age-structure graphs, and use them to make inferences about populations

Inquiry Skills
- organizing data
- analyzing data
- making inferences
- communicating conclusions

Time
- 10–15 min for Prelab Activity
- 45 min for Part A (20 min if Step 1 is assigned as homework or completed by another class or in a previous year)
- 20 min for Part B
- 30 min for Part C
- 20 min for Analysis and Conclusions

The Hanover Green Cemetery was chosen as the data source for this lab in part because it represents an economically and culturally diverse population. Therefore, although it is not the only cemetery in the region, it is a fairly representative sample of the breadth of the population in the area and thus is a reasonable basis for making inferences about the local population.

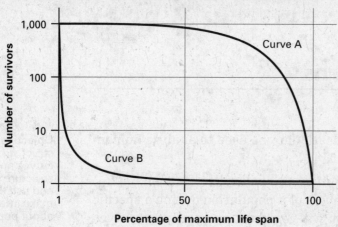

Survivorship Curves for Populations of Two Species

Curve A

Curve B

Number of survivors

1,000

100

10

1

1   50   100

Percentage of maximum life span

Prelab Questions

1. Oysters, which do not provide care for their offspring, may produce millions of eggs at once. Which curve do you think would most likely represent an oyster population? Explain.

Suggested answer: Curve B. The death rate for individuals in the population represented by this curve

is very high, then it levels off. This would be typical of an oyster population, in which parents do not

provide care for offspring.

2. Elephants produce only a few offspring and provide care for their young. Which curve do you think would most likely represent an elephant population? Explain.

Suggested answer: Curve A. The death rate for individuals in the population represented by this curve

is very low early in life and through midlife, and then drops significantly when individuals reach old

age. This would be typical of an elephant population, in which parents provide care for offspring.

3. Which curve do you think would most likely represent a survivorship curve of a human population? How might an event such as a plague that affects mostly young adults change the shape of this survivorship curve?

Suggested answer: Curve A. In the case of such an event, a drastic dip in the curve would occur on

the area of the graph representing the young adults. Then it would most likely level out again through

middle age, and drop off again in old age.

4. What does an age-structure graph with a "bulge" toward the top end of the graph indicate about the probable future size of a population?

Suggested answer: A bulge toward the top of the age-structure graph would indicate the population

size might decrease in the future.

Name _____ Class _____ Date _____

Materials

- birth and death data (included at the end of this lab)
- 50 small cards (per student)
- graph paper
- calculator

Procedure

Part A: Constructing a Survivorship Curve

1. Each lab group will be assigned a range of 20 years. For example, if your group is assigned 1840–1859, your group's task is to collect data for all of the people whose birthdates range from 1840–1859. Before beginning the investigation, make a prediction about which age groups in your time span were most vulnerable to death. Also, make a prediction about differences you will see in the survivorship curves of males and females.

Predictions:

Student predictions will vary. Accept all reasonable predictions.

_____

_____

_____

Divide the data collecting among the group to ensure that only one group member will record data for a particular individual. Use a separate card to record the sex (M or F), year of birth (YOB), year of death (YOD), and age at death in years (AAD) for each individual (see example).

```
F
YOB: 1860
YOD: 1950
AAD: 90
```

2. Combine your cards with the rest of your lab group's cards. Sort the cards by sex into two piles. At the top of Data Table 1 on the next page, enter the range of birth years for which your group collected data and the total numbers of males and females born during those years.

3. Since every individual in your study had to be part of Age Group 0–9, record the total numbers of males and females again in Column A: Population in Age Group, Age Group 0–9.

4. Now, sort the cards for each sex into groups by age at death. Each group should represent a 10-year period, as listed in Data Table 1. For example, put all males who died from ages 0–9 in one group, all males who died from ages 10–19 in another group, and so on.

Advance Preparation
Cut 3" × 5" index cards in half. Or, cut construction paper or cardstock into small rectangles.

Assign groups of students to 20-year periods. Recommended periods are 1820–1839, 1840–1859, 1860–1879, 1880–1899, 1900–1919. Note that some ranges will have significantly more individuals with available data than other ranges. Adjust the group sizes accordingly. Remind groups to divide their list so that there is no duplicate data between students within the group.

You could collect and keep the data cards to save time for next year's students.

5. Count the cards in each age group for each sex and enter the numbers in Data Table 1 in Column B: Deaths in Age Group.

6. Next you will calculate the populations of males and females for the rest of the age groups (Column A). To calculate the population for an age group, subtract the number of deaths in that age group from the population in the previous age group. Try the practice data table below before completing Data Table 1.

Example Data Table

Age Group	A. Population in Age Group		B. Deaths in Age Group	
	M	F	M	F
1. 0–9	100	100	6	3
2. 10–19	94	97	2	3
3. 20–29	92	94	2	5
4. 30–39	?	?	1	1

Based on this example data, what are the populations of males and females in the 30–39 age group?

___90___ M   ___89___ F

Share your answer with the other members of your group.

Data Table 1: Population Data
Range of years studied: _____
Total number of individuals born during this
    time period: _____ M _____ F

Age Group	A. Population in Age Group		B. Deaths in Age Group	
	M	F	M	F
1. 0–9				
2. 10–19				
3. 20–29				
4. 30–39				
5. 40–49				
6. 50–59				
7. 60–69				
8. 70–79				
9. 80–89				
10. 90–99				
11. Over 100				

Survivorship curves show different age groups that are most vulnerable to death. For instance, in some populations, the males in the 60–69 age group tend to be very vulnerable, but if a male survives past this age, he is likely to live past 80. These curves also show trends surrounding historical events. For example, the Spanish flu epidemic and the U.S. involvement in World War I are two 1918 events that may affect a survivorship curve of a U.S. population. Both events led to the deaths of many young adults, especially males. Other events to keep in mind for this study population are the Civil War (1861–1865) and World War II (1941–1945).

Name _____ Class _____ Date_____

7. Use the data from Data Table 1 to construct survivorship curves for each sex together on a single graph. Plot age group on the *x*-axis and number of surviving individuals on the *y*-axis. Use different colors for the data points and curves for the males and females, and add a key.

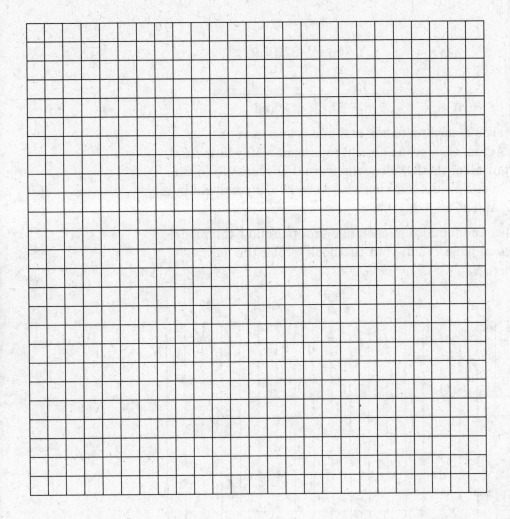

In Part B, assign two specific years for the age-structure graphs. Two recommended years are 1820 and 1920.* Have each group separate the male and female cards that include each target year and those that include neither. Divide the class into two large groups assigned by year. There will be significantly more data for the 1920 group than the 1820 group. Adjust the group sizes accordingly. Students should take the appropriate stacks of cards with them to their new group.

You could set up two poster boards in the class. Have students come up individually and draw part of the age-structure graph. This will get as many students involved as possible in the exercise.

*These two dates (1820 and 1920) will give the most interesting data; however, note that depending on the ranges you assigned in Part A, students may not have data cards for individuals born before 1820 or in 1920.

Part B: Constructing an Age-Structure Graph

1. Your teacher will assign your group one year for which to construct an age-structure graph. If, for example, your group is assigned 1820, the group will gather the cards for every individual who was alive in the year 1820. (**NOTE:** *As in Part A, keep males and females in separate piles.*) Your teacher will give you specific instructions on organizing the data.

2. Once you have all of the cards that include the year your group was assigned, calculate all the individuals' ages in that year. On the back of each card, record the person's age in that year. (See the example below.)

Year assigned: 1820

<table>
<tr><td>F
YOB: 1811
YOD: 1901
AAD: 90</td><td>Age in 1820 = 9</td></tr>
<tr><td style="text-align:center">**Front of card**</td><td style="text-align:center">**Back of card**</td></tr>
</table>

3. Separate the cards according to sex and age group in your assigned year. Again, each group should represent a 10-year period. For example, put all of the females who were 0–9 years old in the assigned year in one group; females who were 10–19 years old in another group, and so on.

4. Count the males and females in each age group. Follow the model in Figure 35-11 on page 775 in your textbook to plot the data as an age-structure graph.

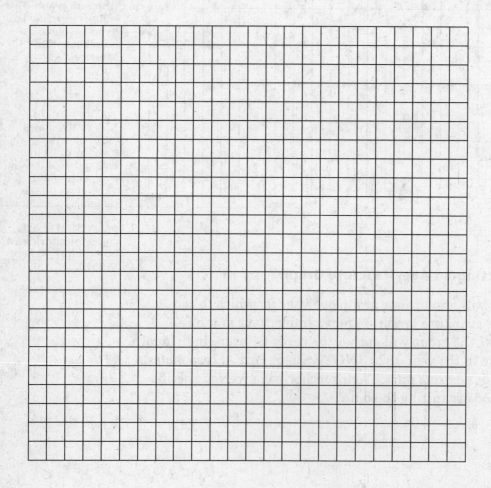

Part C: Comparing Group Data

1. Members of the original lab groups will take turns presenting their survivorship curves to the rest of the class. Record similarities and differences in the different graphs below.

_____

_____

_____

_____

_____

_____

_____

2. Compare and discuss the different age-structure graphs created by the class. Record similarities and differences below.

_____

_____

_____

_____

Analysis and Conclusions

1. What age groups were most vulnerable to death in different time spans? What events or health challenges do you hypothesize might have caused these higher death rates?

   Students may note that during the early years of the cemetery's use, many more young children and

   young-adult females died than in later years. They may note that many more young-adult males died

   during certain time periods. They may cite instances such as lack of medications or hospitals to explain

   the deaths of children and young-adult females. They may cite wars as reasons for the deaths of

   young-adult males.

2. Describe any differences in your group's original survivorship curves for males and females in your particular time span.

   Students' results will vary depending on the time span.

_____

_____

_____

3. How do your answers to questions 1 and 2 compare to the predictions you made in Part A? Suggest reasons for any differences.

Students' answers will vary based on their original predictions and data.

4. Discuss some reasons why your graphs may not be completely accurate reflections of the population you studied.

Possible answers: The number of individuals studied is too small. Students do not know how large

the population of this area was during different time periods. Perhaps there are other large cemeteries

in the area. Students do not know if many people who were born in this town moved

away and may be buried in other locations.

5. What predictions about the future of the study population could you make based on the age-structure graph for the earliest year the class graphed? Did the shape of the age-structure graph of the later year follow those predictions? Suggest reasons for any differences.

Students' answers will vary based on the shape of the graphs. Students could check their predictions by

counting how many individuals were alive during the year used for the second age-structure graph.

Extension

Research the 20-year time span you were assigned in Part A for factors that could have affected people's lifespans. Keep the following types of questions in mind as you do your research. What types of historical, social, and economic events occurred during that time? What were typical healthcare issues of that time? Were there any scientific breakthroughs that could have affected the health and overall survival rates of a population? After conducting your research, go back to your survivorship curves and age-structure graphs. Based on your research, develop hypotheses to explain the shapes of each type of graph.

Extension
There are many events in the last few centuries that could cause noticeable dips and rises in a U.S. population's survivorship curve. Some examples are World War I (1917–1918), World War II (1941–1945), the Civil War (1861–1865), the Spanish flu epidemic (1918), enhanced cleanliness in the medical community (late nineteenth century), and the discovery of penicillin (after World War II).

	Sex	YOB	YOD	AAD		Sex	YOB	YOD	AAD		Sex	YOB	YOD	AAD
Inm, E	M	1718	1804	86	Dan, A	M	1812	1872	60	Mor, S	F	1847	1913	66
Inm, S	F	1721	1809	88	Mil, J	M	1814	1820	6	Wil, M	F	1847	1928	81
Fis, M	F	1725	1830	105	Dea, G	M	1816	1901	85	Dav, D	M	1848	1918	70
Fis, R	M	1726	1809	83	Chr, E	F	1817	1879	62	Hug, T	M	1848	1921	73
Kei, A	F	1738	1811	73	Gre, A	M	1817	1868	51	Jen, J	M	1848	1910	62
Ben, R	M	1754	1842	88	Owe, D	M	1817	1865	48	May, W	M	1848	1915	67
Gar, C	M	1756	1825	69	Siv, M	F	1817	1899	82	Pen, S	M	1848	1921	73
Beh, G	M	1758	1816	58	Lon, C	F	1818	1856	38	Swa, N	M	1848	1921	73
Inm, J	M	1758	1804	46	Mil, M	F	1818	1895	77	Wil, D	M	1848	1915	67
Con, R	M	1759	1829	70	Rum, C	M	1819	1843	24	Jon, C	F	1849	1914	65
Eva, M	F	1759	1825	66	Rob, C	M	1820	1842	22	Mor, J	M	1849	1924	75
Moo, S	M	1762	1798	36	San, J	M	1820	1841	21	Sev, A	M	1849	1940	91
Rum, J	M	1767	1835	68	Rum, C	M	1821	1841	20	May, M	F	1850	1937	87
Car, C	M	1768	1838	70	Geo, A	F	1822	1889	67	Mor, L	F	1850	1926	76
Ste, R	M	1770	1796	26	Geo, W	M	1822	1890	68	Tho, M	F	1850	1929	79
Smi, A	M	1774	1830	56	Beh, C	M	1826	1828	2	Tho, S	M	1850	1931	81
Rob, J	M	1776	1821	45	Beh, Z	M	1828	1831	3	Ale, L	F	1851	1919	68
Ste, F	F	1777	1855	78	Wil, W	M	1828	1869	41	Fin, W	M	1851	1916	65
Ste, S	F	1780	1871	91	Jer, J	M	1829	1891	62	Leu, S	M	1851	1913	62
Nag, C	M	1781	1857	76	Geo, I	M	1831	1875	44	Mil, S	F	1851	1873	22
Aum, E	F	1782	1827	45	Dur, S	F	1833	1835	2	Wil, H	M	1851	1931	80
Con, M	F	1782	1820	38	Wil, R	M	1833	1910	77	Gre, A	F	1852	1935	83
Hoo, J	M	1782	1866	84	Opl, M	F	1834	1920	86	Mor, R	M	1852	1911	59
Lut, J	M	1784	1847	63	Obr, M	F	1835	1861	26	Opl, A	F	1852	1925	73
Min, H	M	1785	1845	60	Mil, S	M	1836	1923	87	Wil, F	M	1852	1920	68
Pet, W	M	1787	1869	82	Ste, I	M	1836	1923	87	Jon, G	M	1853	1905	52
Inm, D	M	1788	1807	19	Cyr, E	F	1837	1859	22	Mor, M	F	1853	1919	66
Ben, N	M	1789	1872	83	Dil, J	M	1838	1851	13	Str, H	M	1853	1910	57
Siv, G	M	1789	1854	65	Jon, L	F	1838	1904	66	Der, J	F	1854	1924	70
Rum, C	F	1790	1811	21	Wel, C	M	1839	1923	84	Eva, D	M	1854	1918	64
Kli, S	F	1793	1821	28	Bee, M	F	1840	1921	81	Hec, C	M	1854	1936	82
Kno, E	F	1793	1818	25	Bee, W	M	1840	1919	79	Hug, C	F	1854	1883	29
Ree, P	M	1793	1816	23	Jon, J	F	1840	1937	97	Ree, T	M	1854	1911	57
Ash, H	M	1794	1820	26	Lon, J	M	1840	1907	67	Rin, J	M	1854	1924	70
Ash, J	M	1795	1841	46	Sol, T	M	1840	1927	87	All, C	M	1855	1913	58
Ben, A	F	1795	1866	71	Moo, S	F	1841	1910	69	Jon, Z	F	1855	1922	67
Kno, J	M	1796	1819	23	Jon, W	M	1842	1918	76	Mor, W	M	1855	1927	72
Pel, S	M	1796	1872	76	Sev, J	M	1842	1914	72	Tho, M	F	1855	1920	65
Apl, H	F	1797	1822	25	Wel, A	F	1842	1923	81	Cur, J	F	1856	1868	12
Wri, E	F	1797	1853	56	How, J	M	1843	1928	85	Fal, T	M	1856	1900	44
Car, T	M	1798	1871	73	Jon, M	F	1843	1922	79	Gun, M	F	1856	1917	61
Mil, A	F	1800	1818	18	Geo, E	F	1844	1919	75	Law, J	M	1856	1926	70
Mil, P	M	1800	1871	71	Geo, H	M	1844	1888	44	Lew, E	F	1856	1935	79
Sti, E	F	1801	1851	50	Mun, J	M	1844	1908	64	Mor, M	M	1856	1920	64
Dra, C	M	1803	1830	27	Dav, W	M	1845	1927	82	Pia, R	M	1856	1938	82
Inm, E	M	1803	1835	32	Mor, D	M	1845	1887	42	She, E	F	1856	1921	65
Car, E	F	1805	1871	66	Mor, L	M	1845	1929	84	Wil, M	F	1856	1937	81
Min, W	M	1805	1831	26	Opl, J	M	1845	1915	70	Chr, M	F	1857	1919	62
Mil, E	F	1806	1823	17	Wil, L	M	1845	1920	75	Con, C	M	1857	1943	86
Lio, C	M	1807	1815	8	Bol, G	M	1846	1917	71	Dur, H	M	1857	1941	84
Pel, M	F	1807	1881	74	How, A	F	1846	1928	82	Edw, R	M	1857	1915	58
Inm, A	M	1808	1817	9	Mar, A	F	1846	1926	80	Eva, C	F	1857	1940	83
Pfo, B	M	1809	1874	65	Jon, M	F	1847	1917	70	Gun, J	M	1857	1913	56
Fis, S	F	1810	1812	2	Kis, W	M	1847	1923	76	Leu, J	F	1857	1923	66

	Sex	YOB	YOD	AAD		Sex	YOB	YOD	AAD		Sex	YOB	YOD	AAD
Mor, M	F	1857	1931	74	Sch, G	M	1864	1939	75	Ada, A	F	1871	1949	78
She, V	M	1857	1939	82	Tho, E	M	1864	1909	45	Ada, H	F	1871	1921	50
Swa, C	F	1857	1941	84	Wil, A	F	1864	1946	82	Dre, P	M	1871	1967	96
But, E	F	1858	1936	78	Eva, O	M	1865	1894	29	Eva, E	F	1871	1924	53
Fin, J	M	1858	1931	73	Mil, R	F	1865	1926	61	Ful, M	F	1871	1949	78
Fin, M	F	1858	1938	80	Pri, R	M	1865	1938	73	Hil, M	F	1871	1927	56
Ful, F	F	1858	1945	87	Rob, M	F	1865	1948	83	Hum, M	F	1871	1949	78
Dur, A	F	1859	1918	59	Ada, J	M	1866	1934	68	Joh, W	M	1871	1945	74
Epp, A	F	1859	1928	69	Eva, I	M	1866	1939	73	Jon, M	F	1871	1946	75
Llo, S	F	1859	1935	76	Gra, J	M	1866	1939	73	Low, J	M	1871	1951	80
Smi, L	M	1859	1929	70	Ham, H	F	1866	1953	87	San, L	F	1871	1907	36
Tho, M	F	1859	1910	51	Hod, M	F	1866	1947	81	Coo, F	F	1872	1937	65
Wil, A	F	1859	1935	76	Rei, A	M	1866	1953	87	Dev, J	M	1872	1936	64
Wir, A	F	1859	1935	76	Rip, L	F	1866	1958	92	Hil, A	M	1872	1951	79
Bac, M	F	1860	1950	90	Tho, E	F	1866	1916	50	Jon, M	F	1872	1936	64
Coo, J	M	1860	1941	81	Tho, M	F	1866	1932	66	Mar, L	F	1872	1944	72
Hoy, C	M	1860	1952	92	Wil, W	M	1866	1929	63	Tho, J	M	1872	1951	79
Jan, M	F	1860	1953	93	Eva, A	M	1867	1933	66	Wai, M	F	1872	1958	86
Pau, J	M	1860	1913	53	Gra, A	F	1867	1953	86	Ale, W	M	1873	1923	50
Rhy, E	F	1860	1932	72	Gun, L	F	1867	1917	50	Ben, A	F	1873	1936	63
Tho, A	F	1860	1935	75	Hae, I	F	1867	1935	68	Dan, I	M	1873	1937	64
Tho, J	M	1860	1919	59	Hil, G	M	1867	1926	59	Dif, N	F	1873	1944	71
Wit, J	M	1860	1872	12	Hof, E	F	1867	1949	82	Hum, C	M	1873	1929	56
Dav, F	M	1861	1929	68	Hof, G	M	1867	1929	62	Mil, S	F	1873	1941	68
Dev, M	F	1861	1943	82	Pay, S	F	1867	1952	85	Ric, J	M	1873	1949	76
Hoo, J	M	1861	1861	0	Pia, B	M	1867	1916	49	Rob, H	M	1873	1937	64
Jen, M	M	1861	1927	66	Pri, E	F	1867	1929	62	Sav, I	F	1873	1947	74
Jon, S	F	1861	1951	90	Spe, L	M	1867	1937	70	Sch, I	F	1873	1954	81
Ree, M	F	1861	1927	66	Ble, A	F	1868	1930	62	Tro, C	M	1873	1941	68
Rob, J	M	1861	1946	85	Dav, A	F	1868	1919	51	Tug, T	M	1873	1941	68
Ste, J	M	1861	1862	1	How, E	M	1868	1953	85	Bam, J	M	1874	1943	69
Tho, E	M	1861	1917	56	Hoy, C	F	1868	1955	87	Dav, J	M	1874	1946	72
Tho, W	M	1861	1917	56	Jon, T	M	1868	1931	63	Dre, M	F	1874	1963	89
Wir, J	M	1861	1913	52	Pia, M	F	1868	1928	60	Eyn, D	M	1874	1948	74
Fin, M	F	1862	1936	74	Sin, H	M	1868	1935	67	Joh, J	F	1874	1954	80
Jon, M	F	1862	1950	88	Wol, P	M	1868	1933	65	Mcc, R	M	1874	1941	67
Kei, S	F	1862	1926	64	Gri, J	F	1869	1931	62	Mon, E	F	1874	1933	59
Lon, H	M	1862	1938	76	Ham, D	M	1869	1937	68	Nor, J	M	1874	1947	73
Olc, Z	M	1862	1938	76	Ham, M	F	1869	1944	75	Rob, A	F	1874	1875	1
Opl, M	F	1862	1940	78	Hoo, J	M	1869	1925	56	Swe, F	F	1874	1934	60
Ree, J	M	1862	1933	71	Pia, A	F	1869	1953	84	Wil, M	F	1874	1950	76
Rot, C	F	1862	1925	63	Rip, M	F	1869	1962	93	Win, M	F	1874	1926	52
Col, H	F	1863	1947	84	Sin, L	F	1869	1926	57	Wlo, A	M	1874	1947	73
Eva, R	F	1863	1938	75	Spe, M	F	1869	1935	66	Dev, A	M	1875	1952	77
Jon, E	F	1863	1943	80	Wil, J	M	1869	1941	72	Eva, D	M	1875	1922	47
Mon, A	M	1863	1940	77	Bey, M	F	1870	1951	81	Eva, M	F	1875	1933	58
Pau, J	F	1863	1929	66	Cor, S	F	1870	1947	77	Fre, G	M	1875	1951	76
Rou, J	M	1863	1946	83	Dan, M	F	1870	1945	75	Hoo, L	F	1875	1963	88
Shi, W	M	1863	1930	67	How, G	F	1870	1944	74	Lew, H	M	1875	1951	76
Wil, G	M	1863	1936	73	Lon, R	M	1870	1903	33	Mcg, L	F	1875	1917	42
Chr, J	M	1864	1913	49	Nic, J	M	1870	1956	86	Neu, A	F	1875	1959	84
Con, E	F	1864	1944	80	Shi, E	F	1870	1941	71	Poh, R	M	1875	1955	80
Die, C	M	1864	1917	53	Wil, E	M	1870	1924	54	Pro, T	M	1875	1953	78
Hug, E	F	1864	1919	55	Wil, T	F	1870	1948	78	Ric, D	M	1875	1966	91

Name	Sex	YOB	YOD	AAD
Ros, E	M	1875	1941	66
Rou, B	F	1875	1960	85
Ste, M	F	1875	1949	74
And, E	F	1876	1947	71
Bar, S	M	1876	1946	70
Fur, M	F	1876	1942	66
Geo, C	F	1876	1965	89
Han, E	F	1876	1939	63
Hic, W	M	1876	1961	85
Nic, W	F	1876	1917	41
Nor, G	M	1876	1937	61
Opl, A	M	1876	1932	56
Par, S	F	1876	1959	83
Rob, J	M	1876	1916	40
Rob, L	F	1876	1958	82
Tho, W	M	1876	1929	53
Wil, S	F	1876	1948	72
Ale, B	F	1877	1878	1
Dav, J	M	1877	1948	71
Eva, J	F	1877	1961	84
Hah, R	M	1877	1939	62
Jon, O	M	1877	1957	80
Jon, W	M	1877	1972	95
Mag, S	M	1877	1958	81
Nor, A	F	1877	1960	83
Pro, R	F	1877	1964	87
Ric, E	F	1877	1961	84
Rob, J	M	1877	1949	72
Smi, F	M	1877	1958	81
Wil, P	M	1877	1942	65
Alb, O	M	1878	1941	63
And, C	M	1878	1965	87
Dan, R	M	1878	1942	64
Die, C	F	1878	1962	84
Ebe, Z	F	1878	1955	77
Hec, C	M	1878	1923	45
Jon, T	M	1878	1928	50
Phi, E	F	1878	1950	72
Smi, C	M	1878	1922	44
Smi, F	M	1878	1929	51
Sor, E	F	1878	1954	76
Str, H	F	1878	1886	8
You, O	M	1878	1940	62
And, M	F	1879	1933	54
Bev, S	M	1879	1942	63
Eve, F	M	1879	1931	52
Geo, F	M	1879	1923	44
Gun, G	M	1879	1954	75
Han, G	M	1879	1946	67
Kas, A	M	1879	1950	71
Llo, T	M	1879	1918	39
Mag, M	F	1879	1962	83
Mai, J	M	1879	1952	73
Mil, D	F	1879	1918	39

Name	Sex	YOB	YOD	AAD
Pen, M	F	1879	1961	82
Rei, L	M	1879	1943	64
Ric, E	F	1879	1931	52
Tud, A	F	1879	1967	88
Van, C	M	1879	1972	93
Van, M	F	1879	1969	90
Wei, S	F	1879	1974	95
All, J	M	1880	1956	76
Bee, W	M	1880	1891	11
Bro, E	F	1880	1920	40
Dan, W	M	1880	1946	66
Eva, A	F	1880	1962	82
Eyn, A	F	1880	1949	69
Gen, W	M	1880	1966	86
Gou, G	M	1880	1961	81
Gri, B	M	1880	1922	42
Hou, P	M	1880	1934	54
Lew, H	F	1880	1948	68
Low, F	M	1880	1942	62
Mac, M	F	1880	1929	49
Mai, G	F	1880	1940	60
Pre, M	F	1880	1966	86
Pry, H	M	1880	1921	41
Row, L	F	1880	1936	56
Smi, M	F	1880	1960	80
Swa, C	F	1880	1949	69
Tug, B	F	1880	1958	78
Wri, T	M	1880	1937	57
Zie, J	M	1880	1939	59
All, L	F	1881	1961	80
Cro, F	M	1881	1955	74
Geo, W	M	1881	1922	41
Hea, H	M	1881	1943	62
Jon, H	M	1881	1951	70
Phi, M	M	1881	1923	42
Sti, A	F	1881	1957	76
Tho, H	M	1881	1931	50
Wes, W	M	1881	1962	81
You, A	M	1881	1946	65
Bru, J	M	1882	1957	75
Cam, L	M	1882	1958	76
Cob, J	F	1882	1975	93
Dan, E	F	1882	1960	78
Jon, E	F	1882	1912	30
Jon, R	M	1882	1965	83
Mac, M	F	1882	1945	63
Smi, G	M	1882	1933	51
Tho, E	F	1882	1948	66
Tho, R	M	1882	1952	70
Var, S	M	1882	1957	75
Wan, W	M	1882	1940	58
You, E	M	1882	1971	89
Zie, E	F	1882	1975	93
Alb, E	F	1883	1917	34

Name	Sex	YOB	YOD	AAD
Ale, D	F	1883	1883	0
Dav, L	M	1883	1949	66
Edw, S	F	1883	1933	50
Fre, D	F	1883	1932	49
Gri, C	F	1883	1940	57
Hag, R	F	1883	1969	86
Hoo, O	M	1883	1964	81
Iba, W	M	1883	1967	84
Jam, A	M	1883	1973	90
Lam, G	M	1883	1909	26
Luc, C	F	1883	1962	79
Pas, E	M	1883	1920	37
Rei, G	F	1883	1962	79
Tem, H	M	1883	1968	85
Tho, E	F	1883	1945	62
Wal, E	M	1883	1958	75
Wes, A	F	1883	1973	90
Bon, J	M	1884	1945	61
Bro, C	M	1884	1938	54
Bul, W	M	1884	1943	59
Eva, L	F	1884	1950	66
Fre, B	F	1884	1928	44
Jam, T	M	1884	1943	59
Kas, G	M	1884	1960	76
Kei, E	M	1884	1918	34
Loc, F	M	1884	1951	67
Lon, A	M	1884	1971	87
Min, M	F	1884	1952	68
Ols, H	M	1884	1925	41
Reg, F	M	1884	1949	65
Rhy, K	F	1884	1961	77
Rob, J	F	1884	1952	68
Rot, J	M	1884	1918	34
Var, A	F	1884	1945	61
Wil, F	F	1884	1941	57
Wil, I	M	1884	1944	60
Woj, W	M	1884	1938	54
Bee, R	F	1885	1891	6
Bra, A	F	1885	1971	86
Bus, R	F	1885	1930	45
Con, C	M	1885	1976	91
Dav, G	F	1885	1967	82
Gal, I	F	1885	1945	60
Gri, S	F	1885	1965	80
His, T	M	1885	1938	53
Jon, J	M	1885	1950	65
Leu, C	F	1885	1950	65
Loc, E	F	1885	1949	64
Lub, M	M	1885	1936	51
Mes, M	F	1885	1955	70
Mun, A	F	1885	1987	102
Opl, T	M	1885	1938	53
Pow, E	M	1885	1942	57
Rot, W	M	1885	1896	11

Sex	YOB	YOD	AAD		Sex	YOB	YOD	AAD		Sex	YOB	YOD	AAD
Sch, A	F	1885	1943	58	Opl, D	M	1888	1977	89	Far, L	F	1891	1942	51
Swa, O	M	1885	1968	83	Phi, G	F	1888	1963	75	Fei, I	F	1891	1916	25
Tho, P	M	1885	1935	50	Reg, A	F	1888	1943	55	Fin, H	M	1891	1913	22
Tre, S	M	1885	1941	56	Row, C	F	1888	1966	78	Jam, A	F	1891	1935	44
Wil, B	F	1885	1937	52	She, G	M	1888	1964	76	Las, J	F	1891	1931	40
Woo, A	M	1885	1963	78	Sta, B	F	1888	1968	80	Mil, L	F	1891	1985	94
Ale, A	M	1886	1886	0	Str, F	M	1888	1891	3	Pay, W	M	1891	1910	19
Bee, J	F	1886	1891	5	Swi, G	F	1888	1933	45	Pie, A	M	1891	1943	52
Dav, P	M	1886	1952	66	All, W	M	1889	1967	78	Rhy, G	F	1891	1975	84
Eva, M	F	1886	1919	33	Bee, C	F	1889	1891	2	Sma, M	F	1891	1970	79
Gat, N	F	1886	1986	100	Cas, A	F	1889	1946	57	Smi, A	F	1891	1971	80
Hag, R	M	1886	1941	55	Jam, L	F	1889	1955	66	Smi, H	M	1891	1978	87
Hop, W	M	1886	1930	44	Joh, J	M	1889	1967	78	Tho, H	M	1891	1959	68
Hug, T	M	1886	1939	53	Jon, F	F	1889	1973	84	Tho, W	M	1891	1944	53
Jon, E	M	1886	1947	61	Jon, M	F	1889	1988	99	Beg, H	M	1892	1940	48
Jon, L	M	1886	1945	59	Klu, E	M	1889	1942	53	Coe, A	M	1892	1924	32
Kan, G	M	1886	1978	92	Lut, S	M	1889	1943	54	Eva, J	F	1892	1911	19
Kin, B	F	1886	1919	33	Man, M	F	1889	1950	61	Geo, S	F	1892	1984	92
Lei, J	F	1886	1930	44	May, N	F	1889	1947	58	Hor, P	F	1892	1977	85
Mat, J	M	1886	1950	64	Mcd, L	F	1889	1942	53	Kin, H	M	1892	1915	23
Maz, B	M	1886	1929	43	Nic, G	F	1889	1946	57	Lay, E	M	1892	1958	66
Mcg, J	F	1886	1968	82	Par, A	F	1889	1956	67	Lit, G	M	1892	1941	49
Mye, E.	F	1886	1980	94	Shi, P	F	1889	1915	26	Pea, J	M	1892	1969	77
Phi, S	F	1886	1954	68	Smi, A	F	1889	1981	92	Pre, S	M	1892	1961	69
Smi, H	M	1886	1959	73	Tro, G	M	1889	1961	72	Ree, E	M	1892	1955	63
Str, L	M	1886	1957	71	Vet, J	M	1889	1966	77	Rox, A	M	1892	1944	52
Tho, E	F	1886	1913	27	Web, W	M	1889	1957	68	Wil, S	M	1892	1915	23
Wil, T	M	1886	1950	64	Woo, E	F	1889	1940	51	Ada, A	F	1893	1976	83
Bol, R	M	1887	1921	34	Ada, B	F	1890	1892	2	Bri, I	M	1893	1977	84
Bul, B	F	1887	1966	79	Ada, T	M	1890	1892	2	Dav, E	M	1893	1969	76
Dur, F	M	1887	1918	31	Ant, Z	F	1890	1985	95	Geo, A	M	1893	1979	86
Eva, R	F	1887	1971	84	Ben, E	M	1890	1980	90	Gri, R	M	1893	1967	74
Geo, E	F	1887	1971	84	Far, W	M	1890	1969	79	How, D	M	1893	1961	68
Hag, E	F	1887	1961	74	Gri, T	M	1890	1937	47	Hum, E	M	1893	1942	49
Hes, H	M	1887	1927	40	Gri, T	F	1890	1959	69	Jon, P	F	1893	1978	85
Jon, A	F	1887	1970	83	Gri, W	M	1890	1956	66	Kli, A	M	1893	1982	89
Jon, T	M	1887	1945	58	Hug, L	F	1890	1982	92	Kli, F	F	1893	1945	52
Jon, W	M	1887	1941	54	Iba, M	F	1890	1944	54	Lea, E	F	1893	1965	72
McC, J	M	1887	1932	45	Jon, E	M	1890	1955	65	Lee, E	F	1893	1964	71
Mor, T	M	1887	1939	52	Jon, G	M	1890	1956	66	Mat, A	M	1893	1979	86
Pry, M	F	1887	1956	69	Klu, I	F	1890	1977	87	Mck, C	F	1893	1970	77
Sch, P	F	1887	1974	87	Mcg, H	M	1890	1922	32	Mel, E	F	1893	1967	74
Vet, M	F	1887	1971	84	Men, A	M	1890	1958	68	Pia, F	M	1893	1977	84
Wil, G	M	1887	1964	77	Mil, E	F	1890	1935	45	Ree, B	M	1893	1957	64
Wil, M	F	1887	1982	95	Roa, A	M	1890	1930	40	Rog, J	F	1893	1974	81
But, S	F	1888	1965	77	Str, E	F	1890	1944	54	Ruc, T	M	1893	1952	59
Gen, I	F	1888	1959	71	Tho, E	F	1890	1941	51	Wil, E	F	1893	1952	59
Het, I	F	1888	1927	39	Tho, J	M	1890	1954	64	Wil, F	F	1893	1983	90
Jon, E	F	1888	1939	51	Wil, M	F	1890	1959	69	Wil, H	F	1893	1921	28
Jon, K	F	1888	1985	97	Wil, M	F	1890	1955	65	Beg, M	F	1894	1943	49
May, R	M	1888	1976	88	Wil, M	F	1890	1940	50	Cra, J	M	1894	1944	50
Mcd, H	M	1888	1950	62	Wil, N	M	1890	1965	75	Dan, M	F	1894	1980	86
Mid, C	F	1888	1972	84	Bus, A	M	1891	1961	70	Gui, A	F	1894	1979	85
Mil, E	F	1888	1976	88	Cam, G	F	1891	1953	62	Hag, F	F	1894	1949	55

Name	Sex	YOB	YOD	AAD	Name	Sex	YOB	YOD	AAD	Name	Sex	YOB	YOD	AAD
Isa, D	M	1894	1972	78	Sau, H	M	1897	1983	86	Eva, W	M	1902	1939	37
Jen, M	F	1894	1915	21	Tro, A	F	1897	1975	78	Lar, A	M	1902	1965	63
Joh, E	F	1894	1972	78	Edw, M	F	1898	1979	81	Maj, E	M	1902	1977	75
Lau, H	M	1894	1941	47	Est, S	F	1898	1981	83	Rin, M	F	1902	1997	95
Law, M	F	1894	1920	26	Gri, E	F	1898	1956	58	All, C	M	1903	1915	12
Pia, E	F	1894	1898	4	Hof, J	F	1898	1988	90	Ast, R	M	1903	1978	75
Pug, R	M	1894	1966	72	Jon, E	M	1898	1977	79	Ero, C	M	1903	1990	87
Ree, E	M	1894	1950	56	Jon, P	M	1898	1964	66	Kin, E	F	1903	1955	52
Rin, D	F	1894	1946	52	Lew, W	M	1898	1918	20	Man, M	F	1903	1980	77
Ruc, H	F	1894	1971	77	Mar, M	M	1898	1975	77	Man, W	M	1903	1984	81
She, K	M	1894	1952	58	Nor, W	M	1898	1968	70	May, G	F	1903	1995	92
Viv, R	M	1894	1993	99	Ric, L	F	1898	1984	86	Obr, L	F	1903	1975	72
Wir, C	M	1894	1937	43	Rob, A	M	1898	1965	67	Pay, C	M	1903	1963	60
Bur, G	F	1895	1986	91	Rob, N	F	1898	1953	55	Pen, F	M	1903	1978	75
Car, R	F	1895	1971	76	Rot, W	M	1898	1938	40	Ric, I	F	1903	1993	90
Dav, M	F	1895	1977	82	Sul, F	M	1898	1972	74	Smi, M	F	1903	1986	83
Dre, L	F	1895	1913	18	Wil, C	F	1898	1939	41	Sto, M	F	1903	1991	88
Enk, S	M	1895	1958	63	Wlo, M	F	1898	1985	87	Van, N	M	1903	1967	64
Goo, W	M	1895	1975	80	Bri, P	M	1899	1960	61	Woo, H	M	1903	1975	72
Gri, M	F	1895	1980	85	Con, R	M	1899	1944	45	Ast, M	F	1904	1945	41
Mat, S	F	1895	1942	47	Cra, D	F	1899	1984	85	Bus, M	F	1904	1981	77
Mil, H	M	1895	1975	80	Err, M	F	1899	1992	93	But, L	M	1904	1994	90
Mil, W	M	1895	1966	71	Kei, B	M	1899	1964	65	Cou, D	F	1904	1994	90
Ric, A	F	1895	1968	73	Phi, A	M	1899	1971	72	Dav, G	M	1904	1958	54
You, E	F	1895	1958	63	Pia, E	F	1899	1940	41	Ero, M	F	1904	1984	80
Ave, C	M	1896	1965	69	Sch, E	F	1899	1972	73	Gab, L	M	1904	1947	43
Bat, E	M	1896	1970	74	Sul, C	M	1899	1930	31	Joh, B	M	1904	1991	87
Bat, M	F	1896	1973	77	Sul, L	M	1899	1965	66	Joh, D	M	1904	1984	80
Eck, E	F	1896	1970	74	Whi, J	M	1899	1964	65	May, L	F	1904	1983	79
Eva, E	F	1896	1981	85	Bro, L	M	1900	1961	61	Mil, F	M	1904	1985	81
Geo, E	M	1896	1966	70	Dar, R	M	1900	1934	34	Nau, A	F	1904	1984	80
Gre, T	F	1896	1908	12	Gro, B	M	1900	1972	72	Pat, F	F	1904	1980	76
Lar, E	F	1896	1950	54	Gru, C	F	1900	1965	65	Ric, C	F	1904	1968	64
Lee, D	M	1896	1939	43	Jon, J	M	1900	1981	81	Rot, C	M	1904	1938	34
Lun, A	M	1896	1924	28	Lac, D	M	1900	1940	40	Sau, I	F	1904	1973	69
Lut, L	F	1896	1987	91	Pen, B	M	1900	1971	71	Tud, H	M	1904	1977	73
Pia, M	F	1896	1971	75	Pic, E	M	1900	1954	54	Bus, H	M	1905	1992	87
Pia, R	M	1896	1971	75	Pru, L	M	1900	1930	30	Dav, M	F	1905	1949	44
Sac, W	M	1896	1986	90	Rog, H	M	1900	1976	76	Egg, J	M	1905	1961	56
Sch, E	F	1896	1985	89	Viv, B	F	1900	1967	67	Eng, E	M	1905	1964	59
Ada, J	M	1897	1968	71	Wil, O	F	1900	1913	13	Jam, E	M	1905	1968	63
Cro, R	M	1897	1984	87	Zim, W	M	1900	1956	56	Kil, H	M	1905	1996	91
Cul, G	F	1897	1951	54	Eva, G	F	1901	1946	45	Lar, E	F	1905	1976	71
Dil, J	M	1897	1966	69	Gra, W	M	1901	1970	69	May, J	M	1905	1990	85
Gom, M	M	1897	1950	53	Gri, T	F	1901	1985	84	Pat, S	F	1905	1969	64
Hof, L	M	1897	1956	59	Hal, T	M	1901	1952	51	Pen, E	F	1905	1982	77
Hum, P	M	1897	1967	70	Jon, V	F	1901	1988	87	Pry, F	F	1905	1980	75
Kis, M	F	1897	1974	77	Leg, E	F	1901	1975	74	Rin, M	F	1905	1967	62
Lon, F	M	1897	1975	78	Llo, R	F	1901	1986	85	Rot, C	M	1905	1907	2
Mil, G	M	1897	1980	83	Lun, F	M	1901	1976	75	Wil, W	M	1905	1978	73
Pay, S	F	1897	1898	1	Pay, M	F	1901	1902	1	Ast, M	F	1906	1977	71
Ric, H	M	1897	1977	80	Rob, C	M	1901	1943	42	Bro, A	F	1906	1968	62
Ric, J	M	1897	1933	36	She, L	F	1901	1990	89	Fai, R	F	1906	1981	75
Rob, E	M	1897	1937	40	Cro, W	M	1902	1958	56	Gab, T	M	1906	1949	43

	Sex	YOB	YOD	AAD		Sex	YOB	YOD	AAD		Sex	YOB	YOD	AAD
Hoo, A	M	1906	1941	35	Car, E	F	1910	1938	28	How, H	M	1915	1994	79
Lew, J	M	1906	1989	83	Fin, D	M	1910	1974	64	Jam, M	M	1915	1917	2
Mar, C	F	1906	1976	70	Fre, J	M	1910	1979	69	Per, R	M	1915	1952	37
Nas, W	M	1906	1994	88	Hag, R	M	1910	1954	44	Ree, A	M	1915	1989	74
Obr, J	M	1906	1988	82	Las, W	M	1910	1980	70	Rin, M	M	1915	1983	68
Phi, W	M	1906	1967	61	Til, W	M	1910	1997	87	Ros, J	M	1915	1975	60
Rap, P	M	1906	1967	61	Web, D	F	1910	1960	50	Row, E	F	1915	1928	13
Ros, W	F	1906	1937	31	Wil, S	F	1910	1972	62	Sie, A	M	1915	1951	36
Tra, E	M	1906	1972	66	Con, P	M	1911	1974	63	Sma, A	F	1915	1936	21
Wai, M	F	1906	1931	25	May, B	F	1911	1996	85	Str, M	F	1915	1990	75
Bau, S	M	1907	1960	53	Mil, M	F	1911	1997	86	Wil, E	M	1915	1995	80
Cor, G	M	1907	1943	36	Nor, B	F	1911	1919	8	Bab, E	F	1916	1974	58
Dav, D	M	1907	1947	40	Pea, G	F	1911	1989	78	Hal, B	M	1916	1992	76
Egg, A	F	1907	1996	89	Row, M	M	1911	1936	25	Hal, W	M	1916	1998	82
Ole, C	F	1907	1991	84	Smi, A	F	1911	1989	78	Par, E	F	1916	1993	77
Pea, W	M	1907	1958	51	Smi, I	M	1911	1972	61	Pen, D	F	1916	1944	28
Phi, M	F	1907	1990	83	Ste, J	M	1911	1985	74	Wit, C	M	1916	1986	70
Pie, M	F	1907	1997	90	Tra, E	F	1911	1981	70	Wit, M	F	1916	1973	57
Rod, L	M	1907	1986	79	Wil, F	M	1911	1974	63	Eve, A	M	1917	1990	73
Sto, A	M	1907	1979	72	You, D	M	1911	1966	55	Mor, R	F	1917	1988	71
Str, C	F	1907	1999	92	Amo, J	F	1912	1992	80	Pia, R	M	1917	1974	57
Sul, E	M	1907	1962	55	Dan, E	F	1912	1981	69	Rin, C	M	1917	1926	9
Wes, W	M	1907	1975	68	Dil, E	F	1912	1966	54	Row, D	F	1917	1993	76
Dav, T	M	1908	1970	62	Jon, T	M	1912	1959	47	She, L	F	1917	1917	0
Dip, W	M	1908	1964	56	Pet, A	M	1912	1989	77	Sul, R	M	1917	1985	68
Edi, E	F	1908	1975	67	Pro, R	M	1912	1929	17	Vet, J	F	1917	1992	75
Fai, H	M	1908	1989	81	Ree, M	F	1912	1939	27	War, S	F	1917	1986	69
Gou, T	M	1908	1925	17	Sul, L	F	1912	1966	54	Dyk, R	M	1918	1974	56
Jon, M	F	1908	1976	68	Wlo, H	M	1912	1927	15	Pia, C	M	1918	1972	54
Lew, C	M	1908	1969	61	Van, C	F	1912	1970	58	Pri, R	M	1918	1966	48
Lun, E	F	1908	1982	74	Alb, E	M	1913	1921	8	Wil, F	F	1918	1974	56
Mas, S	F	1908	1937	29	Bar, E	F	1913	1974	61	Wil, T	M	1918	1941	23
Rot, A	M	1908	1983	75	Bar, L	M	1913	1984	71	Dav, E	F	1919	1952	33
Rot, K	M	1908	1918	10	Coo, J	M	1913	1973	60	Dev, D	M	1919	1965	46
Ste, R	M	1908	1975	67	Coo, S	M	1913	1999	86	Jam, A	M	1919	1939	20
Vet, J	M	1908	1977	69	Jas, T	M	1913	1976	63	Oel, R	F	1919	1947	28
Wat, M	F	1908	1993	85	Jef, R	M	1913	1981	68	Alb, R	F	1920	1981	61
Wes, A	F	1908	1985	77	Ric, V	F	1913	1983	70	Bie, S	M	1920	1983	63
Wil, A	M	1908	1990	82	Til, L	F	1913	1995	82	Hib, J	M	1920	1971	51
Woo, G	F	1908	1988	80	Ure, D	F	1913	1984	71	Kai, M	M	1920	1984	64
Zei, M	F	1908	1914	6	Bro, R	M	1914	1977	63	Lit, J	M	1920	1981	61
Ada, P	M	1909	1966	57	Edw, R	M	1914	1970	56	Pet, A	M	1920	1999	79
Ann, M	F	1909	1995	86	Fin, D	F	1914	1971	57	Rea, D	M	1920	1995	75
Bar, S	M	1909	1954	45	Fre, D	F	1914	1999	85	Smi, R	M	1920	1935	15
Ber, G	F	1909	1968	59	Hec, M	F	1914	1993	79	Bat, E	F	1921	1977	56
Edw, G	F	1909	1994	85	Pen, V	F	1914	1926	12	Bat, J	M	1921	1997	76
Geo, J	M	1909	1969	60	Pow, C	F	1914	1985	71	Den, A	M	1921	1978	57
Hor, A	M	1909	1984	75	Row, J	M	1914	1993	79	Eva, W	M	1921	1990	69
Kac, S	M	1909	1991	82	Ste, J	M	1914	1980	66	Gri, J	F	1921	1973	52
Smi, L	F	1909	1983	74	Woo, M	F	1914	1914	0	Las, L	F	1921	1996	75
Str, L	M	1909	1970	61	Car, M	F	1915	1991	76	Pri, F	M	1921	1988	67
Ten, J	M	1909	1980	71	Che, F	M	1915	1986	71	Sul, A	F	1921	1988	67
War, A	M	1909	1974	65	Che, J	M	1915	1969	54	Wil, F	M	1921	1944	23
Bog, C	M	1910	1991	81	Hil, R	M	1915	1980	65	Bel, A	M	1922	1987	65

Name	Sex	YOB	YOD	AAD	Name	Sex	YOB	YOD	AAD	Name	Sex	YOB	YOD	AAD
Gei, W	M	1922	1970	48	Mos, M	F	1925	1927	2	Bro, J	M	1937	1964	27
Jon, W	M	1922	1988	66	Bar, A	F	1926	1979	53	Cot, D	F	1937	1939	2
Ric, C	F	1922	1997	75	Bar, T	M	1926	1994	68	Pis, R	M	1937	1990	53
Viv, D	F	1922	1929	7	Bar, I	F	1927	1967	40	Sul, R	F	1938	1993	55
Bar, M	M	1923	1982	59	Har, D	M	1927	1995	68	Zet, M	F	1939	1999	60
Dev, L	F	1923	1983	60	Hug, T	M	1927	1999	72	Ast, G	M	1940	1967	27
Hil, A	M	1923	1974	51	May, N	F	1927	1928	1	Fai, C	M	1940	1978	38
Hon, J	F	1923	1997	74	Wil, J	M	1927	1991	64	Phi, M	F	1941	1944	3
Tru, A	M	1923	1995	72	Dav, E	M	1928	1988	60	Bam, J	M	1943	1998	55
Cam, R	M	1924	1976	52	Dif, J	M	1928	1969	41	How, B	F	1943	1958	15
Eva, K	F	1924	1993	69	Err, C	F	1928	1967	39	Cam, L	F	1946	1987	41
Fra, P	F	1924	1996	72	Eve, A	F	1928	1979	51	Nov, D	M	1952	1968	16
Fra, R	M	1924	1993	69	Gib, W	M	1928	1980	52	Dun, W	M	1953	1998	45
Lel, M	F	1924	1949	25	Pen, J	M	1929	1983	54	Jes, H	M	1954	1987	33
Mar, F	F	1924	1992	68	Sir, F	F	1929	1969	40	Gab, A	M	1956	1963	7
Mos, E	F	1924	1931	7	Jon, E	F	1930	1986	56	Dif, K	F	1957	1958	1
Phi, E	M	1924	1988	64	Fed, A	M	1931	1967	36	Hon, W	M	1957	1983	26
Rin, W	M	1924	1924	0	Kin, S	M	1931	1970	39	Ure, J	M	1957	1976	19
Sch, I	F	1924	1983	59	Han, J	F	1932	1991	59	Pri, R	M	1958	1958	0
Ath, M	F	1925	1993	68	Har, H	M	1932	1971	39	Gol, W	M	1961	1998	37
Bog, I	F	1925	1996	71	Wil, B	F	1932	1949	17	Dic, B	M	1962	1962	0
Kam, B	M	1925	1975	50	Dwy, J	M	1934	1953	19	Kow, G	F	1970	1990	20
Kov, F	F	1925	1948	23	Zet, B	M	1934	1979	45	Dav, K	M	1973	1997	24
Kre, J	M	1925	1995	70	Jon, G	M	1935	1984	49	Mad, E	M	1989	1990	1
Mor, J	M	1925	1995	70	Mye, J	F	1936	1972	36					

Can Lake Life Remain Despite Acid Rain?

Acid Rain and the Chemistry of Lake Water

Question Why does acid rain harm some lakes more than others?

Lab Overview In this investigation you will test how simulated acid rain changes the pH of lake water samples, including a sample of local lake water. You will use your results to make predictions about the effects of acid rain on lake ecosystems and explore how these effects may vary.

Introduction In the Prelab Activity you will compare and contrast three Adirondack lakes that receive significant amounts of acid rain. You will study the characteristics of each lake and develop possible hypotheses explaining why acid rain affects each lake differently.

Background Acid rain is caused by chemical pollutants in the air, mainly sulfur oxides and nitrogen oxides that form when coal and other fossil fuels are burned in factories and cars. These compounds dissolve in rainwater as it falls, forming sulfuric acid and nitric acid. In Chapter 4 you learned that acidity is measured on the pH scale, from 0 to 14. Pure distilled water has a pH of 7.0, which is neutral. Solutions with a pH of less than 7 are acidic. Rainwater in unpolluted environments normally contains small amounts of dissolved carbon dioxide and is slightly acidic, about pH 5.5. Rainwater with a pH lower than 5.5 is considered to be acid rain.

As acid rain falls and collects in lake environments, it can change the pH of the lake water and have a profound impact on plant and animal life. Lake water is a solution containing minerals and salts dissolved from rocks and soil, as well as suspended organic material from decomposed plant and animal life. As these components vary in different locations, so does the natural pH of the lake water in different locations.

Prelab Activity Read the information below about three lakes in the Adirondack Mountains of New York and study Data Table 1 on the next page. Then, answer the Prelab Questions.

The Adirondack lakes, and the woods around them, have long been a popular vacation area. In some of the lakes, aquatic life has been dying off in recent years. Scientists have determined that acid precipitation is one cause. Although there is very little air pollution produced in the Adirondack wilderness, the wind carries air pollutants from surrounding industrial areas to the wilderness.

Objective to learn how soil composition and elevation can affect how resistant a lake is to acid precipitation

Inquiry Skills
- observing
- making inferences
- collecting data
- controlling variables
- drawing conclusions

Time
- 20 min for Prelab Activity
- 15 min for Part A
- 20–30 min for Part B
- 20 min for Analysis and Conclusions

Data Table 1

Characteristic	Brant Lake	Big Moose Lake	Blue Mountain Lake
Size (approximate)	5.7 km²	5.2 km²	5.5 km²
Elevation (approximate)	243 m	556 m	545 m
Water color	clear	brown	clear
pH	7.6	5.5	7.2
Algae growth	moderate	low	low
Phosphorus levels	low	low	low
Nitrogen levels	low	moderate to high	moderate

Generally, lakes at higher elevations are less resistant to acid rain than lakes at lower elevations. While higher-elevation lakes receive water from precipitation only, lower elevation lakes may also receive water with dissolved minerals and salts from other sources. The type of rocks and soil found in a lake are also important to buffering capacity. For example, limestone contains minerals that are basic when dissolved.

Lakes found in areas rich in limestone are rarely affected by acid precipitation. Some organic molecules also act as buffers. However, an excess of decaying material will tend to lower the pH of lake water because decomposing organisms also release acid byproducts.

Prelab Questions

1. What physical features do Big Moose Lake and Blue Mountain Lake have in common?

   Suggested answer: Both lakes are about the same size and are located in the same area at about the same elevation.

2. What characteristics do Brant Lake and Blue Mountain Lake have in common?

   Suggested answer: Both lakes are similar in size and have clear water that is not acidic (pH 7.6 and 7.2 respectively).

3. An ecology student noticed that Big Moose Lake has a higher nitrogen level than Brant Lake, but has lower algae growth. This data surprised her, because algae often flourish in water with high nitrogen levels. Develop a hypothesis to explain the surprisingly low algae growth in Big Moose Lake.

   Sample answer: The low pH may be affecting algae growth.

4. In lakes with low pH, such as Big Moose Lake, the normal decomposition of plant and animal debris slows down. How might this explain the difference in appearance between Big Moose Lake and the other two lakes?

Suggested answer: Big Moose Lake may be brown in color because it contains more

undecomposed plant and animal debris.

5. The table below shows the pH ranges at which certain aquatic animals can survive. Use the chart to answer the following questions.

Organism	pH 6.5	pH 6.0	pH 5.5	pH 5.0	pH 4.5	pH 4.0
Trout	■	■	■	■		
Bass	■	■	■			
Perch	■	■	■	■	■	
Frogs	■	■	■	■	■	■
Salamanders	■	■	■	■		
Clams	■	■				
Crayfish	■	■	■			
Snails	■	■				
Mayflies	■	■	■			

SOURCE: Environmental Protection Agency, Acid Rain Program

a. Which animal listed in the table is most sensitive to acid rain? Which is least sensitive? Explain.

Clams and snails are most sensitive since they cannot survive when the pH drops below 6.

Frogs are least sensitive. They can survive even when the lake drops to pH 4.

b. Based on this data, which animals might you expect to find in Brant Lake that would not be found in Big Moose Lake?

Clams and snails are likely to be present in Brant Lake (pH 7.6), but not in Big Moose Lake

(pH 5.5).

6. In the lab activity, you will use a chemical called a pH indicator that changes color as the pH of a solution changes. If you added a pH indicator to two different solutions and they both turned the same color, what would this tell you about the pH of each solution?

They are the same.

Materials

- 5 clear plastic cups or beakers (500-mL size)
- graduated cylinder
- stirring rods or coffee stirrers
- labeling tape
- marker
- 50 mL local lake water*
- 50 mL simulated Brant Lake water
- 50 mL simulated Blue Mountain Lake water
- 50 mL distilled water
- simulated "acid rain" (dilute acetic acid in small beaker or cup)
- transfer pipette
- universal pH indicator

For simulated Blue Mountain Lake water use plain tap water.

If local lake water is not available:
50 mL of local soil, 100 mL tap water, coffee filter, funnel

Procedure

Part A: Preparing Lake Water Samples

1. **Local lake water sample:** If you have a sample of local lake water, measure 50 mL of it into a plastic cup or beaker. Label the cup or beaker "Local lake water." Then, go to Step 5.

   If you do not have a sample of local lake water, prepare a simulated local lake water sample by following steps 2–4.

2. To prepare a simulated local lake water sample, mix 50 mL of local soil with 100 mL of tap water in a plastic cup or beaker. Stir for 1 min.

3. Line the funnel with the coffee filter. Hold the filter-lined funnel over a clean plastic cup or beaker and carefully pour the soil-water mixture through it.

4. Discard all but 50 mL of the water that has filtered through. Label the cup or beaker "Local lake water."

5. **Other lake water samples:** With a graduated cylinder, measure 50 mL samples of Brant Lake water, Blue Mountain Lake water, and distilled water (for comparison) into separate plastic cups or beakers. Use a paper towel to dry the graduated cylinder between each measurement. Label each cup appropriately.

Part B: Comparing the Effects of Acid Rain on Lake Water Samples

1. Using a transfer pipette, add 1 mL of pH indicator to each cup.

2. Use the pH indicator key to determine the pH of each water sample. Record the data in Data Table 2 on the next page.

Advance Preparation

A day or two before the lab

- Make the buffer solution to serve as "Brant Lake water." Make 1 L of 0.05 M sodium phosphate or potassium phosphate buffer. Adjust the pH of the phosphate buffer so that it is the same pH as your tap water.
- Obtain a sample of local lake water. You will need about 1 L per 30 students. If local lake water is unavailable, see student lab for instructions to prepare simulated local lake water. You may choose to make this in a large batch rather than having each group make their own.

Safety and Disposal
Remind students to handle solutions carefully to avoid spills. The simulated "acid rain" solution may cause skin irritation and should be rinsed off promptly if it comes into contact with the skin. If any of the solutions get into a student's eye, flush the eye with water for 15 min and seek medical attention. Remind students to wash their hands thoroughly with soap after handling lake water and soil. Water samples and "acid rain" solution can be flushed down a lab drain.

3. Add one drop of the "acid rain" to each water sample and stir gently to mix. Note any changes in pH. Record the pH in Data Table 2. Then, add another drop of "acid rain" and repeat.

4. Continue to add "acid rain" two drops at a time while stirring, until all samples have reached pH 4. Keep track of how many drops you have added to each lake sample.

Data Table 2

	Blue Mountain Lake	Brant Lake	Local Lake	Distilled Water
Initial pH of water sample (no acid rain added)	8	7	7	6
pH of water sample after 1 drop of acid rain	7	7	7	4
pH of water sample after 2 drops of acid rain	6	7	7	
pH of water sample after 4 drops of acid rain	5	7	6	
pH of water sample after 6 drops of acid rain	4	7	5	
Drops of acid rain needed to lower water sample pH to 4	6	15	8	1

Expected Results
Since the simulated Blue Mountain Lake water is tap water, it will probably show some buffering ability. The simulated Brant Lake water is a buffer solution and will take significantly more of the "acid rain solution" to change the pH. Local lake samples will vary, but generally local lake water is more buffered than tap water. Distilled water will change to pH 4 with one drop of vinegar.

Analysis and Conclusions

1. To which lake water sample did you add the most acid before it reached pH 4?

Suggested answer: The Brant Lake water received the most acid before it reached pH 4.

_____

_____

2. Read the following information, then answer the questions that follow.

Some lakes contain particles of rocks, soil, and decaying plant and animal debris that act as buffers (substances that cause a solution to resist changes in pH). These buffers dissolve in the lake water and then bind to free H^+ ions in an acidic solution (the more acidic a solution is, the more H^+ ions the solution contains). When an H^+ ion binds to a buffer, the ion is no longer free in the solution to affect its pH. However, buffers can only bind to a limited number of H^+ ions.

a. Which of the lake water samples you tested do you think contained the most buffers? Explain.

Suggested answer: The Brant Lake water contained the most buffers. Since the Brant Lake

sample took the longest to change pH, it must have contained the most buffers to bind to

H$^+$ ions.

b. Based on your data and observations, make a prediction about what may happen to this lake in the future, if acid rain continues to fall.

Suggested answer: Eventually, the buffers will no longer be able to bind to H$^+$ ions. Then, the

pH will start to decrease and the lake will become acidic.

3. How did your local lake water sample resist the effects of the acid rain compared to the other water samples? Why do you think the local lake water compared as it did?

Suggested answer: The following answer will be true for most natural lakes: The local lake water

sample resisted change better than the distilled water and the Blue Mountain lake water, but

not as well as the Brant Lake water. Student hypotheses will vary depending on results.

4. Which do you think would have a higher concentration of dissolved minerals, a lake at a higher elevation or a lake at a lower elevation? Explain.

Sample answer: Lakes at a lower elevation may receive dissolved minerals in runoff.

5. Based on the information you discovered in this lab, develop a plan to protect vulnerable lakes from acid rain. Consider factors and questions that should be taken into account before the plan is carried out.

Student answers will vary. Students may suggest adding buffers to the lake water or depositing

limestone in the area. Questions to consider could include what impact buffers might have on

local wildlife.

Extension

How could you find out whether or not acid precipitation falls in your local area? Devise a test, and write out the steps of your testing procedure. With your teacher's approval, carry out the testing procedure and report your results to the class.

Extension
Check student experimental design and procedures for proper scientific method and all safety issues before allowing them to proceed with their experiments.

What Is a Solution for Oil-Spill Pollution?

Evaluating the Effectiveness of Oil-Spill Cleanup Methods

Question How can you compare the effectiveness of different oil-spill cleanup methods?

Lab Overview You will add different materials to a mixture of oil and water to test how effectively each material absorbs oil. Then you will determine which material would be the easiest to remove from the ocean's surface, and use that material to clean up an oil spill.

Introduction To start your investigation, you will explore the impact of an oil spill on marine life, and learn about some of the difficulties involved in cleaning up an oil spill. Then, you will evaluate and discuss the cost-effectiveness and environmental impact of five different oil-spill cleanup methods.

Background When an oil spill occurs at sea, a layer of oil (called an oil slick) forms on the surface of the water. When the oil reaches shore, it can be very harmful to wildlife. For example, if the fur of marine mammals or the feathers of seabirds become covered in oil, the animals cannot keep warm. If animals try to clean themselves, or if they eat other oil-soaked organisms, they can become sick or die from ingesting oil.

The quicker an oil spill is cleaned up, the less environmental damage occurs, especially if the oil is cleaned up while it is still floating on the open ocean. Once the oil reaches shore it can harm many more organisms and becomes even more difficult to clean up. Also, some onshore cleaning efforts may cause harm to the environment in other ways.

Prelab Activity Read the following scenario and the five proposed oil-spill cleanup methods listed on the next page. Then, answer the Prelab Questions.

An oil tanker has come too close to shore and has rammed into sharp rocks off the coast. Millions of liters of oil are being released into the ocean. The oil is drifting to shore and is starting to cover rocks, tide pools, and marine animals. Several methods have been proposed to clean up the oil before much more damage is caused. Review the information about the proposed cleanup methods in Table 1 on the next page, and answer the questions that follow.

Objective to test the effectiveness of various materials in absorbing and containing oil spills

Inquiry Skills
- observing
- predicting
- using models
- controlling variables
- drawing conclusions

Time
- 15–20 min for Prelab Activity
- 15 min for Part A
- 15 min for Part B
- 15 min for Part C
- 20 min for Analysis and Conclusions

Table 1

Method	Relative Cost	Other Environmental Problems	Related Cleanup Problems
A. Burn off surface oil.	very inexpensive	pollution from smoke	possible soot and smoke
B. Add detergent or other chemicals to break up oil slick before it reaches shore.	inexpensive	substances from detergents can have negative effects	detergent suds and foam
C. Wash oil off rocks and sand with hot water from high-pressure hoses.	expensive	hot water may kill organisms and harm habitat	oil washes back into ocean
D. Soak up oil with floating material such as cloth or sawdust.	somewhat inexpensive	no immediate problems	disposal of oil-soaked material
E. Surround spill with floating barriers and use skimming devices to collect or contain the oil.	expensive	no immediate problems	disposal or recycling of reclaimed oil

Prelab Questions

1. Based on the information in Table 1, which cleanup method do you think would be the most effective overall? Explain.

Student answers will vary, but should take cost, "side effect," and

disposal issues into account.

2. What further questions would you ask about this cleanup method before deciding to use it?

Student answers will vary.

3. What factors about a particular oil spill might affect the effectiveness of a cleanup method?

Student answers will vary, but could include weather, how far from shore the spill occurred,

temperature of the water, or the type of wildlife most affected.

_____

_____

_____

Materials

- 4 petri dishes
- masking tape and pen
- 60 mL Marvel® Mystery Oil
- 60 mL water
- measuring teaspoon (5 mL) and tablespoon (15 mL)
- 1 tbsp Enviro-bond™ 403
- 1 tsp (5 mL) sodium polyacrylate
- 1 tbsp (15 mL) oat or wheat bran
- five squares of cloth (about 1 cm² each)
- 5 self-sealing plastic bags
- 50-mL graduated cylinder
- Dawn® liquid detergent
- small kitchen sponge or heavy-duty paper towels

Marvel® Mystery Oil is a red-colored engine-protecting fluid. Enviro-bond absorbs this oil better than regular motor oil.

You could have some students use synthetic cloth strips and others use natural cloth strips and see if there is a difference.

Advance Preparation

A couple weeks before the lab
Order sodium polyacrylate from a biological supply company. Enviro-bond™ 403 is available through Flinn Scientific. Marvel® Mystery Oil is also available through Flinn Scientific or can be purchased at an auto supply store.

Locate an oil service shop where you can bring oil waste products for disposal. To reduce the amount of waste, you may want to create lab groups of 4–6 students.

Procedure

Part A: Comparing Oil-absorbing Materials

1. Label each petri dish with the name of one of the four types of oil-absorbing materials you will test.

2. Add 1 tbsp (15 mL) of water to each petri dish.

3. Add 1 tbsp (15 mL) of oil to each dish.

4. To each petri dish, add the oil-absorbing material a little at a time until you can determine the effect on the oil-water mixture. Cover the petri dish to reduce your exposure to oil fumes. Observe how each material interacts with the liquid. Write your observations in Data Table 1 on the next page. Note if the material is absorbing oil, water, or both.

Safety and Disposal
Remind students to wear goggles, gloves, and aprons. Keep the room well ventilated. Oil is volatile and flammable and is a hazardous waste. Gather the sealed plastic bags containing oil waste and the sponges or paper towels used in Part C for proper disposal. Many oil service shops will take the waste for little or no charge. Check that all oil has been removed from petri dishes before storing them for reuse.

Data Table 1

Material	Observations
Oat or wheat bran	absorbs oil and water
Enviro-bond™ 403	absorbs oil only and forms a solid
Sodium polyacrylate	absorbs only water
Cloth	absorbs oil and water

Enviro-bond™ 403 is a hydrophobic powder that absorbs oil, forming a solid mass that can be dramatically lifted out of the water.

Part B: Evaluating Overall Effectiveness

1. Allow enough time for each material to soak up oil. Then, clean up the "oil spill" by using a plastic spoon to scoop the oil-absorbing material in each petri dish into a separate plastic bag. (**NOTE:** *Only scoop up the material. Leave the water and any remaining oil behind.*) Seal the bags to prevent leaks.

2. Examine the water left behind in the petri dishes. Evaluate each material for ease of cleanup and the condition of the water after treatment. Use brief descriptions and a numbered rating system in which 1 means "not effective" and 10 means "very effective." Write your evaluations in Data Table 2 below.

Sodium polyacrylate, often used in disposable diapers, is hydrophilic and only absorbs water. When added to the water and oil mixture, a slushy semi-solid will form, but the oil layer remains intact. Students will see the obvious need for a hydrophobic molecule to absorb oil.

Data Table 2

Material	Ease of Cleanup	Water Condition After Treatment	Oil-absorbing Ability (fill in after Part B, Step 3)
Oat or wheat bran	1, poor, much of it stays in the water	3, murky	5, moderate
Enviro-bond™ 403	10, excellent	7, looks clean, but has an oily smell	10, excellent
Sodium polyacrylate	1, poor	1, mixture has gelled	1, poor
Cloth	3, moderate	1, still lots of oil	1, poor

3. To get a sense of how well each material absorbed oil, carefully pour the contents of the first petri dish into a graduated cylinder. Measure the amounts of oil and water in the cylinder and record the results below. **CAUTION:** *Be very careful not to spill the oil and water as you pour.* Carefully pour the water back into the appropriate petri dish. Repeat with the other petri dishes. Then, rate each material's oil-absorbing abilities in Data Table 2 on the previous page.

Oat or wheat bran   Oil: _____ mL   Water: _____ mL

Enviro-bond™ 403   Oil: _____ mL   Water: _____ mL

Sodium polyacrylate   Oil: _____ mL   Water: _____ mL

Cloth   Oil: _____ mL   Water: _____ mL

Part C: Cleaning Up

1. Once you have decided on the cleanup method you think is best, put it to work on the remaining oil spills. Add the material to the petri dishes to soak up any remaining oil. Discard the material in a plastic bag and seal the bag.

2. Hold each dish under running water and scrub the petri dishes with a sponge or heavy-duty paper towel and detergent until the oil is removed completely.

To clean the graduated cylinders, used in Part B, you could use a round bottle brush wrapped in a heavy-duty paper towel.

Analysis and Conclusions

1. Which material was the most effective at cleaning up the oil spill? Describe the properties of this material that made it so effective.

Suggested answer: Enviro-bond™ 403 was the most effective method. It stayed on top of the water, absorbed the oil, and formed a solid material that could be easily removed.

2. Which material was the least effective at cleaning up the oil spill? Describe the properties of this material that made it ineffective.

Suggested answer: Sodium polyacrylate was the least effective method. It soaked up water underneath the layer of oil and formed a slushy material that was difficult to remove.

3. Do you think it would be more or less difficult to clean oil from an actual shore after a spill than it was in your model? Explain your answer.

Student answers will vary, but most students will say that they can see how onshore cleanup would

be more difficult. Once oil has stuck to objects such as sand or rocks, more work is involved

than applying a chemical and scooping up the oil.

4. As a scientist devising a cleanup plan, what other information would you like to know about Enviro-bond™ 403 before recommending its use?

Sample questions: Can the oil be separated from the chemical to recycle the oil? What are the disposal

methods for the chemical? Will the chemical cause any further harm to the environment? Can the

chemical be used to clean up oil that has reached shore?

Extension

Another oil-spill cleanup method uses bacteria that consume petroleum products as a food source. This method is especially useful if the oil has reached the shore.

Design an experiment to test the effectiveness of these bacteria in cleaning up an oil spill. **CAUTION:** *Do not carry out any investigations without permission from your teacher.*

Extension
Review students' experimental designs. You could have students perform this experiment. Kits containing oil-eating microbes are available from several biological supply companies, such as Neo Sci. See the front of this Laboratory Manual Teacher's Edition for contact information.